Articles of Impeachment

against
Sex Change Surgery

Walt Heyer

ARTICLES OF IMPEACHMENT

AGAINST SEX CHANGE SURGERY

Copyright © 2020 by Walt Heyer

ISBN: 978-1-7323453-7-9

Page layout and editing by Kaycee Heyer

Cover design by Kaycee Heyer

Attributions for articles appearing in this book:

Public Discourse

> Pieces originally appeared in Public Discourse: Ethics, Law, and the Common Good, the online journal of the Witherspoon Institute of Princeton, NJ and are reprinted with permission.

> thepublicdiscourse.com

The Federalist

> Pieces originally appeared in The Federalist, a wholly independent division of FDRLST Media and are reprinted with permission.

> thefederalist.com

The Daily Signal

> Pieces originally appeared in The Daily Signal, part of the Heritage Foundation and are reprinted with permission.

> dailysignal.com

Table of Contents

Introduction

I endured sex change surgeries, lived eight years as the opposite sex, sought emotional and psychological healing and thankfully, built a full life restored in my original male sex.

My purpose in assembling "articles of impeachment" is to indict the practice of sex change surgeries from my viewpoint as an insider. Fifty-five of my sixty-plus articles published in *The Daily Signal*, *Public Discourse*, *The Federalist* and other news outlets over the last five years make a compelling case for how destructive and catastrophic sex change surgeries are for too many people.

What comprises sex change surgery? For men, surgeries may include feminizing procedures such as genital surgery to form a pseudo-vagina, breast implants and various cosmetic surgeries to the face. For women, taking testosterone provides many of the masculinizing effects such as facial hair growth, voice deepening and male pattern baldness. Surgeries to sculpt a masculine-appearing body may include removing the breasts, removing the uterus and vagina, and constructing a penis.

By gathering first-person stories, medical studies, history and politics, these "articles of impeachment" detail the harmful and irreversible consequences this social and medical experiment continues to inflict on real people—adults, teenagers, and even children—and lay out the reasons to stop it.

Especially culpable are the medical professionals of the so-called "gender" clinics. The Oath expressly says that as a doctor "I will come for the benefit of the sick, remaining free of all intentional injustice, of all mischief" but doctors and counselors are causing far too much mischief by asserting, without scientific backing, that hormones and sex change surgeries are effective and reduce the risk of suicide. Both claims are false.

Regrettable outcomes can be linked directly to the attitude of medical providers who say their role is to assist the client to achieve an "authentic life," however the patient defines "authentic" at the time. These medical professionals live in a fantasy world populated by drug pushers and surgeons who introduce powerful hormone treatments and irreversible, radical cosmetic surgical procedures to vulnerable individuals who do not need any of it.

Frankly, their attitude shocks me every time I interact with one of these providers. A highly-regarded therapist in this field wrote me: "It is NOT the therapist or the doctor or the surgeon who makes this choice for their clients. Yet, when a client changes their mind about their gender identity, they all too easily choose to blame someone other than themselves. It is they who made the choice to seek treatments. The clients blame their caregivers for what they ultimately have chosen for themselves."

It is true—patients do diagnosis themselves and convince themselves that transition is the answer. Desperate for relief, they go to "gender experts" and often demand hormones and surgery. Many see any attempt to dissuade or delay as hateful and "gatekeeping." Even so, patients are not the medical experts.

I believe the psychologists, psychiatrists and surgeons have a responsibility to evaluate, uncover and treat any psychological, emotional, sexual or social disorders that may be present. Instead, they see their only duty to be getting patients to sign consent documents acknowledging awareness of the risks of treatment. Having this legal defense allows the "experts" to wash their hands of any responsibility for the regrettable outcomes that follow.

Over the last five years I have become convinced only an infinitesimal, rarefied group of people have breathed in the air of truth about "changing genders." I wrote this book so everyone will have a chance to breathe deeply of that air of truth, sitting in a chair, book in hand, ready and willing to dive into the articles of impeachment against sex change surgery.

Now you will learn in these articles why their "impeachable offense" should be judged as the crime it is—medical malpractice which contributes to suicides, unhappiness, regret and detransitions.

Notes

This book doesn't need to be read front to back. Feel free to dive in at any place, choosing topics as needed from the table of contents at the front and the index in the back.

A word about vocabulary used throughout the articles—The articles span five years and the political correctness of words and terms keeps changing. I'm not here to offend anyone with word usage. The debate about "gender" versus "sex" will go on.

The fundamentals remain true:

- Sex is fixed in the human body at conception; no amount of surgery can change it.
- Regret is not rare. In fact, reports of regret are growing. My inbox overflows with emails from people who wish they could undo the changes and get back wasted time. More and more people post videos on YouTube to share their reasons for detransitioning and the number of participants in online support groups devoted to detransitioners is escalating.

Chapter 1.
Regret Is Real

I Was a Transgender Woman

The reprieve provided by surgery and life as a woman was only temporary. Hidden deep underneath the make-up and female clothing was the little boy hurt by childhood trauma, and he was making himself known.

BY WALT HEYER
PUBLIC DISCOURSE, APRIL 1, 2015
WWW.THEPUBLICDISCOURSE.COM/2015/04/14688/

It was a pivotal scene. A mom was brushing a boy's long hair, the boy slowly turned his head to look at her. In a tentative voice, he asked, "Would you love me if I were a boy?" The mom was raising her boy to become a trans-girl.

In that split second, I was transported back to my childhood. I remembered my grandmother standing over me, guiding me, dressing me in a purple chiffon dress. The boy in that glowing documentary about parents raising transgender kids dared to voice a question I always wanted to ask. Why didn't she love me the way I was?

I am haunted by that boy and his question. What will the trans-kids of 2015 be like sixty years from now? Documentaries and news stories only give us a snapshot in time. They are edited to romanticize and normalize the notion of changing genders and to convince us that enlightened parents should help their children realize their dreams of being the opposite gender.

I want to tell you my story. I want you to have the opportunity to see the life of a trans-kid, not in a polished television special, but across more than seven decades of life, with all of its confusion, pain, and redemption.

The Trans-Kid

It wasn't my mother but my grandmother who clothed me in a purple chiffon dress she made for me. That dress set in motion a life filled with gender dysphoria, sexual abuse, alcohol and drug abuse, and finally, an unnecessary gender reassignment surgery. My life was ripped apart by a trusted adult who enjoyed dressing me as a girl.

My mom and dad didn't have any idea that when they dropped their son off for a weekend at Grandma's that she was dressing their boy in girls' clothes. Grandma told me it was our little secret. My grandmother withheld affirmations of me as a boy, but she lavished delighted praise upon me when I was dressed as a girl. Feelings of euphoria swept over me with her praise, followed later by depression and insecurity about being a boy. Her actions planted the idea in me that I was born in the wrong body. She nourished and encouraged the idea, and over time it took on a life of its own.

I became so accustomed to wearing the purple dress at Grandma's house that, without telling her, I took it home so I could secretly wear it there too. I hid it in the back of a drawer in my dresser. When my mom found it, an explosion of yelling and screaming erupted between my mom and dad. My father was terrified his boy was not developing into a man, so he ramped up his discipline. I felt singled out because, in my view, my older brother didn't receive the same heavy-handed punishment as I did. The unfairness hurt more than anything else.

Thankfully, my parents decided I would never be allowed to go to Grandma's house again without them. They couldn't know I was scared of seeing Grandma because I had exposed her secret.

Uncle Fred's Influence

My worst nightmare was realized when my dad's much younger adopted brother, Uncle Fred, discovered the secret of the dress and began teasing me. He pulled down my pants, taunting and laughing at me. At only nine years of age, I couldn't fight back, so I turned to eating as a way to cope with the anxiety. Fred's teasing caused a meal of six tuna-fish sandwiches and a quart of milk to become my way of suppressing the pain.

One day Uncle Fred took me in his car on a dirt road up the hill from my house and tried to take off all my clothes. Terrified of what might happen, I escaped, ran home, and told my mom. She looked at me accusingly and said, "You're a liar. Fred would never do that." When my dad got home, she told him what I said, and he went to talk to Fred. But Fred shrugged it off as a tall tale, and my dad believed him instead of me. I could see no use in telling people about what Fred was doing, so I kept silent from that point on about his continuing abuse.

I went to school dressed as a boy, but in my head that purple dress lived on. I could see myself in it, standing in front of the mirror at my grandma's house. I was small, but I participated and excelled in football, track, and other sports. My way to cope with my gender confusion was to work hard at whatever I did. I mowed lawns, delivered newspapers, and pumped gasoline. After high school graduation, I worked in an automotive shop, then took classes in drafting to qualify for a job in aerospace. After a short time, I earned a spot on the Apollo space mission project as associate design engineer. Ever eager for the next challenge, I switched to an entry-level position in the automobile industry and quickly rocketed up the corporate ladder at a major American car company. I even got married. I had it all—a promising career with unlimited potential and a great family.

But I also had a secret. After thirty-six years, I was still unable to overcome the persistent feeling I was really a woman. The seeds sown by Grandma developed deep roots. Unbeknownst to my wife, I began to act on my desire to be a woman. I was cross-dressing in public and enjoying it. I even started taking female hormones to feminize my appearance. Who knew Grandma's wish in the mid-1940s for a granddaughter would lead to this?

Adding alcohol was like putting gasoline on a fire; drinking heightened the desire. My wife, feeling betrayed by the secrets I had been keeping from her and fed up by my out-of-control drunken binges, filed for divorce.

Life as a Woman

I sought out a prominent gender psychologist for evaluation, and he quickly assured me that I obviously suffered from gender dysphoria. A gender change, he told me, was the cure. Feeling that I had nothing to lose and thrilled that I could finally attain my lifelong dream, I underwent a surgical change at the age of forty-two. My new identity as Laura Jensen, female, was legally affirmed on my birth record, Social Security card, and driver's license. I was now a woman in everyone's eyes.

The gender conflict seemed to fade away, and I was generally happy for a while.

It's hard for me to describe what happened next. The reprieve provided by surgery and life as a woman was only temporary. Hidden deep underneath the make-up and female clothing was the little boy carrying the hurts from traumatic childhood events, and he was making himself known. Being a female turned out to be only a cover-up, not healing.

I knew I wasn't a real woman, no matter what my identification documents said. I had taken extreme steps to resolve my gender conflict, but changing genders hadn't worked. It was obviously a masquerade. I felt I had been lied to. How in the world had I reached this point? How did I become a fake woman? I went to another gender psychologist, and she assured me that I would be fine; I just needed to give my new identity as Laura more time. I had a past, a battered and broken life that living as Laura did nothing to dismiss or resolve. Feeling lost and depressed, I drank heavily and considered suicide.

At the three-year mark of life as Laura, my excessive drinking brought me to a new low. At my lowest point, instead of committing suicide I sought help at an alcohol recovery meeting. My sponsor, a lifeline of support and accountability, mentored me in how to live life free from alcohol.

Sobriety was the first of several turning points in my transgender life.

As Laura, I entered a two-year university program to study the psychology of substance and alcohol abuse. I achieved higher grades than my classmates, many of whom had PhDs. Still, I struggled with my gender identity. It was all so puzzling. What was the point of changing genders if not to resolve the conflict? After eight years of living as a woman, I had no lasting peace. My gender confusion only seemed to worsen.

During an internship in a psychiatric hospital, I worked alongside a medical doctor on a lock-down unit. After some observation, he took me aside and told me I showed signs of having a dissociative disorder. Was he right? Had he found the key that would unlock a childhood lost? Rather than going to gender-change activist psychologists like the one who had approved me for surgery, I sought the opinions of several "regular" psychologists and psychiatrists who did not see all gender disorders as transgender. They agreed: I fit the criteria for dissociative disorder.

It was maddening. Now it was apparent that I had developed a dissociative disorder in childhood to escape the trauma of the repeated cross-dressing by my grandmother and the sexual abuse by my uncle. That should have been diagnosed and treated with psychotherapy. Instead, the gender specialist never considered my difficult childhood or even my alcoholism and saw only transgender identity. It was a quick jump to prescribe hormones and irreversible surgery. Years later, when I confronted that psychologist, he admitted that he should not have approved me for surgery.

Becoming Whole

Coming back to wholeness as a man after undergoing unnecessary gender surgery and living life legally and socially as a woman for years wasn't going to be easy. I had to admit to myself that going to a gender specialist when I first had issues had been a big mistake. I had to live with the reality that body parts were gone. My full genitalia could not be restored—a sad consequence of using surgery to treat psychological illness. Intensive psychotherapy would be required to resolve the dissociative disorder that started as a child.

But I had a firm foundation on which to begin my journey to restoration. I was living a life free from drugs and alcohol, and I was ready to become the man I was intended to be.

At age fifty-six, I experienced something beyond my wildest dreams. I fell in love, married, and began to fully re-experience life as a man. It took over fifty years, but I was finally able to unwind all the damage that purple chiffon dress had done. Today, I'm seventy-four years old and married to my wife of eighteen years, with twenty-nine years of sober living.

Changing genders is short-term gain with long-term pain. Its consequences include early mortality, regret, mental illness, and suicide. Instead of encouraging them to undergo unnecessary and destructive surgery, let's affirm and love our young people just the way they are.

Transgender Regret Is Real Even If The Media Tell You Otherwise

They don't want you to know: regret 20 percent, attempted suicides 41 percent, mental illness 60-90 percent among transgendered population.

BY WALT HEYER
THE FEDERALIST, FEBRUARY 2, 2016
THEFEDERALIST.COM/2015/08/19/TRANSGENDER-
REGRET-IS-REAL-EVEN-IF-THE-MEDIA-TELL-YOU-OTHERWISE/

The Washington Post reported Tuesday that the White House has appointed its first openly transgender staff member. Raffi Freedman-Gurspan has been hired as an outreach and recruitment director for presidential personnel in the White House Office of Presidential Personnel.[1]

I do not know how this will work out for the White House but everyone needs to know the truth about regret, suicides and untreated mental illness among the transgender population.

When Carol Costello, CNN reporter, interviewed me in June on the subject of Olympian, trans-Jenner, she couldn't help beginning with a false narrative that only 2 percent regret of transgender have regrets. That is, the media's propensity to fluff over the regret statistics.

Early in the interview, she made the statement, "We have researched… and we found a recent Swedish study that found only 2.2 percent of transgenders, male and female, suffered from sex change regret."[2]

Costello is a bright reporter. That it is why it was so puzzling she would use her interview of me to misinform her audience, unless the intent was to diminish and dismiss reports of sex change regret among the transgender population. Costello used only one study to reach a conclusion on the frequency of regret. She or her staff did not look at the wealth of other studies that suggest sex change regret is quite common. One such study commissioned by The Guardian of the UK in 2004 reviewed 100 studies and reported that a whopping 20 percent (one fifth) of transgenders regret changing genders[3], ten times more than CNN's Costello reported.

The review of 100 studies also revealed that many transgenders remained severely distressed and even suicidal after the gender change operation. Suicide and regret remain the dark side of transgender life.

The Media—Unwilling to Show the Dark Side

The media cover-up of regret and suicides isn't a new phenomenon; it was in play 36 years ago. In 1979 Dr. Charles Ihlenfeld, who worked alongside the famous Dr. Harry Benjamin for six years administering hormone therapy to some 500 transgenders, spoke to an audience in New York about

[1] http://www.washingtonpost.com/news/the-fix/wp/2015/08/18/the-white-house-has-appointed-its-first-transgender-staffer/
[2] https://www.youtube.com/watch?v=ZWb9vtl5n1c
[3] http://www.theguardian.com/society/2004/jul/30/health.mentalhealth

his experience: "There is too much unhappiness among people who have had the surgery. Too many of them end as suicides."[4]

Thirty-six years of the insanity of ignoring poor outcomes and hoping they will go away is long enough.

The media was unwilling to report the unhappiness then, and ever since has downplayed any results that would raise the alarm about poor outcomes. Albert Einstein said that insanity is doing the same thing over and over again and expecting different results. Thirty-six years of the insanity of ignoring poor outcomes and hoping they will go away is long enough.

The unhappiness continues. Last month, Jenner used the occasion of accepting the ESPY award for courage to tell the world that 41 percent of transgenders attempt suicide. We can debate all day long the various reasons why trans-people have regret and attempt suicide because the reasons are many and diverse. But no debate is needed in the face of the evidence that, for some, changing genders causes unhappiness and ends in suicide.

Come on, Carol, it's time to stop perpetuating the misinformation that transgender regret is rare.

Transgender regret is not rare

The study commissioned by The Guardian of the UK in 2004 reviewed 100 studies and found 20 percent regret. Consider the findings of a 2011 Swedish study (not the study Ms. Costello used) published seven years after the 2004 UK review. It looked at mortality and morbidity after gender reassignment surgery and found that people who changed genders had a higher risk of suicide.[5]

What are suicide and attempted suicide but symptoms of tremendous depression and unhappiness?

In this study, all the sex-reassigned persons in Sweden from 1973–2003 (191 male-to-females, 133 female-to-males) were compared to a comparable random control group. The sex-reassigned persons had substantially higher rates of death from cardiovascular disease and suicide, and substantially higher rates of attempted suicide. What are suicide and attempted suicide but symptoms of tremendous depression and unhappiness?

My life story and the stories of those who contact me speak of regret over transitioning. Often, the stories include attempted suicide or suicide ideation.

I was a 4 year old trans-kid who grew up with gender confusion and underwent gender reassignment surgery at age 42. I lived for 8 years as a so-called trans-female named Laura Jensen. But no matter how feminine I appeared, like all transgenders, I was just a man in a dress. I was unhappy, regretful of having transitioned and I attempted suicide. Gender surgery is not effective treatment for depression, anxiety or mental disorders.

---

4 http://lvtgw.jadephoenix.org/Info_htm/Herbal_G/ginko_b2.htm
5 https://journals.plos.org/plosone/article?id=10.1371/journal.pone.0016885

Astonishing evidence of other illness

According to several studies, the majority of transgenders have co-existing disorders that need to be treated. This helps to explain why regret and suicide are prevalent among transgenders. The following studies provide irrefutable evidence that transgenders overwhelmingly suffer from a variety of mental disorders. Neither CNN nor Carol Costello will report studies such as these.

1. "90 percent of these diverse patients had at least one other significant form of psychopathology" reported Case Western Reserve University, Cleveland, Ohio, Department of Psychiatry in a 2009 studyof transgender outcomes at their clinic.[6] In other words, 90 percent of the patients were suffering from a mental illness that gender surgery did not alleviate.

2. 61 percent of the patients treated for cross-gender identification (359 people) had other psychiatric disorders and illnesses, notably personality, mood, dissociative, and psychotic disorders according to a 2003 Dutch survey of board-certified Dutch psychiatrists.[7]

3. A 2013 University of Louisville, KY study of 351 transgender individuals found that the rates of depression and anxiety symptoms within the study "far surpass the rates of those for the general population." About half had depressive symptoms and more than 40 percent had symptoms of anxiety.[8]

In all the rhetoric about gender change success you cannot find one sound bite from any media source that acknowledges that even one transgender suffers from a serious mental illness, much less reporting the 90 percent like Case Western Reserve University found, or the 61 percent that the survey of Dutch psychiatrists reported. The numbers are astonishingly high, yet no media reports it.

Fair-minded individuals would see the cumulative effect of the findings—20 percent have regret, 41 percent attempt suicide, 90 percent have a "significant form of psychopathology", 61 percent also have other psychiatric disorders and illnesses, 50 percent had depressive symptoms, 40 percent showed symptoms of anxiety—and be troubled by the push to surgery and transition as the first course of treatment for transgenders.

Yet the media is silent. It's so much easier to deliver the LGBT talking point than to dig into the science.

True compassion starts with the truth

The fallout of the media's inclination to overlook the negative findings is simple: nothing will change. It's insanity to continue the cover-up and expect different outcomes. Thirty years from now, the environment will be the same. Co-existing mental illnesses in transgenders won't be treated. The attempted suicide rate will be high; transition regret will occur with frequency. Every time a transgender ends his or her life, the LGBT will blame society or the victim and push for more laws to "protect" them.

---

[6] http://www.ncbi.nlm.nih.gov/pubmed/19105079

[7] http://ajp.psychiatryonline.org/article.aspx?articleID=176330

[8] http://www.ncbi.nlm.nih.gov/pubmed/23398495

Apparently transgender lives do not matter: not to the LGBT and not to the media. It's time for the media to stand up and provide the overwhelming evidence for all to see that mental illness, regret and suicide exist among transgenders. Only then will we see true improvement in the outcomes for all.

I believe that true compassion is shown by raising factual issues, based on scientific research, and having the best minds follow the evidence to provide the best care for this segment of our society that is suffering. Packaging the issue in the wrapper of political correctness or withholding the negative findings is not compassion. Political correctness hinders research and treatment of the medical conditions and muzzles a media that's willing to participate in a false narrative. Who's the loser? The transgender who regrets transitioning.

The White House plays politics with a vulnerable part of our population to score points with the LGBT but the risks of regret, suicide and untreated mental issues remain for the transgender population.

50 Years of Sex Changes, Mental Disorders, and Too Many Suicides

Early pioneers in gender-reassignment surgery and recent clinical studies agree that a majority of transgender people suffer from co-occurring psychological disorders, leading tragically high numbers to commit suicide.
Outlawing psychotherapy for transgender people may be politically correct, but it shows a reckless disregard for human lives.

BY WALT HEYER
PUBLIC DISCOURSE, FEBRUARY 2, 2016
WWW.THEPUBLICDISCOURSE.COM/2016/02/16376/

Early pioneers in gender-reassignment surgery and recent clinical studies agree that a majority of transgender people suffer from co-occurring psychological disorders, leading tragically high numbers to commit suicide. Outlawing psychotherapy for transgender people may be politically correct, but it shows a reckless disregard for human lives.

Dateline Oct 4, 1966: The *New York Daily News* gossip column reported a girl was making the rounds in Manhattan clubs who admitted to being a man in 1965. She had undergone a sex-change operation in Baltimore at the Johns Hopkins gender clinic.

By 1979, thirteen years later, enough gender surgeries had been performed to evaluate the results. It was time for a report card based on actual patients.

1970s: How effective was the change surgery? What were the outcomes for transgender people?

The first report comes from Dr. Harry Benjamin, a strong advocate for cross-gender hormone therapy and gender-reassignment surgery, who operated a private clinic for transsexuals. According to an article in the *Journal of Gay & Lesbian Mental Health*, "By 1972, Benjamin had diagnosed, treated, and befriended at least a thousand of the ten thousand Americans known to be transsexual."[9]

Dr. Benjamin's trusted colleague, endocrinologist Charles Ihlenfeld administered hormone therapy to some 500 transgender people over a period of six years at Benjamin's clinic—until he became concerned about the outcomes. "There is too much unhappiness among people who have the surgery," he said. "Too many of them end as suicides. 80% who want to change their sex shouldn't do it." But even for the 20% he thought might be good candidates for it, sex change is by no means a solution to life's problems. He thinks of it more as a kind of reprieve. "It buys maybe 10 or 15 years of a happier life," he said, "and it's worth it for that."

---

[9] http://www.tandfonline.com/doi/full/10.1080/19359700802111619

But then, Ihlenfeld himself never had a sex change. I did, and I disagree with him on that last point: The reprieve is not worth it. After I had a reprieve of seven or eight years, then what? I was worse off than before. I looked like a woman—my legal documents identified me as a woman—yet I found that at the end of the "reprieve" I wanted to be a man every bit as passionately as I had once yearned to be a woman. Recovery was difficult.

Nevertheless, based on his experience treating 500 transgenders, Dr. Ihlenfeld concluded that the desire to change genders most likely stemmed from powerful psychological factors. He said in *Transgender Subjectivities: A Clinician's Guide*, "Whatever surgery did, it did not fulfill a basic yearning for something that is difficult to define. This goes along with the idea that we are trying to treat superficially something that is much deeper." Dr. Ihlenfeld left endocrinology in 1975 to begin a psychiatry residency.

About three years ago, while writing my book *Paper Genders*, I was curious and called Dr. Ihlenfeld to ask if anything had changed his mind about the remarks he made in 1979. Ihlenfeld was polite to me on the phone and quickly said that no, nothing had changed his mind. It is interesting in today's atmosphere of political correctness that Dr. Ihlenfeld, a homosexual, holds the view that gender-reassignment surgery isn't the answer to alleviate the psychological factors that drive the compulsion to change genders. I appreciate his honest, clinical evaluation of the evidence and refusal to bend the medical results to fit a particular political viewpoint.

Next let's take a look at the Johns Hopkins University Gender Clinic where the transgender girl gossiped about in the *New York Daily News* had her surgery. Dr. Paul McHugh became director of psychiatry and behavioral science in the mid-1970s and asked Dr. Jon Meyer, director of the clinic at the time, to conduct a thorough study of the outcomes of people treated at the clinic. McHugh says,

> [Those who underwent surgery] were little changed in their psychological condition. They had much the same problems with relationships, work, and emotions as before. The hope that they would emerge now from their emotional difficulties to flourish psychologically had not been fulfilled.[10]

In 2015 I sat across from Dr. McHugh in his office at Johns Hopkins University and asked him the same question I had asked Dr. Ihlenfeld: Had anything changed his mind regarding surgically made genders? McHugh told me that he has yet to see a medical justification for the surgical alteration of genitalia and that it is the obligation of medical practitioners to follow the science where it leads, rather than ignoring the science to advance political correctness.

These two powerful and influential doctors were early pioneers in the treatment of transsexualism. Dr. Ihlenfeld is a homosexual psychiatrist; Dr. Paul McHugh is a heterosexual psychiatrist. Both came to the same conclusion, then and now: Having surgery did not resolve the patients' psychological issues.

---

[10] http://www.firstthings.com/article/2004/11/surgical-sex

2000s: Were the psychological factors from the Hopkins and Benjamin clinics supported by later studies?

Studies show that the majority of transgender people have other co-occurring, or comorbid, psychological disorders.

A 2014 study found 62.7% of patients diagnosed with gender dysphoria had at least one co-occurring disorder, and 33% were found to have major depressive disorders[11], which are linked to suicide ideation. Another 2014 study of four European countries found that almost 70% of participants showed one or more Axis I disorders, mainly affective (mood) disorders and anxiety.[12]

In 2007, the Department of Psychiatry at Case Western Reserve University in Cleveland, Ohio, committed to a clinical review of the comorbid disorders of the last 10 patients interviewed at their Gender Identity Clinic. They found that "90% of these diverse patients had at least one other significant form of psychopathology . . . [including] problems of mood and anxiety regulation and adapting in the world. Two of the 10 have had persistent significant regrets about their previous transitions."[13]

Yet in the name of "civil rights," laws are being passed at all levels of government to prevent transgender patients from receiving therapies to diagnose and treat co-occurring mental disorders.

The authors of the Case Western Reserve University study seemed to see this legal wave coming when they said:

This finding seems to be in marked contrast to the public, forensic, and professional rhetoric of many who care for transgendered adults . . . Emphasis on civil rights is not a substitute for the recognition and treatment of associated psychopathology. Gender identity specialists, unlike the media, need to be concerned about the majority of patients, not just the ones who are apparently functioning well in transition.

As one who went through the surgery, I wholeheartedly agree. Politics doesn't mix well with science. When politics forces itself on medicine, patients are the ones who suffer.

What about the suicides?

Let's connect the dots. Transgender people report attempting suicide at a staggering rate—above 40%. According to Suicide.org, 90% of all suicides are the result of untreated mental disorders. Over 60% (and possibly up to 90% as shown at Case Western) of transgender people have comorbid psychiatric disorders, which often go wholly untreated.

Could treating the underlying psychiatric disorders prevent transgender suicides? I think the answer is a resounding "yes."

The evidence is staring us in the face. Tragically high numbers of transgender people attempt suicide. Suicide is the result of untreated mental disorders. A majority of transgender people suffer from

---

[11] http://www.ncbi.nlm.nih.gov/pubmed/25180172
[12] http://bjp.rcpsych.org/content/204/2/151.full
[13] http://www.ncbi.nlm.nih.gov/pubmed/19105079

untreated comorbid disorders—yet against all reason, laws are being enacted to prevent their treatment.

I write out of deep concern for the transgender men and women who attempt suicide, who are unhappy, and who want to go back to their birth gender. The other ones—those who appear to be functioning well in transition, at least for now during their "reprieve"—are celebrated in the media. But I hear from others—the ones who prefer to stay hidden, who are contemplating suicide, whose lives are torn apart, who have had the surgery but still have debilitating physical or psychological issues—the ones whose reprieve is over.

In the 1970s and now, gender-reassignment surgery is routinely performed when requested. Transgender people are the one population allowed to diagnose themselves with gender dysphoria solely on the basis of their desire for sex-reassignment surgery, and not because the medical community has found objective proof that such surgery is medically required.

After fifty years of surgical intervention in the United States, a scientific basis for surgical treatment of transgender people is still lacking. A task force commissioned by the American Psychiatric Association did a review of the literature on the treatment of gender identity disorder and in 2012 stated, "The quality of evidence pertaining to most aspects of treatment in all subgroups was determined to be low."[14] In 2004, the review of more than 100 international medical studies of post-operative transsexuals found "no robust scientific evidence that gender reassignment surgery is clinically effective."[15]

We hear the echoes from the pioneers at the Hopkins and Benjamin clinics and see their early conclusions confirmed in today's studies, showing again and again that psychiatric and psychological disorders exist in the psyches of gender-changers—but who is paying attention?

Scorn and vilification await anyone who dares to suggest that psychotherapy is needed to effectively treat gender dysphoria. Dr. McHugh, Dr. Ihlenfeld, and others like them display great integrity when they publicly raise concerns about psychological issues existing in the gender-changers, and when they push back against the "steamroller approach" of treatment that provides hormones and reassignment surgery without first pursuing less-invasive and life-altering treatment.

Advocates and trans-clients fear that if a psychologist or a psychiatrist looks too deeply into the patient's psyche they could discover the presence of a disorder that, if properly treated, would take away the dream of sex change, a fantasy they nurtured most of their lives. Living in denial is often a means of escape, a way to avoid looking back at early childhood events and doing the hard work of dealing with a painful past. The causes of these disorders lie buried so deep, and stirring them up leads to such high levels of anxiety, that changing one's identity and appearance—while extreme— seems preferable.

Thirty-three years ago I underwent gender-reassignment surgery only to discover it was a temporary reprieve, not a solution to the underlying comorbid disorders. I have written books, published articles,

---

[14] http://www.ncbi.nlm.nih.gov/pubmed/22736225
[15] http://www.theguardian.com/society/2004/jul/30/health.mentalhealth

and spoken publicly around the world to enlighten people on the prevalence of suicide among transgender people and on the risks and regrets of changing genders.

Television networks such as ABC that glamorize transgenders like Bruce Jenner, in his psychological turmoil, do a great disservice to transgender people and to those who treat them by denying them a safe environment in which to tackle the deeper issues of comorbid disorders and suicide. Continuing to ignore history and the warnings in studies and reports—however inconvenient or politically incorrect they may seem—is no solution to the treatment of psychological disorders. Ignoring suicides will not help to prevent them. Outlawing certain medical interventions when we know that 90% of suicides are due to untreated mental disorders and that a majority of transgender people have coexisting psychological disorders doesn't advance effective treatment protocols; it shuts down the freedom to follow where science leads.

Allowing a political agenda to override and silence the scientific process will not prevent suicides or lead to better treatments for this population. It's not compassion; it's reckless disregard for people's lives.

9 Transgender Patients Complain Of Mutilation, Botched Sex-Change Surgeries In Oregon

'The doctor basically used a bunch of trans people to experiment on and gain experience without being properly trained.'.

BY WALT HEYER
THE FEDERALIST, DECEMBER 6, 2018
THEFEDERALIST.COM/2018/12/06/9-TRANSGENDER-PATIENTS-
COMPLAIN-MUTILATION-BOTCHED-SEX-CHANGE-SURGERIES-OREGON/

Note: This article contains graphic details about transgender body mutilation and sex acts.

Ashe underwent a gender-change surgery in 2016 at the Oregon Health and Science University (OHSU) Hospital in Portland, to change his appearance from male to female. A mere 13 months later, Ashe was suicidal. Now, two years after surgery, Ashe wants to undo the surgery. (Ashe is a pseudonym.)

I found Ashe a bright, intelligent man who sincerely wants transgender people to have access to the care they need and want. But in his opinion, much improvement is needed in the OHSU Transgender Health Program (THP), which its website touts as "one of the most comprehensive and highest volume gender programs in the nation."[16]

The program may be "most comprehensive and highest volume," but what prospective patients care most deeply about is the quality of outcomes, not the quantity. To measure the quality of the health program, the data need to be measured, collected, and reported transparently in an unbiased way. Transparency and accountability about outcomes are some of the things Ashe told me he desires to see change.

Ashe is one of 16 patients he knows who are dissatisfied with their experience, nine of whom anonymously participated in a July 2018 letter to OHSU to point out their concerns and suggest specific recommendations to take transgender patient care to a higher level. Frustrated by the lack of response, and wanting the OHSU THP to provide better information to future transgender patients, Ashe gave me permission to publish his story and the group's permission to publish their letter.

'I Was Very Much Pushed into Transition'

The first recommendations in the letter are to implement advanced transgender-specific surgical training for the surgeons and a formal grievance procedure for the patients. Ashe told me in an email

---

[16] https://www.ohsu.edu/transgender-health, accessed Dec. 1, 2018

he felt rushed and pushed into having surgery by all his medical providers — therapist, general practitioner and surgeon. He wrote:

> The doctor [Dr. Daniel Dugi III] basically used a bunch of trans people to experiment on and gain experience without being properly trained. I was denied by him for an orchiectomy [removal of the testicles] and coerced into having SRS [Sex Reassignment surgery] by him and my GP [general practitioner] who was stressing that I needed to be castrated ASAP. I had previously told my therapists who wrote my letters [of approval] I never wanted surgery. I feel like I was very much pushed into transition as an answer to my mental health problems that were ignored by my 'gender' therapist.

The OHSU THP surgeon, Dugi, a urologist with a fellowship in trauma, reconstructive urology, and prosthetics[17], became interested in sex-change surgery during his career at OHSU. In 2015, with the blessing of OHSU, Dugi traveled to Belgium and Serbia to receive training and practiced the vaginoplasty procedure (formation of a vagina out of male genitalia) on cadavers. In May 2016, he performed his first vaginoplasty at OHSU.[18] Three months later, Ashe was on the gurney, headed for vaginoplasty surgery with Dugi.

No wonder Ashe felt that the surgeon was experimenting on him — Dugi was in the earliest stages of his newfound specialty. Other patients of Dugi dating from two years ago to January 2018 are among those who shared their surgical complications in the letter:

Note: This letter contains graphic details about transgender body mutilation and sex acts.

> Patient 1. I had surgery with Dr. Dugi almost a year ago. … The most significant issue being what appears to be an unfinished urethroplasty, leaving a hole where my urethra should be, large enough to place a thumb into. … The scrotum still was hair-producing, scrotal tissue was still used internally. I subsequently have internal hair growth. My clitoris is exceptionally large, and I have substantial holes on either side that never healed shut. My general aesthetic is not anatomical. I have what is believed to be permanent nerve damage in my right ankle, from the surgical positioning of my body during my 12-hour surgery.
>
> Patient 2. I had surgery with Dr. Dugi a couple years ago. … I've had extreme difficulty achieving orgasm to the extent that I no longer bother masturbating. I've had maybe ten orgasms in nearly two years, and rarely via sex. This lack of stimulation has led to me having near constant sexual dreams like I'm a teenager again, which is distracting and frustrating.
>
> Patient 3. I had gender confirmation surgery with Dr. Dugi a year ago [2017] this July 29th … Stimulus and response of my clitoris is marginal at best, and totally depressing at worst. Ninety per cent of the time that I urinate, I have an orgasm. Not sure how this came about, but the novelty has certainly paled significantly. The cosmetic appearance/value of the GCS I received isn't all that great …

---

[17] https://www.ohsu.edu/providers/daniel-d-dugi/F79D4C09578A4B0AB1E99567BFD8FA2F
[18] https://www.oregonlive.com/transgender-health/2016/05/ohsu_daniel_dugi.html

> Patient 4. Drs. Dugi and Berli performed my phalloplasty surgery (construction of a penis) almost two years ago. I had numerous complications, including lingering bad side effects from anesthesia and surgical trauma. Both surgeons misrepresented their expertise, experience, and readiness. My first of three surgeries was incomplete, and took 17 hours, more than twice as long as it should have. My penis is half as long as it's supposed to be due to poor surgical technique and cutting the flap shorter than agreed …
>
> Patient 5. [Ashe is Patient 5 and his story in the letter is similar to what he shared in his email above.]
>
> Patient 6. I had vaginoplasty in January with Dr. Dugi. I was off work for 8 weeks on medical leave. I had a series of post-op appointments after my surgery. I voiced concerns, as I felt like I was not urinating normally, and was assured that everything was fine. I experienced a "waterfall effect" when I was urinating, with no control over urine stream. My urethra lacks external structure to guide urine flow. I knew it was a major surgery, and the reality is that it would take time to heal. I knew for sure that there was something wrong when I began to experience discharge and became sick …

As the stories in the letter to the university clearly show, the number of surgical complications in this small group far exceeds the program's publicly stated total of three. These six stories and three more in the letter demonstrate why the group recommends that the OHSU THP begin collecting, evaluating, and independently reviewing patient results.

From their experience, they clearly see that the current data available from the program, reported by the surgeons themselves and not from an independent body, severely underreports the true number of surgical complications. They wrote:

> To be honest, the number of 'issues' we are aware of, represent higher rates of complications than what are expected with these surgeries.
>
> We feel the THP at OHSU has not been honest in reporting its outcomes thus far. While there is not currently a data system tracking outcomes for patients, the program has publicly stated that there have been a total of 3 surgical complications. We need a standardized process of assessment, with agreed upon benchmarks as determined by patients and surgeons … Ethical concerns abound when surgeons self-report their data, and determine the variable of success on behalf of the patient at the points of query. Further concerns are found when the THP is reporting a number significantly lower than what is factual based on patient stories. This discrepancy must be addressed by the THP at OHSU immediately.

Of Course, Taxpayers Are Paying for This

OHSU THP is the major provider of sex change surgery in Oregon. In January 2015, Oregon Medicaid (known as Oregon Health Plan) started paying for sex reassignment surgery — the same year that Dugi went abroad for training. State regulators estimated 175 patients would use the benefit that first year at a cost to taxpayers of less than $150,000. The reality was different by orders of magnitude — more than 700 people used it and the budget was three times higher than estimated.[19]

Any Oregon resident whose income falls below a certain threshold is eligible for Medicaid benefits. A quick look on social media shows one solution being touted for free gender change surgery is to move to Oregon, keep one's income below the limit, and allow Medicaid to pay the entire cost.

Ashe told me he believes the OHSU THP is prone to fast-tracking Medicaid recipients for gender-change surgery. The group letter shares concerns about potential harm done as a result to the indigent patients at OHSU THP:

> What is perhaps the most troubling to us, are the demographics associated with who is accessing surgery at the THP at OHSU. While OHSU is not responsible for holding a monopoly on genital surgery options, the fact remains that most recipients of Medicaid in Oregon who seek these surgeries, are funneled toward the THP at OHSU. The intersection of no additional options for low-income folks on Medicaid, and a program that has had as many issues as the THP has, means that too many people have come out of the program harmed without the financial or social means to do anything about it… While we do not believe that this is the intention on the part of the THP, the facts remain.

Historically, doctors and hospitals don't get rich by treating Medicaid patients, but if they are looking to establish a transgender health program quickly, Medicaid patients would be an extra source of cases, over and above self-paying and insured patients. Certainly, the perception that THP gained surgical experience at the expense of low-income folks because that population lacks the wherewithal to fight back bears further investigation.

Having taxpayers pay for gender changes for poor people might sound humanitarian and caring to some people, but neglects to answer the longer-term funding questions, such as: Who pays for fixing surgical complications? Who pays for gender change reversals when patients like Ashe want to detransition? Will Medicaid pay? Will the surgeons work for free? Will OSHU THP provide the care and absorb the costs?

No Psych Evaluation Required to Change Your Life Forever

For Ashe, now 24, the OHSU THP failed to provide effective pre-surgical protocols to keep him from having surgery he didn't want. He says at the time of his surgery the THP did not require an extensive psychiatric evaluation.

In fact, many gender clinics (and their clients) are opposed to psychiatric evaluations, even though that could help prevent people like Ashe from being suicidal after surgery. I can tell you from my personal view 35 years post-surgery that people who take their own lives after surgery are the collateral damage inflicted by the existing flawed transgender health system. Psychiatric evaluation before life-altering surgery is a must.

As the group letter points out, putting improvements in place is fundamental to safeguarding patients. Their recommendations include transparency of the data regarding gender change outcomes,

---

[19] https://www.oregonlive.com/transgender-health/2016/04/oregon_health_plan_transgender.html

independent evaluation, and access to formal grievance procedures. But in today's transgender medical environment, the proverbial foxes are guarding the hen house and negative outcomes are kept under wraps. Ashe says when he raised questions about his care, his claims were dismissed by the hospital as being irrelevant.

Based on the people who write me with sex change regret, the happenings at OHSU THP aren't rare occurrences. Stories hauntingly similar have come into my inbox over the years and are captured in my book, "Trans Life Survivors," from people like Ashe who felt they were rushed into surgery or whose feelings later changed and they want to detransition.

Ashe said he didn't want the surgery, but his therapists approved him, his GP pushed him, and his gender therapist ignored his mental health issues. Like most people with gender dysphoria, Ashe trusted the medical professionals' expert advice and went ahead with surgery, only to realize after that surgery was a mistake.

My own sex change surgery story 35 years ago exhibits the same themes — a rush to surgery, failure to diagnose or treat co-existing mental health problems, and later, regret and detransition. Fortunately, I survived it all.

As I've written before[20], I believe that true compassion for this segment of our society that is suffering is shown by raising factual issues, based on scientific research, and having the best minds follow the evidence to provide the best scientifically proven care. Packaging the issue in the wrapper of political correctness or withholding the negative findings is not care or compassion.

---

[20] https://thefederalist.com/2015/08/19/transgender-regret-is-real-even-if-the-media-tell-you-otherwise/

This Man Received 167 Sex-Change Surgeries.
He Lives in a World of Regret.

Blair Logsdon's 167 surgeries cost him $220,000 and left him, in his words, "disfigured."

BY WALT HEYER
THE DAILY SIGNAL, JANUARY 12, 2018
WWW.DAILYSIGNAL.COM/2018/01/12/
MAN-RECEIVED-167-SEX-CHANGE-SURGERIES-LIVES-WORLD-REGRET/

Recently I interviewed a person whose experience with gender-change surgeries was so extreme, it gained him entry in the Guinness World Records book for the most gender-reassignment surgeries for an individual person.[21]

Blair Logsdon's story is a cautionary tale for anyone today who is considering the use of cross-gender hormones and gender-change surgery to feel better about themselves.

Logsdon underwent 167 surgeries from 1987 to 2005 in his quest to resolve gender dysphoria with surgery. On a cold, snowy December morning in a Maryland coffee shop, he shared with me his story.

In 1987, at the age of 26, he underwent the first of many cosmetic surgeries to change his gender/sex appearance from male to trans-female. Within a few months, he said he deeply regretted becoming a trans-woman.

For the next five years, he struggled in his life as a woman before undergoing a genital surgical change to restore his original male self.

But peace with his gender eluded him.

With gender dysphoria still present and feeling unsettled, Logsdon underwent yet another gender change and returned to self-identifying as trans-female.

Doctors, apparently with total and reckless disregard for Logsdon's emotional, psychological, and sexual well-being, ignored his obvious distress about previous cosmetic surgeries and indulged his requests for more.

Logsdon said he continued to have regrets about the feminizing surgeries, even as he strongly felt the need for more, caught in a cycle of hope followed by disappointment.

By 2005, seven cosmetic surgeons had performed 167 gender-affirming surgeries on his body, filling their bank accounts to the tune of more than $220,000 and leaving him, in his words, "disfigured."

Logsdon says he regrets all 167 surgeries. No longer turning to the surgeons to discover his "true self," he has found his true male self in following Jesus Christ.

---

[21] http://www.guinnessworldrecords.com/world-records/most-gender-reassignment-surgery

I do not blame Logsdon one bit in his case. The doctors and surgeons failed him in their responsibility to "first, do no harm"—as the Hippocratic Oath says—and wrongfully profited from the 167 disfiguring surgeries. Yet, they will not be held accountable or responsible for gross medical misconduct or malpractice against this good man.

At some point, these surgeons should have refused requests for more surgery and protected Logsdon from harming himself further. Instead, they chose to take advantage of his emotionally, psychological, or sexually unhealthy and unstable psyche.

Transgender People Could Benefit from Hearing the Truth

As a society we, too, fail transgender people by withholding the truth from them in the belief that telling the truth is somehow offensive and hateful. No—following the evidence is not hate speech, it is the foundation of the scientific research.

Several core truths have been relegated to the category of hate speech. For example:

- There is no objective evidence to show that transgender people even exist, beyond the person's own feelings and gender-dysphoric imagination.
- Strong persistent feelings of being the opposite sex are not based in biology ("born this way"), but stem from emotional, psychological, or sexual factors.
- Ignoring the protocols of effective psychological diagnosis harms trans-people because it guarantees they will not get effective treatment for coexisting disorders.

The Truth: Psychotherapy Is Important

For the last 50 years, the transgender ideology has grown progressively more deadly and destructive as it takes lives via suicide, destroys marriages, rips family relationships apart (including my own), and now expects the whole of society to reject the physical truth about sex and gender in public places and in social interactions, under the threat of ostracization and legal prosecution.

Transgender people are provided only one remedy: to wholeheartedly embrace an alternative gender/sex ideology that attempts to redefine their gender/sex and promises healing.

When the cross-gender hormonal and surgical protocols and lifestyle changes fail to bring relief to those experiencing gender dysphoria, as Logsdon found, often what remains is depression, despair, and regret, leading some to attempt suicide.

Doctors should focus on uncovering the parallel disorders that often lie at the root of the trans-person's distorted self-identity. These often include alcohol abuse, drug usage, chronic depression, and personality disorders.

Uncovering these disorders results from engaging in effective psychotherapy, not surgery.

Providing psychotherapy first in the treatment of gender dysphoria could be a key factor in reversing the staggering 41 percent rate of suicide attempts among transgender individuals.

It could also reduce the number of people who seek out self-mutilation in an attempt to find inner peace, and thus prevent these people from digging deep wells of regret.

I'm sure I will catch some heat for publicly sharing the truth here. But saving one life is worth the heat.

If you've seen the 1992 film "A Few Good Men," you'll remember the pivotal courtroom scene where Col. Nathan Jessup (played by Jack Nicholson) shouts at the cross-examination lawyer (played by Tom Cruise) the now-famous line, "You can't handle the truth!"

The same can be said today to those who declare that the only treatment for gender dysphoria is to affirm it, to give patients cross-gender hormones, and to perform gender-change surgeries: "You can't handle the truth!"

In The Past 5 Years, The Transgender Explosion Has Wounded More And More People

---

What's changed in the last five years is the explosion in the number of children and adolescents diagnosed with gender dysphoria and the lack of help for them.

BY WALT HEYER
THE FEDERALIST, JANUARY 13, 2020
THEFEDERALIST.COM/2020/01/13/IN-THE-PAST-5-YEARS-THE-
TRANSGENDER-EXPLOSION-HAS-WOUNDED-MORE-AND-MORE-PEOPLE/

Five years ago, I started writing about gender identity and the harm of gender change not because I was a psychiatrist, college professor, or some extraordinarily brilliant guy, but because of living it.[22] I underwent the full physical surgery from male to female at age 42, lived as "Laura Jensen" for eight years, then came to realize my unresolved childhood trauma drove the overwhelming desire to escape into another gender.

Through hard work and effective psychological counseling, I resolved the wounds of the past and my desire to be a woman dissipated. I re-identified as Walt Heyer legally and socially, removed the breast implants, and with the support of an amazing group of friends, built my life anew, this time on psychological wholeness. I've been happily married to a biological woman for more than 22 years now.

Having been given a second chance at life, I feel compelled to share this hope with others by writing and speaking out against the lie that "regret is rare"[23] and to expose the lies of the sex change movement from an insider's perspective. What's changed in the last five years is the explosion in the number of children and adolescents diagnosed with gender dysphoria[24] and the tight stranglehold excluding other treatment options.

Real Help for Trans People Has Evaporated

Five years ago, my first article, "What Parents of Trans Kids Need to Know,"[25] gave background and advice that still stands. Children might identify as the opposite gender due to co-existing disorders or a history of abuse. I advised parents to work with a professional to identify the cause of the stress and cautioned them to avoid any professional who advocates for gender change. I assured parents that they are in the best position to identify the root cause of their child's distress.

---

[22] https://www.thepublicdiscourse.com/2015/04/14688/

[23] https://thefederalist.com/2015/08/19/transgender-regret-is-real-even-if-the-media-tell-you-otherwise/

[24] https://www.thepublicdiscourse.com/2019/03/50118/

[25] https://thefederalist.com/2015/01/09/heres-what-parents-of-transgender-kids-need-to-know/

Now parents tell me that finding a therapist who doesn't advocate for gender change is almost impossible. Sixteen states and innumerable cities have outlawed counseling for children that dares to explore the cause of the gender distress.[26] A distinguished university child psychiatry chair, Dr. Josephson, lost his position[27] at the University of Louisville because he publicly stated the need for medical professionals to ask "Why?" when a young person rejects his or her sex.

Counselors or researchers who pursue such answers or consider other factors, such as sexual or emotional abuse, are at risk of being ostracized. In states that have banned the therapy, they will lose their license to practice.

Parents, do not take your children to "gender clinics." Gender clinics exclude any option except transgenderism. They hand out[28] powerful cross-sex hormones like Halloween candy to anyone who knocks at the door. Surgeons stand ready to carve up the bodies of young people, performing double mastectomies on healthy girls as young[29] as 13 and refashioning the genitalia of teenage boys, channeling Doctor Frankenstein. The negative outcomes do not matter[30] to them.

Public schools and universities loom large as contributors to the boom in gender transition among youth. I routinely hear from parents whose children as college freshmen "come out" as transgender after a semester or two away at school, when previously they exhibited no signs of gender incongruity or distress.

I have a new warning for parents of trans kids, based on the past five years of experience. Be extremely aware and wary of school authority figures—teachers, counselors, social workers—and the internet. These often collaborate to misguide teens toward gender change.

Reports of Regret from Former Trans Kids

It was inevitable and predictable: As more children are misdiagnosed with gender dysphoria and loaded onto the transition train, the more reports of regret emerge. I have recently received a steady stream of emails from young adults who followed the pathway to transition and now want help in undoing it. Here are some of their stories

Sydney, a bright and engaging woman on the verge of her 21st birthday, regretted only two years after going from female to male using hormones at age 19. She's one of the lucky ones—still young enough to have a "do-over" without having wasted many years like so many of us.

She wrote about her experience in an article, "I Spent a Year as a Trans Man. Doctors Failed Me at Every Turn."[31] Her masculine physical appearance will gradually fade as the effects of taking testosterone wear off. But living through the upheaval of detransition takes patience and perseverance.

---

[26] https://www.usnews.com/news/best-states/articles/2019-04-11/these-states-have-banned-conversion-therapy

[27] https://www.adflegal.org/detailspages/press-release-details/univ.-of-louisville-to-faculty-express-your-views-at-your-own-risk

[28] https://www.lifesitenews.com/news/state-coerced-child-gender-transitioning-is-here-parents-are-horrified

[29] https://thefederalist.com/2018/09/12/u-s-doctors-performing-double-mastectomies-healthy-13-year-old-girls/

[30] https://www.dailysignal.com/2020/01/02/transgender-clinics-are-ruining-young-lives/

[31] https://www.dailysignal.com/2019/10/07/i-spent-a-year-as-a-trans-man-doctors-failed-me-at-every-turn/

Nathaniel, who as a teen questioned his gender identity, at age 18 had the full "bottom surgery" that altered his male genitalia into a pseudo-vagina. He regretted it just a year later and asked me to help him.

In elementary school, Nathaniel says he was bullied by boys because he was sensitive and preferred playing girl games. When he was a bit older, he discovered internet pornography, heard about transgenderism, and "convinced myself that's what I was." Nathaniel started seeing the doctor a week after his 15th birthday, and from how he describes the next years of his teens, I'd say going to the clinic didn't improve his life.

"From then on," he says, "I slowly detached from everything until I was just staying home, playing video games, and going on the internet all day. I stopped reading, drawing, riding my bicycle. I surrounded myself in an echo chamber that supported and validated my poor decisions, because the others were also, unfortunately, stuck in that pit, too."

His parents were not in favor of his detransition back to male, but after reading my article, "1 Year After Sex Change, This Teen Regrets His 'Frankenstein Hack Job,'"[32] they are helping him.

The Economist 1843 Magazine told the story of Max's detransition[33] in September 2017, which I included in an article[34] for The Federalist. Max came out as transgender to her parents around age 15, saw a therapist, and against the therapist's advice insisted that she had to have hormones and surgery. She started testosterone shortly before she turned 17 and had a mastectomy the following year.

It was a happy time for Max. But only six months after she began successfully passing as a male, she realized, deep down, that she wasn't sure anymore. When Max was 19, a little more than three years after she came out as transgender, she realized she'd made a mistake and began detransitioning.

Explosion in Trans Identification and Media Attention

Do not surrender to the trans madness. I witness too many people with too much unhappiness after a gender transition. Having a front-row seat to people's pain through their personal, vulnerable emails fuels my drive to expose what goes on behind the scenes in the gender change industry today.

I have written books to help people learn about the regret of transitioning. My latest, "Trans Life Survivors,"[35] has sections on children, research and resources, and importantly, it shares stories of 30 people who were swept up by gender change. They share what they think caused the desire for a new persona and why they decided to go back to identifying as their God-given sex. Often the cause can be traced to childhood abuse.

---

[32] https://www.dailysignal.com/2019/11/17/1-year-after-sex-change-this-teen-regrets-his-frankenstein-hack-job/
[33] https://www.1843magazine.com/features/when-girls-wont-be-girls
[34] https://thefederalist.com/2017/11/16/three-transgenders-celebrate-election-victories-detransitioners-tell-different-story/
[35] https://www.amazon.com/Trans-Life-Survivors-Walt-Heyer/dp/173234535X/ref=sr_1_1?crid=3W2M70L1DKUET&keywords=walt+heyer&qid=1576798960&s=books&sprefix=walt+heyer%2Caps%2C326&sr=1-1

Writer Stella Morabito asks:[36] "Can you imagine what it must be like to tell a therapist of your experience being abused as a child, which you offer as a possible explanation for your dysphoria, only to have the psychiatrist totally ignore that aspect of your past and instead push you to sex-change procedures as the only way to overcome your angst?"

That's what happened to me more than 30 years ago and continues to happen to children and adults today. My attempt to shine a light on the ongoing wreckage on vulnerable people, especially children, due to the rampant practice of mutilating people's bodies to match the error in their self-perception has resulted in more than 50 articles published over the last five years in publications like The Federalist, USA Today, The Washington Times, and others.

The purpose of my website, sexchangeregret.com, is to provide hope and resources to anyone who wants them and offer a listening ear to those in distress—the thousands of people who transitioned, found it wasn't for them, and want their "true self" back.

My true self is found in my biological sex. Gender and sex is fixed and does not change because of hormones, red pumps, or plastic surgery. I won't surrender to the trans-madness and I suggest you don't give up or give in to the insanity either.

---

[36] https://thefederalist.com/2019/01/03/30-transgender-regretters-come-closet-new-book/

Chapter 2.
Children

The Experiment on Our Children:
Doctors Don't Know Who the Real Trans Kids Are

Doctors currently have no way of predicting which gender dysphoric children will persist in their gender dysphoria, and yet they are pushing the minimum age for irreversible hormone therapy and surgery as low as possible.

BY WALT HEYER
PUBLIC DISCOURSE, JUNE 12, 2017
HTTPS://WWW.THEPUBLICDISCOURSE.COM/2017/06/19512/

According to the wisdom of the day, kids experiencing gender dysphoria need to be treated affirmingly as early—and as radically—as possible. For the time being, surgery and hormone therapy have to wait until age sixteen. But before that, adolescents can be prescribed puberty blockers, and even younger children are encouraged to transition "socially," by adopting the name, dress, and mannerisms of their preferred gender.

All of this is in spite of the fact that gender dysphoria in children sees very low rates of persistence—ranging from 2.2% to 30% in males and from 12% to 50% in females, according to the DSM-5. As Dr. Kristina Olson, a research psychologist at the University of Washington, put it, "We just don't have definitive data one way or another." The truth is that no one can predict whether a gender dysphoric kid will feel the same way years later. That's why Olson is leading a study of 300 trans kids that will track outcomes over twenty years. "To be able to, hopefully, answer which children should or should not transition," she said.[37] In the meantime, many of those children will be encouraged to go ahead and make life-altering medical decisions in light of scientific ignorance.

Standards Are Getting Looser, Not More Stringent

The standard medical and social response to gender dysphoria is to encourage and affirm the child's self-diagnosis and to provide hormone therapies and unnecessary social and medical gender transitions without thoroughly exploring alternative effective treatment plans.

In fact, a team of international doctors affiliated with The Endocrine Society, the Pediatric Endocrine Society, and the World Professional Association of Transgender Health—all of which are held in esteem in this field of medicine—is rewriting treatment guidelines so that a medically induced gender change may be recommended for children even younger than sixteen.[38] This represents a huge

---

[37] http://www.nbcbayarea.com/investigations/Transgender-Kids-Eligible-for-Earlier-Medical-Intervention-Under-New-Guidelines-423082734.html

[38] http://www.pbs.org/wgbh/frontline/article/when-transgender-kids-transition-medical-risks-are-both-known-and-unknown/

departure from what were already lenient guidelines for treating children who feel they are in the wrong gender.

Until now, the guidelines recommended giving preadolescent children puberty blockers to give more time to decide about going forward with more invasive treatment. But under the new guidelines, the more invasive treatment of cross-gender hormones will be recommended for children younger than age sixteen. Many physical effects of hormones, such as reduced bone density and reduced fertility, are irreversible. Other risks haven't been studied at all.

Making an Informed Decision Is Impossible

Recently an email arrived in my inbox with the subject "I wish I listened to you" from a young man who regrets taking cross-sex hormones and undergoing surgery.

> I'm only in my mid [twenties]. I transitioned in my teens and had surgery. I was [too] young to make such a decision. I've sunken into such a deep regret. I don't even feel transgender anymore. I feel like my old self. I am happy with a female appearance but that is all I really needed. I feel like I was brainwashed by the transgender agenda and by gender norm expectations. I would do anything to [have] my penis back. My feelings were confusing and I thought they would never go away. I'm just a guy who's really in touch with my feminine side. I can't believe what I've done to my life. And now I have no choice but to take hormones forever. I don't know what to do. I feel like I'm losing my mind. All I would have had to do was discontinue my hormones and everything would have been alright. I honestly feel 100% normal and okay . . . if only I had never had that surgery.

This young man's body is permanently damaged because doctors, who have no definitive idea as to who will persist in a condition of gender dysphoria, propose irreversible treatments for young people who feel conflicted about gender. But as this young man found out, even strongly held feelings change.

My own story was similar: I was a trans kid, and I underwent gender change surgery after waiting until I became an adult. Living in unrelenting gender confusion for most of my life and desiring a resolution, I took the transition path that top gender doctors recommended for me. I trusted their guidance. But that didn't prevent the wave of regret that followed.

Firsthand accounts such as this one confirm the empirical data: no one knows who should transition or at what age, if anyone ever should. Given our inability to predict the future of children's dysphoria, any doctor who is actively administering hormone blockers based on a child's feelings is ignoring or dismissing the biological facts and pretending to knowledge he or she cannot have. Ignoring the science is malpractice and places the children and parents at risk of deep lifelong regret for having agreed to unnecessary procedures.

Young children are making this "decision" based on feelings, not verifiable lab tests, but children are much too young to make such a life-changing, and likely regrettable, decision.[39] Kids and parents need to be able to trust that doctors will not play a game of Russian roulette with their lives.

Social Transition Is Not Harmless Either

Even if it's unwise to make hormonal and surgical interventions into gender dysphoric kids' lives, isn't it a good idea to help them socially transition, in case they want to transition years later, as adults? No: this practice is not without serious risks either.

As Eric Vilain, a geneticist and leader of the Center for Genetic Medicine Research at Children's National Health System, points out, social transitioning is liable to influence children's thinking. "If the children are pushed in this belief it will be much harder for them to get out of this belief because everyone will have agreed on it very, very early on," Dr. Vilain says. It's one thing to grow up confused about one's gender; it's another thing to grow up being told that one belongs to a special group of "trans kids."[40]

But getting everyone—parents, siblings, fellow students—to agree that a young boy is a girl doesn't make it so, and it doesn't change the empirical fact that no one is able to predict which gender dysphoric children will remain gender dysphoric as time goes on. None of this is even to address the question of whether those who do persist in their gender dysphoria will find the relief they desire by transitioning. Yet children encouraged to socially transition are being placed "on a path that will have a lot of medical and surgical consequences," and they will be all the more likely to take irreversible steps because they have been told for their whole lives that they are "trans," that they are "really" the gender they think they are.

But—according to the most recent scientific evidence on the persistence of childhood gender dysphoria—many of these children would have grown out of their gender dysphoria on their own. Lowering the minimum age for surgery only increases the chance that kids will agree to a procedure that they will deeply regret.

Transgender children should not be placed on the path of unnecessary and irreversible medical interventions that include cross-gender hormones and body-altering surgeries. The scientific community simply has not demonstrated the long-term efficacy or studied the risks and harms being done.

In the meantime, don't let the rhetoric surrounding this issue distract you from the fact: we are performing an experiment on our children. We will learn twenty years from now, when Dr. Olson's study is complete, whether the doctors were wrong. So we wait.

---

[39] http://thefederalist.com/2015/02/02/what-parents-should-know-about-giving-hormones-to-trans-kids/
[40] http://www.nbcbayarea.com/investigations/Transgender-Kids-Eligible-for-Earlier-Medical-Intervention-Under-New-Guidelines-423082734.html

Kids Aren't Born Transgender, So Don't Let Advocates Bamboozle You

---

The American Psychological Association and the weight of historical evidence both challenge society's affirmation of cross-sex identities.

BY WALT HEYER
THE DAILY SIGNAL, MARCH 29. 2019
WWW.DAILYSIGNAL.COM/2019/03/29/KIDS-ARENT-BORN-TRANSGENDER-SO-DONT-LET-ADVOCATES-BAMBOOZLE-YOU/

People who pursue a cross-sex identity aren't born that way, and children should not be encouraged to "transition" to the opposite sex, according to a reference work endorsed by the American Psychological Association.

Yet every day I hear from another parent who tells me that a child's therapist, after an appointment or two, strongly recommends that the parent allow the child to change his or her name and personal pronouns, live as the opposite sex, and get on the track toward irreversible medical interventions.

Laura Haynes, a licensed psychologist in California, recently reviewed[41] the APA Handbook of Sexuality and Psychology[42] and highlighted its research findings about transgender children.

Among those findings, cited on page 744 of Volume 1:

- "In no more than about one in four children does gender dysphoria persist from childhood to adolescence or adulthood," with the majority of affected boys later identifying as gay, not transgender, and up to half of affected girls identifying as lesbian, not transgender.
- "Early social transition (i.e., change of gender role, such as registering a birth-assigned boy in school as a girl) should be approached with caution to avoid foreclosing this stage of gender identity development."
- "Early social transition may be necessary for some; however, the stress associated with possible reversal of this decision has been shown to be substantial."

Yet we all have been bamboozled by distorted claims to the contrary from sex-change advocates, who insist the science is settled.

---

[41] http://www.therapyequality.org/american-psychological-association-says-born-way-cant-change-not-true-sexual-orientation-gender-identity

[42] https://www.amazon.com/APA-Handbook-Sexuality-Psychology-Handbooks/dp/1433813696/ref=sr_1_fkmrnull_2?crid=12574SGT1BDRX&keywords=apa+handbook+of+sexuality+and+psychology&qid=1551456712&s=gateway&sprefix=the+apa+handbook+of+sexu%2Caps%2C251&sr=8-2-fkmrnull

They say people who identify as the opposite sex will never change their mind, the cross-sex identity is fixed and the earlier the child, teen, or adult is affirmed as the opposite sex and makes the transition, the better off he or she will be.

In fact, however, the American Psychological Association and the weight of historical evidence both challenge society's affirmation of cross-sex identities.

The preface to the APA Handbook of Sexuality and Psychology, published in 2014, says it is endorsed and approved by the American Psychological Association, which describes itself as "the largest scientific and professional organization representing psychology in the United States and the largest association of psychologists in the world."

I underwent my own "sex change" in April 1983. I had no idea then that I would be here today talking about the subject, or that the evidence against "born that way" had started oozing out as early as 1979, four years before I was mutilated.

In 1979 an endocrinologist, Dr. Charles L. Ihlenfeld, sounded a warning on using hormones and surgery on the transgender population in remarks to a group of clinicians. Ihlenfeld had administered hormone therapy for six years to a large sample of 500 trans-identified adults.

Ihlenfeld, who is gay, told the clinicians that "80 percent of the people who want to change their sex shouldn't do it." Desires to change sex, he said, "most likely stem from powerful psychological factors—likely from the experiences of the first 18 months of life."[43]

Ihlenfeld's comments 40 years ago foreshadowed the evidence provided in the APA Handbook, where page 743 of Volume 1 says that identifying as the opposite sex is "most likely the result of a complex interaction between biological and environmental factors."

"Research on the influence of family of origin dynamics," it adds, "has found some support for separation anxiety among gender-nonconforming boys and psychopathology among mothers."

Ihlenfeld and the APA, generations apart in time, came to a similar conclusion: The desire to change sex most likely stems from early life experiences and psychological factors.

As to the wisdom and effectiveness of using cross-sex hormones and sex-change surgery to treat gender dysphoria, the evidence does not exist.

In the United Kingdom, the University of Birmingham's Aggressive Research Intelligence Facility conducted a review in 2004 of 100 international medical studies of "post-operative transsexuals." It found "no conclusive evidence [that] sex-change operations improve the lives of transsexuals."[44]

Additionally, the evidence showed that the transsexual person, after undergoing reassignment surgery, "remains severely distressed to the point of suicide."

A professor at Oxford University, Carl Heneghan, is one recent voice questioning cross-sex hormone use in children and adolescents. Heneghan is editor-in-chief of a respected British medical journal, BMJ Evidence-Based Medicine.

---

[43] http://lvtgw.jadephoenix.org/Info_htm/Herbal_G/ginko_b2.htm
[44] https://www.theguardian.com/society/2004/jul/30/health.mentalhealth

On Feb. 25, Heneghan and a fellow researcher reported significant problems with how evidence is collected and analyzed, concluding:

> Treatments for under 18 gender dysphoric children and adolescents remain largely experimental. There are a large number of unanswered questions that include the age at start, reversibility, adverse events, long-term effects on mental health, quality of life, bone mineral density, osteoporosis in later life and cognition.[45]

So the negative findings stack up, and alarms are raised about the lack of proof concerning effectiveness and safety. But administering unnecessary hormones and rearranging healthy body parts with sex-change surgeries continue undaunted by a deaf medical community.

I feel like I'm standing alongside the road shouting to warn approaching drivers: "The bridge is out! The bridge is out!"

Because I know—I drove off that cliff, and I'm still affected 35 years later.

The APA Handbook of Sexuality and Psychology, again, says that transgender people are not born that way, that cross-sex identification can change, and that the majority of children grow out of a desire to change sex if they don't engage in social transition.

Strangely, the medical and psychological community doesn't follow its own evidence and seems oblivious to the experiment they're conducting on real lives, especially those of children.

The sex-change cheerleaders falsely claim, "Affirmation is the only solution." They use distorted doctrine to lobby for laws that punish counselors and parents who say otherwise, laws that take away the rights of patients to choose their own therapy goals.

Organizations such as The Trevor Project are lobbying in all 50 states to outlaw any therapy that suggests interest in cross-sex transition can change.[46]

Meanwhile, accounts such as these of families[47] and lives being ripped to shreds by sex change appear in my inbox daily. I have compiled 30 of the stories I've received, along with recent research, in my own book "Trans Life Survivors."

We must wake up and use the evidence provided in the APA Handbook to counter those who say transgender people are born that way.

Instead, we must fight loudly for the rights of patients to choose their counseling goals and against laws that legislate affirmation as the only therapy allowed.

---

[45] https://blogs.bmj.com/bmjebmspotlight/2019/02/25/gender-affirming-hormone-in-children-and-adolescents-evidence-review/

[46] https://www.usatoday.com/story/opinion/voices/2018/12/27/gay-conversion-therapy-lgbtq-law-harm-column/2413310002/

[47] Public Discourse, "In Their Own Words: Parents of Kids Who Think They Are Trans Speak Out," February 26, 2019, by Five Anonymous Moms, https://www.thepublicdiscourse.com/2019/02/49686/

There Is No Solid Evidence of Genetic Basis for Trans Identity

A recent study exploring whether genes may play a role in transgender identity was inconclusive, despite some media suggestions to the contrary.

BY WALT HEYER
THE DAILY SIGNAL, APRIL 3. 2018
WWW.DAILYSIGNAL.COM/2018/04/03/
NO-SOLID-EVIDENCE-GENETIC-BASIS-TRANS-IDENTITY/

A new study into the genes of those who identify as transgender has picked up decent amount of media attention.

The Times in the United Kingdom hailed what it called a genetic "discovery" with the headline "Science pinpoints DNA behind gender identity."[48] LGBTQ Nation ran a more inconclusive headline: "Scientists discover DNA that could be responsible for gender identity."[49]

The Times should have paid more attention to Dr. John Theisen, the lead researcher, who said the genes they identified pointed to a "possibility, not a fact." He cautioned that his research, still in its early stages, used only a small sample size (30 people) and has yet to be peer reviewed—both reasons for exercising major caution when interpreting the results.

In fact, closer examination of the abstract from the research paper reveals that finding a genetic basis for transgender identity wasn't even the intended purpose of the study. The purpose was much narrower in scope: to identify genes that might point to a potential biological basis so future research could know where to focus its efforts.

In the conclusion, the researchers say, "We identified genetic variants in 20 genes that may play a role in transgender identity." [50] Words are important, and the word "may" indicates a possibility, not a fact.

Another much larger study is being conducted to explore whether transgender identity has any biological basis. That study, which includes 10,000 participants, is looking to the genome—a person's complete set of DNA—for clues about whether transgender identity has a biological basis. The findings are years away, though, and completion of the project depends on securing more funding.[51]

In the meantime, no absolute conclusions can be made about a genetic basis for transgender identity.

---

[48] https://www.thetimes.co.uk/article/science-pinpoints-dna-behind-gender-identity-3vmrgrdnv

[49] https://www.lgbtqnation.com/2018/03/scientists-discover-dna-responsible-gender-identity/

[50] http://www.abstractsonline.com/pp8/#!/4592/presentation/578

[51] https://www.reuters.com/article/us-usa-lgbt-biology/born-this-way-researchers-explore-the-science-of-gender-identity-idUSKBN1AJ0F0

Some of the difficulty in fashioning a study to find a biological link to transgender identities arises from the definition of the term "transgender." Medically speaking, a transgender person is defined as someone who has been diagnosed with gender dysphoria, a condition where a person experiences discomfort or distress arising from a mismatch between their biological sex and internal sense of gender identity.

The problem is that transgender identity is based solely on subjective criteria. There is no objective, robust physical test to prove whether "transgender persons" exist beyond a person strongly insisting that he or she is a transgender person.

It's difficult to even discern who truly has gender dysphoria. Those who self-identify as "transgender" represent a challenging cross-section of individuals. They may be simple cross-dressers, transvestites, or drag queens, yet they may or may not have gender dysphoria.

Many transgender persons are suffering emotionally, psychologically, or psychiatrically, sometimes due to early childhood trauma or co-existing mental disorders. Studies have shown that nearly 70 percent of people diagnosed with gender dysphoria also suffer from a wide variety of co-existing disorders that often go undiagnosed and untreated.

With no medical proof to help diagnose gender dysphoria, and with most who identify as transgender having other issues that need treatment, one could argue that too many people are being gathered under the blanket term "transgender" and being inappropriately directed toward cross-gender hormone therapies and surgeries.

The original advocates of gender change started a social experiment in the 1960s that continues today. Alfred Kinsey, Dr. Harry Benjamin, and Dr. John Money fell short in providing proof that cross-gender hormone therapies and surgeries provide long-term, effective results for gender disorders. The 50 years of reported suicides and a suicide attempt rate of 40 percent suggest that treatments have failed the gender distressed population.

As a young person, I was correctly diagnosed with gender dysphoria and then approved for hormones and surgery by Dr. Paul Walker, the original author of the "Harry Benjamin International Standards of Care." The treatment was not effective.

I discovered firsthand that society wasn't the cause of transgender suicide and suicide attempts. The cause was an unfulfilled expectation that cross-gender hormones and surgery would effectively resolve gender distress.

I remain open to the possibility that a biological predisposition to transgender identities may be found. Whether it is found or not, my hope is that today's barbaric, mutilating gender-change procedures will be replaced by an effective treatment that eliminates the high rate of suicide ideation and brings long-lasting relief to those with gender dysphoria.

Here's What Parents Of Transgender Kids Need To Know

Immediately treating a transgender child as his opposite sex without addressing his underlying psychological needs will hurt him—probably forever.

BY WALT HEYER
THE FEDERALIST, JANUARY 9, 2015
THEFEDERALIST.COM/2015/01/09/HERES-
WHAT-PARENTS-OF-TRANSGENDER-KIDS-NEED-TO-KNOW/

As a former child transgender, my heart goes out to parents whose boy says, "I'm a girl" or whose girl who says, "I'm a boy." The medical diagnosis is gender dysphoria—distress that comes from feeling one's physical gender doesn't match one's internal perception. A flood of questions come with the revelation: What causes it? What treatment will help? What should parents do or not do?

First, do not panic. Studies are showing that kids are not born with this disorder. A 2014 study shows no specific chromosome aberration associated with MtF (male to female) transsexualism.[52] A 2013 study looking for molecular mutations in the genes involved in sexual differentiation found none.[53] Your child was not born in the wrong body.

Transgender Children Typically Need Treatment for Other Disorders

Studies indicate that two-thirds of transgenders suffer from multiple disorders at the same time, or comorbidity.[54] The top three disorders evidenced in transgenders are depression (33 percent), specific phobia (20 percent) and adjustment disorder (15 percent). A child who states a desire to identify as the opposite sex has a two-thirds chance of having a co-existing disorder.

Let's look at the one at the top of the list: depression. Depression is a leading cause of suicide. A survey of over 6,000 transgenders revealed that 41 percent reported having attempted suicide at some time in their lives. Without effective psychiatric intervention or sound psychotherapy for the underlying depression, the risk of suicide will remain high. As a parent, it is important to look for depression and treat it if it is present.

Your child needs psychiatric or psychological help, not a change of wardrobe or hairstyle. Anyone working with a transgender needs to look for, and treat, comorbid disorders. Biologically, it is impossible for a doctor to change a boy into a girl, no matter how much surgery is performed or how many hormones are administered. I know; they tried it on me.

---

[52] http://www.ncbi.nlm.nih.gov/pubmed/25124466

[53] http://www.pubfacts.com/detail/23324476/Hormone-and-genetic-study-in-male-to-female-transsexual-patients

[54] http://www.ncbi.nlm.nih.gov/pubmed/25180172

I came into this world a boy. Starting in early childhood, I frequently cross-dressed as a girl. I thought I was born in the wrong body. A nationally-prominent PhD diagnosed me as a transgender with gender dysphoria. Eventually, I underwent the full recommended hormone therapy and the gender reassignment surgery and became the female Laura Jensen. I lived and worked successfully as a female transgender in San Francisco for several years until I was diagnosed with my own comorbid disorder.

With proper diagnosis and treatment with psychotherapy, I found the sanity and healing gender change could not provide. Transgenderism was my outward expression of an undiagnosed comorbid disorder, and gender-change surgery was never necessary. I detransitioned and returned to my male gender, like so many others do who regret changing genders.

What Causes the Comorbid Disorders that Exist in So Many Transgenders?

After receiving hundreds of emails over the last several years, it became evident to me that comorbid disorders develop in childhood. Some of the stresses people with gender dysphoria have reported are:

- An unstable unsafe home environment, real or perceived
- Separation from a parent by death or other events
- Serious illness among the family or child
- Domestic violence in the home
- Neglect, perceived or real
- Sexual, physical, or verbal abuse
- A strong opposition disorder from social norms

The key for parents to helping young transgenders is to work with a professional to identify the cause of the stress the child faces and correctly diagnose any comorbid disorder that exists concurrently with the gender dysphoria. Parents are in the best position to identify the cause of the stress the child faces.

A caution about the choice of medical professional: parents need to find medical professionals who are not advocates for gender change, and who will look beyond the surface of gender dysphoria symptoms for the comorbid disorders, fetishes, phobias, and adjustment disorders common among the transgender population. Only then can an effective treatment plan be devised that truly targets the child's needs.

As a child transgender myself, I can tell you I needed help. I did not need to dress as a girl at home and at school, with all the stress that would have brought. There is no doubt in my mind that if I would have been encouraged to go off to school dressed up as a female it would have escalated my anxiety and deepened my depression and my desire to commit suicide.

I understand some parents might dismiss the idea of comorbid disorders. They might feel strongly that they need to allow their child the freedom to change genders or experiment with gender. They may think that will help reduce the child's depression because the child seems happier under these conditions. I know—I seemed happier, too, after my gender change, until the novelty wore off and it no longer provided a distraction from my troubles. Happiness turned to despair when the surgery didn't work as treatment and my despair led to attempted suicide. Ignoring the possibility of comorbidity and giving kids the freedom to change gender is, I suggest, killing too many of them.

My web site, sexchangeregret.com, has many real-life examples of the results of changing genders taken from the headlines and from the letters I receive on a steady basis from gender change regretters.

I can suggest two books to help you as parents better understand your transgender child: my research book, "Paper Genders," and my novel based loosely on my life titled "Kid Dakota and the Secret at Grandma's House."

What Parents Should Know About Giving Hormones To Trans Kids

Medical guidelines advise against doing what many U.S. doctors are to kids who feel like the opposite gender: Giving them life-altering hormones early.

BY WALT HEYER
THE FEDERALIST, FEBRUARY 2, 2015
THEFEDERALIST.COM/2015/02/02/WHAT-PARENTS-
SHOULD-KNOW-ABOUT-GIVING-HORMONES-TO-TRANS-KIDS/

The United States Endocrine Society says that cross-gender hormones should not be used on kids under the age of 16. The standards in the Netherlands, United Kingdom, and Australia agree. The reason is simple: Cross-sex hormones have irreversible effects on fertility. Cross-gender hormone treatments can sterilize kids—not even Dr. Frankenstein would do that.

So I was shocked to learn that physicians administer cross-gender hormones to kids under the recommended age of 16 and many gender specialists believe "it is best to slowly initiate cross-gender hormones at the same time that the patient's peers are entering puberty, typically around age 12-14."[55]

Johanna Olson, medical director of the Los Angeles Children's Hospital Center for Trans Youth Health and Development, in a message directed to medical students, said that she has been "skipping the blockers" and placing children twelve years old and even younger directly on cross-gender hormones.[56]

The blockers she references are hormone blockers, which suspend the natural development of puberty. The idea is to give trans kids more time before the natural course of puberty occurs, with its gender-specific alterations to the body. Blockers are routinely considered to be the first course of treatment for trans-kids of puberty age because if you stop the blockers, puberty resumes.

Hormones Have Irreversible Effects

But cross-gender hormones are another matter. Taking cross-gender hormones is the first step in medical transitioning. As a transgender adult who was a trans kid, I know transitioning has consequences. I know that adults can't fully anticipate the long-term effects, much less little kids. It's a case of short-term gain with long-term pain. That's reality.

Lisa Brinkmann, a clinical psychologist specializing in gender issues in Dublin, Ireland, says about cross-gender hormones, "We are talking about changes that impact the kids' reproductive systems for

---

[55] https://nwhn.org/transgender-youth-providing-medical-treatment-for-a-misunderstood-population/
[56] https://gendertrender.wordpress.com/2014/11/11/skipping-the-puberty-blockers-american-transgender-children-doctors-are-going-rogue/

a lifetime. We have to be sure it's the right thing to do. Cross-sex hormones have irreversible effects on fertility. There's no going back."[57]

Most Kids Will Grow Out of Gender Dysphoria

A September 2014 report from the Hastings Center by Jack Drescher and Jack Pula says a diagnosis of gender dysphoria in childhood "does not inevitably continue into adulthood" the majority of the time.[58] The majority of trans kids will not choose to transition as adults.

The same physicians who suggest administering cross-gender hormones to kids at age 12 to 14 also say that they have no sure way to identify which kids will become transgender adults. No one can objectively provide proof that the kids they are treating with hormones are really transgender. The entire basis for treatment is what the kids say.

Gender dysphoria has been theorized to be a consequence of differences in the brain, but studies don't find any. A recent study at the Department of Clinical Neuroscience, Karolinska Institute, Stockholm, Sweden, says; "The present data do not support the notion that brains of male to female transgenders are feminized." The study could not find a difference in the brains between heterosexual men and that of male to female transsexuals. The brains in trans boys are no different than non-trans boys.[59]

Normal Kids Are At Risk

With no test to tell which kids will become transgender adults, but knowing that a majority will not, it is highly likely that doctors are administering powerful hormones with irreversible effects to normal boys and girls.

My concern for trans kids is forged from my own life as a child transgender. I was told that because my strong feelings of being a girl on the inside had persisted for so long that I needed to alter my external appearance to match, from man to woman. Because I was desperate for relief, I followed all the recommendations for someone with gender dysphoria and underwent the transition. I successfully lived and worked as a female for eight years. But after eight years, the male came back.

My biological sex had never changed, no matter how many procedures I underwent or how many hormones I took. My life was never the same and my body was forever mutilated. People say to me now, "Too bad. It was your choice. You should have made a more informed decision."

Through my website, SexChangeRegret.com, I hear from people with similar experiences as mine, and in every case, the gender dysphoria is a result of childhood developmental issues. Treating the psychological or psychiatric disorder is the answer, not changing genders.

It is crazy to routinely experiment on kids at any age when it carries the risk of irreversible changes and could lead to regrettable outcomes as an adult.

---

[57] http://www.irishexaminer.com/lifestyle/transgender-people-face-uphill-struggle-296638.html
[58] http://www.ncbi.nlm.nih.gov/pubmed/25231780
[59] http://www.ncbi.nlm.nih.gov/pubmed/21467211

Transgender Clinics Are Ruining Young Lives

"These doctors and clinics need to be held accountable for destroying people's lives, especially for the vulnerable youths they exploit," writes Walt Heyer.

BY WALT HEYER

THE DAILY SIGNAL, JANUARY 02, 2020

WWW.DAILYSIGNAL.COM/2020/01/02/

TRANSGENDER-CLINICS-ARE-RUINING-YOUNG-LIVES/

Gender clinics blithely guide 18-year-olds through the radical steps of gender transition, but abandon them later when they regret it.

After exploiting these troubled and vulnerable youths, the clinicians often want nothing more to do with them, and even deny the existence of regret among patients they assisted in transitioning.

These clinics need to be held accountable for ruining young lives. But don't expect the liberal mainstream media, which practically celebrate transgenderism, to do so.

Three teens who transitioned at age 18 or 19 and who regretted it soon after contacted me for help in going back. They are living proof of that cavalier attitude prevalent among gender clinics.

Their stories illuminate the ease with which doctors and clinics facilitate gender change on vulnerable youths, but turn their back on these young adults when they want to undo a tragic mistake.

The Callousness of Trans Clinics

Take the case of Abel Garcia, a 22-year-old born male from Southern California. (Able is a pseudonym to protect his identity.)

Abel first wrote me in June about the conflicting feelings he's had about continuing along the path of transition to female. He allowed me to share his story here to warn others.

> Hello, Walter, I am a transgender woman who's been struggling with myself in regard to continuing or to detransition for the last year," he wrote. "[I've] been watching videos about you and interviews you've been in. And since then, I have been questioning myself more and more every day.

Abel began his journey from male to female with cross-sex hormones in November 2016 at age 19. He changed his legal identity six months later, and in May 2018 had breast augmentation, aka "top surgery."

His attitude toward transitioning is a bit different from most. He decided to take it slowly so he wouldn't regret his decision. After he recovered from top surgery is when the questioning began.

In the year and a half since his breast augmentation, Abel has had a job that helped him mature, which has made a big difference in his decision.

> I am much more mature [at 22], compared to myself when I was 18. I had a feeling that there was a small chance I would regret my decision, and I would want to detransition.

Abel felt unappreciated as a young boy and subconsciously thought transitioning would make him the focus of attention.

> Growing up, I was a very shy, quiet boy compared to other boys my age, and I also didn't see my father growing up, because he worked almost every day as a truck driver, which left me and my two brothers being left alone to be raised by my mother and not having much of a male role figure in my life growing up.
>
> I knew I would never be a real woman. I would just be a man with a mutilated body to present as a woman.

Abel has concluded he wants to go back to identifying as a man.

"Ultimately, I knew even if I transitioned 100% completely, I knew I would never be a real woman," he said. "I would just be a man with a mutilated body to present as a woman."

The gender clinic doctors could have prevented Abel from a needless gender transition through psychotherapy, but they preferred the reckless use of hormones and surgeries. It's criminal what's happening to young people.

Then there's Sydney Wright, a young woman from the South, who wrote to me last spring.

"Hey, Walt! I myself was searching for positive detransitioning articles when I found your website," she wrote. "I transitioned from female to male as soon as I turned 19 … it has been the biggest regret of my life."

Sydney shared her story with The Daily Signal, "I Spent a Year as A Trans Man. Doctors Failed Me at Every Turn,"[60] in which she wrote:

> It's insane to me that our society is letting this happen to young people. At age 18, I wasn't even legal to buy alcohol, but I was old enough to go to a therapist and get hormones to change my gender.

Sydney related how she had no trouble finding a therapist willing to write her an approval letter for cross-gender hormones and a physician who gave her a prescription for testosterone and told her to watch YouTube videos to figure out how to inject herself.

Neither so-called "professional" questioned her motives or recommended counseling.

Nor did clinicians counsel or caution Nathaniel, a young man from the Northeast, who started on hormones at age 15 with his parents' approval and underwent the full surgical reassignment from male to female at age 18.

---

[60] https://www.dailysignal.com/2019/10/07/i-spent-a-year-as-a-trans-man-doctors-failed-me-at-every-turn/

After he regretted having the surgery, the clinic washed its hands of him.

Less than a year later, he wrote me about his regret and wanting his male body parts back. With Nathaniel's permission, I shared his story, "1 Year After Sex Change, This Teen Regrets His 'Frankenstein Hack Job,'"[61] in November.

Nathaniel, like so many others, received no effective counseling before surgery—which would have prevented this horrible mistake. Instead, the gender clinic and surgeons affirmed his false thinking and enticed him down the primrose path.

After he regretted having the surgery, the clinic washed its hands of him.

Hold the Clinics Accountable

People who regret their gender change contact me for help because their gender doctors and clinics abandon them when they want their life back.

None of us will ever be counted among the regretters or detransitioners in any studies or statistics. In fact, the doctors and clinics routinely refuse to acknowledge the existence of even one patient who regrets transitioning or detransitions.

As I reported in my book "Paper Genders,"[62] 90% of transgender research subjects are lost to follow-up, so no one knows how many go back to identifying as their birth gender.

We who detransition do exist, and we deserve to be heard.

The gender doctors and clinics need to be held accountable for destroying people's lives, especially for the vulnerable youths they exploit.

---

[61] https://www.dailysignal.com/2019/11/17/1-year-after-sex-change-this-teen-regrets-his-frankenstein-hack-job/
[62] Heyer, Walt, "Paper Genders", 2011, ISBN: 978-0615468594, amazon.com

Public Schools Force Kids Into Transgender Wars

In concert with transgender activists, the federal government is pushing schools across the country to let boys expose themselves to girls in showers, locker rooms, and bathrooms.

BY WALT HEYER

THE FEDERALIST, DECEMBER 2, 2015

THEFEDERALIST.COM/2015/12/02/

PUBLIC-SCHOOLS-FORCE-KIDS-INTO-TRANSGENDER-WARS/

Recent high-profile demands that schools let boys shower and pee right next to girls are having ripple effects in schools across the country as the transgender wars more militantly encompass young children.

Princeton Public Schools in New Jersey are planning to punish teachers who repeatedly refer to a transgender student with pronouns that correspond with biological reality.[63] The American Civil Liberties Union is threatening schools across Missouri that are responding to the case of Lila Perry by requiring children to either use a unisex bathroom or the one that corresponds to their biological sex. Perry is a 17-year-old boy who wants to expose his male genitalia to girls in a school locker room and be protected by law because he says he is a girl.[64]

State officials in North Carolina and Virginia are defending in federal court a local school board's policy requiring children to use private bathrooms and locker rooms if they don't want to use the facilities designated for their biological sex.[65] And parents in Wisconsin seem to have won a temporary reprieve from having their grade-schoolers read the gender-confused missive "I Am Jazz" to "help" children understand a classmate who insists he has a "girl brain and a boy body."[66]

The Obama administration has made it clear it will put the weight of the federal government behind the aggressors in these conflicts by recently threatening to yank funds from Virginia and Illinois public schools that asked biological boys to dress and shower privately or in the boy's facilities instead of next to girls.

We Will Only Accommodate People Who Agree with Us

School districts are now being told to accommodate transgender students by allowing simultaneous, unfettered access for gender-nonconforming boys to the showers, bathrooms, and dressing rooms occupied by girls, or lose their substantial federal funding.

---

[63] http://www.nj.com/mercer/index.ssf/2015/11/ princeton_schools_considers_policy_change_for_tran.html

[64] http://www.news-leader.com/story/news/local/ozarks/2015/11/24/following-trend-marionville-school-board-adopts-transgender-policy-one-mother-not-happy/76261696/

[65] http://wncn.com/2015/11/24/transgender-lawsuit-over-va-high-school-bathrooms-divides-mccrory-cooper/

[66] http://www.wnd.com/2015/11/school-pulls-back-plans-for-transgender-promotion/

The source of this craziness lies in how the Office of Civil Rights at the U.S. Department of Education has chosen to enforce Title IX, a federal law that originated in 1972 to prohibit discrimination in education opportunities on the basis of sex. The Obama administration has unilaterally expanded its interpretation of Title IX to provide the same anti-discrimination protection for gender-nonconforming students, i.e., those who act out as the opposite gender or sex.

I was a child gender pretender who started cross-dressing at five years of age. By the time I was 17, my desire to change genders was powerful. But I never had any desire to expose myself to girls at school. That is just sick. The law should not protect boys exposing themselves to adolescent girls, even if the boy identifies as a girl. Is utter insanity to assist, encourage, or provide trans kids access to cross-gender facilities. Girls need privacy, protection, and freedom from the "gender pretenders" in U.S. public schools.

It is sexual madness and social terrorism to deem the practices of sexual predators as acceptable and foist them on innocent children and adolescents. Why are we elevating the preferences of gender pretenders above those of all others, going far beyond political correctness to sexual madness in schools?

This Started a Long Time Ago

Let's look back and unmask the founders who started the gender madness we see infiltrating into our public schools today. As I detail in my book, "Paper Genders," changing boys into girls started in the perverted minds of three abhorrent pedophile activists from the 1950s who were at the forefront of promoting a movement for sexual and gender experimentation:

- Alfred Kinsey, a "violently masochistic masturbation addict" who advocated sex between adult men and young boys and became a leading sexology professor.
- Harry Benjamin, an endocrinologist and sexologist who first coined the term "transsexual" in 1954 and for whom the transgender Standards of Care were originally named. Benjamin praised and publicly endorsed his close friend René Guyon, a well-known pedophile.
- John Money, a psychologist and pioneer of gender reassignment surgery and friend of Benjamin, who falsified his research and told his patients, young boys, to play sex games with each other and photographed them.

One of Benjamin's first cases came as a referral from Kinsey, who asked for advice in the case of an effeminate boy who said he wanted to be a girl.

Benjamin first asked for a psychiatric evaluation of the boy. When several doctors examined him and were unable to agree whether Benjamin's gender change was warranted, Benjamin, undeterred, moved forward. Benjamin provided female hormones and recommended feminizing surgeries.

For the surgeries, the boy and his parents traveled to Germany. They never contacted Benjamin again, so the outcome of the experimental treatment was never known and could have included depression, isolation, perhaps even suicide, given that these frequently happen today with transgenders. The boy who wanted to be a girl never acknowledged if the treatment was effective or a failure. We would think that if the hormones and surgery had been successful the boy would have told Benjamin or Benjamin would have tracked him down to report the success.

Later, colleague of Benjamin who administered hormone therapy at Benjamin's clinic to 500 transgenders over a six-year period told an audience in 1979 that 80 percent of transgenders should not change genders. The doctor also told the audience there was too much unhappiness and too many suicides among Benjamin's transgender clients.

Money, the third on our list and a highly respected psychologist, didn't hide his advocacy of pedophilia. For example, *The Journal of Pedophilia* interviewed Money.

He said it was fine, *even desirable*, for young boys to have sex with adult men.

In private sessions at the prestigious Johns Hopkins Hospital, this pioneer of gender reassignment encouraged his first patients, twins, to play sex games with each other at age 7, and photographed them. Only a sick pervert would do this.

The boys' parents had first contacted Money after a botched circumcision destroyed one boy's penis. Money was able to convince the Reimers that the best penis repair would be surgically fabricating a female vagina so the boy would be a transsexual female. Money had a gender theory he wanted to prove and having twins to use as a test case was his perfect opportunity to make a name for himself in the medical community. Money monitored the twins' progress for years and published his results about the success of the "John/Joan" reassignment in journal articles that garnered much acclaim.

The sad truth didn't come out until much later: Money had falsified his findings.

The transgender twin acted decidedly male and was depressed and suicidal by age 13.

His desperate parents told him the whole story of his upbringing and the boy refused to take any more feminizing hormones and reverted to being a boy, David. But the damage had been done.

As an adult, David went public about the folly of changing genders, just as I'm doing today, to discourage people from reassignment surgery. At age 38, David Reimer committed suicide. His brother had died two years earlier from a drug overdose. Money was directly responsible for the death of the Reimer boys because of his reckless disregard of the long-term consequences of the gender change for David and his pedophilic abuse of both boys for his self-gratification. Only Brian's overdose at age 36 and David's suicide at 38 could make the pain Money had caused them to finally go away.

The Reimers placed their trust in Money and had no idea what consequences would follow. These three pedophile activists unleashed our current social nightmare. Today, parents of young gender pretenders have been sold down this same river of madness and are unable to see the long-term consequences for their children of changing genders.

Law Should Protect Privacy and Innocence, Not Voyeurism

Public schools are becoming centers for gay, lesbian, and gender-pretender activists and only secondarily fulfilling their purpose as institutions for sound academics. The laws are being interpreted far beyond the original intent of non-discrimination based on gender to where they protect gender pretenders at the expense of the rights of non-trans kids. Gender pretenders are assured access to every school facility and program available to the opposite gender, up to and including girls-only dressing rooms and showers.

Every child's rights to privacy and protection from exposure to inappropriate opposite-sex nudity are now in jeopardy. According to these new legal interpretations, if you like your gender and want to keep your gender that's fine, but you cannot keep your freedom, rights, or protections in public-school dressing rooms or restrooms. The current conflict of interest playing out in school locker rooms between girls born as girls and the self-acknowledged gender pretender trans-kids is real and it is not funny. Non-trans students have lost their right to privacy and parents have lost the freedom to parent and protect their children.

A young boy, by making the simple announcement "I was a boy, but now I'm a girl" can sashay his way into the girls' restrooms and locker rooms in our schools. Keep in mind this boy still has his dangling boy parts. The accurate term for him is cross-dresser or transvestite. Supposedly the law protects his right to be in the girls' locker room, to observe girls dressing and undressing, and to expose himself to the girls that are sharing the room.

Parents, pull your kids from school. It's time for those who are able to home school or put their children in non-federally funded schools where sexual activism and inappropriate co-mingling of boys and girls in private spaces is not tolerated.

Now is the time to pass a law called "The Right to Privacy and Freedom Act" for non-transgender students. Make it punishable for a boy to expose his male genitalia to girls at any time, in any location on public school property, no exceptions.

Changing Genders Is Dangerous, Not Benign

I know from personal experience that changing genders is not harmless. I was told by the leading experts that a surgical change to female would bring relief from my intense psychological struggle. But I wasn't told it can also tear a person's life apart.

Regret happens for a multitude of reasons. (See www.SexChangeRegret.com for some examples.) Studies show that people with gender issues also have other psychological issues 62.7 percent of the time. When the co-existing illness is treated, often the desire to change gender dissipates. By not treating the co-existing illnesses first and instead putting the patient through gender reassignment— hormones and surgery—the medical community does irrevocable harm to the patient's body and long-lasting harm to his mind.

The harm is deeper for impressionable children and adolescents who experiment with gender-change behaviors and hormones or hormone blockers. Studies have shown that the majority of kids who are gender confused will grow out of it if they are left alone.

If you want your kids to have a psychologically healthy life, do not assist, encourage, or guide them toward a gender change. If they struggle with gender identity issues, do not take them to a psychologist who will push hormones and gender reassignment.

In fact, the best thing you can do for your kid is to grab him or her by the hand and run as fast as you can the other way. Protect them from becoming one of the 41 percent of gender pretenders who attempt suicide like David Reimer or the many who will become lost and unaccounted for, like the effeminate boy who went off to Germany for surgery and was never heard from again. Fifty years of gender change insanity is long enough.

Gender pretenders—also known as trans-kids, crossdressers, or transvestites—should get counseling, not encouragement. Social terrorists who use child transvestites to advance an agenda of sexual perversion should be shut down, not be guiding public school policy.

It's time for parents and kids to fight against the social terrorism of gender change. It's time to take schools back from males who wish to expose themselves with impunity in the girls' locker room.

Doctors Admit They Don't Know Which Kids Should Gender Transition But Do It To Them Anyway

Anyone playing this 'select-a-gender' game with children is complicit in turning young psyches against themselves and the truth of who they are.

BY WALT HEYER
THE FEDERALIST, JULY 10, 2017
THEFEDERALIST.COM/2017/07/10/
DOCTORS-ADMIT-DONT-KNOW-KIDS-GENDER-TRANSITION-YET-ANYWAY/

A 13-year-old seventh grade girl committed suicide just before the Memorial Day holiday weekend. When the Alabama youth was halfway through sixth grade, she publicly identified as a boy, "Jay," with the support of family and school. In addition to gender identity struggles, Jay's mother says Jay battled depression and anxiety. "We were under the care of a psychologist from day one," she says in an interview with AL.com.[67]

The LGBTQ lobby tell parents they must support and affirm their child's transgender journey to prevent the child from attempting suicide. As this tragic case demonstrates, however, it's an open question whether supporting a child's gender switch adds stress rather than reducing it. In this case, the parents fully affirmed and supported her gender transition, yet tragically, depression led to suicide.

Children are encouraged, affirmed and assisted in "coming out" as transgendered without one word about the consequences of the dangerous game of "gender make-believe." Today, the politically correct response expected from adults, especially parents, is to affirm the child in the desired gender. But affirmation gives young people false hope that they can really become a different gender. It's a lie—a lie told with compassionate motives, but a lie nonetheless. Lying is not compassion.

Lying to People Hurts Them

For a vulnerable young person, pursuing a dream that is physically impossible to achieve can lead to depression, and depression is the leading cause of attempted suicide. The prevalence of suicide attempts among transgender or gender non-conforming youth is 45 percent, according to a 2014 report by the Williams Institute, University of California at Los Angeles School of Law, and the American Foundation of Suicide Prevention.[68] It's a startling statistic.

Many parents choose to tell young children that pretend characters, such as the tooth fairy, Easter Bunny, and Santa Claus, are real. As the children grow up, the parents tell them the truth and everyone stops pretending. Today the tooth fairy is replaced by "select-a-gender," a fantasy where all

---

[67] http://www.al.com/news/birmingham/index.ssf/2017/06/ our_children_just_need_to_be_l.html
[68] https://williamsinstitute.law.ucla.edu/wp-content/uploads/AFSP-Williams-Suicide-Report-Final.pdf

are expected to play along. Doctors and parents tell daughters they can become sons and sons they can become daughters.

But as I found out myself, changing genders is a high-stakes game of make-believe. To make the pretend gender appear real, I had to enlist doctors to prescribe cross-gender hormones and perform cosmetic surgeries. Dr. Frankenstein would be proud. It's important to tell people the truth and stop pretending.

Doctors Admit They Can't Tell Who Should Transition

First of all, we need to stop pretending that doctors have scientific backing for their recommendations for children with gender dysphoria. The truth is that no one can predict whether a gender dysphoric child will feel the same way years later.

Kristina Olson, a research psychologist at the University of Washington, puts it this way: "We just don't have definitive data one way or another." That's why Olson is leading a study of 300 trans children that will track outcomes over 20 years, "to be able to, hopefully, answer which children should or should not transition," she said.[69] In other words, we simply don't know right now, yet parents and children are herded in one direction as if we do.

Some young people desire to identify as the opposite sex to escape the pain of a traumatic event or a perceived abandonment or loss. They subconsciously want to dissociate from who they are and become someone else. Gender change promises a fresh start, free from the past. Like many psychological coping mechanisms, however, gender change provides only a temporary reprieve.

Some teens or pre-teens today want to identify as the other gender for social reasons or to become the center of attention. Younger children can simply be curious about the opposite gender. This doesn't mean adults should encourage experimentation.

If you want to go deeper and learn about people who lived the transgender life, get the just-released documentary, "Tranzformed."[70] It explores the journeys of 15 individuals who eventually walked out of the transgender life. "Tranzformed" provides transgendered people a voice to share in their own words, with authenticity and emotion, how they came to the decision to change genders and why they changed back. It's powerful. Be sure to check out the trailer and watch the movie.

The film made the point clearly: people who identify as the opposite sex have deep emotional pain and need true compassion.

'I Was Convinced It Was the Right Thing to Do'

For 12 years now, people have contacted me after visiting my website, SexChangeRegret.com, to tell me about their dissatisfaction with their gender change and their desire to transition back to their birth gender. Lately, the frequency is rising and I feel a great sense of urgency to warn anyone contemplating a gender change to tread carefully.

---

[69] http://www.nbcbayarea.com/investigations/Transgender-Kids-Eligible-for-Earlier-Medical-Intervention-Under-New-Guidelines-423082734.html

[70] https://www.tranzformed.org/

For instance, a male-to-female teacher emailed me with a heart-wrenching story of regret. This first-person account illustrates that a person can be absolutely convinced that gender transition is the right thing to do and afterwards appears to be successfully living life, but with all that, still is not happy with the gender change.

> I underwent surgery 10 years ago. I was convinced it was the right thing to do—regrettably, it was not. The price I paid was dear: I hurt the ones I love the most—my children, my siblings, my parents and my partner. By all appearances I am a success story. I have a good job as a high school teacher, I have had a fairly active love life, etc., but none of this can ever make up for the pain and guilt I feel every day of my life.
>
> Believe it or not I have gone to a therapist and several surgeons—with little success. I just get told it's a normal part of the adjustment phase (an awfully long adjustment phase). They say, you make a nice woman—be happy! But I'm not happy!
>
> I'm wondering do you know of any surgeons who will remove my breast implants. I really would like to start living as a man again.

People write me who are stuck in a transgender "no man's land." Like the lyrics in the song "Hotel California" by the Eagles, "You can check out any time you like, but you can never leave." Therapists and surgeons gladly help people proceed with the pretend gender transition, but resources are mysteriously absent for finding the way back to reality. The people who contact me are desperate to undo the changes but face roadblocks and discouragement.

Another male-to-female teacher wrote to me recently, so fearful of writing in an email about regret the teacher wouldn't say much, except to ask for a phone call (and hope the NSA won't listen in). This teacher wrote:

> Am a teacher of grade school children, I had surgery 12 years ago. Could we talk sometime? If not, I completely understand. It looks like you are a busy public figure doing amazing work. It's just that as a public-school teacher, I have to be really careful what I say online. If not, thank you for your time here, and best—

We did talk on the phone for nearly an hour. We talked about family, children, and the possibility of transitioning back to male and keeping the same teaching job. This teacher with an unblemished 20-year record is gripped with fear over what the school board could do if he changed back to his birth gender of male after 12 years living as a female.

We Only Encourage Your Desires In One Direction

Those who fight for the "rights" of people to find their "authentic self" and assist gender dysphoric people in changing genders, are the most vocal, vicious critics of the same gender dysphoric people who tried transitioning and found it didn't work. Finding one's authentic self is evidently a one-way trip. The same equality and protective laws, and indeed, the same compassionate attitude and legal assistance that advocates lavish on people who want to abandon their birth gender, should apply to those who are disillusioned with their gender pretending. But it doesn't.

For those who look on from afar and see the explosion of young people playing the game of "select-a-gender" remember: 45 percent of them will attempt suicide. Why? Because this emerging group of young gender changers are suffering from emotional, psychological, or social identity discomfort far deeper than new pronouns can rectify.

Doctors admit they do not know which children will remain gender dysphoric into adulthood, yet they condone gender identity change, socially and medically, for youth. This is child abuse. I can tell you that from my own life. It's child abuse to tell a child he or she can select a gender. It is a false hope. Such a suggestion is factually a lie, not a lie with the innocence of pretending the tooth fairy exists, but a lie with life-long destructive ramifications.

The effect of gender "make believe" is the destruction of core identity. It plants the notion inside the minds of young people that the essence of who they are is wrong. They are not someone to be loved or embraced, but eradicated. Affirming someone as the opposite gender reinforces the deep discomfort already undermining his or her identity. Overwhelmed by the weight of these messages cloaked as "affirmation" and a lack of attention to the real issues driving their desire to switch gender appearances, 45 percent attempt suicide. Anyone playing this "select-a-gender" game with children is complicit in turning young psyches against themselves and the factual truth of who they really are.

It is time to stop all this gender-changing madness when the doctors themselves admit they cannot tell who the "real" long-term gender dysphoric children are and affirmed children like Jay die needlessly.

Public School LGBT Programs Don't Just Trample Parental Rights. They Also Put Kids at Risk.

No matter what well-intentioned teachers and administrators believe, LGBT acceptance programs designed by GLSEN and funded by the CDC are designed to encourage kids to question their gender identity and sexual orientation.

BY WALT HEYER
PUBLIC DISCOURSE, JUNE 8, 2015
WWW.THEPUBLICDISCOURSE.COM/2015/06/15118/

Through his executive appointments, President Obama has helped expose American schoolchildren to activism that places them at risk.

On May 19, 2009, a few short months after his inauguration, Obama gave the green light to Secretary of Education Arne Duncan to appoint Kevin Jennings to a top position to influence school policy: the post of Assistant Deputy Secretary for the Office of Safe and Drug-Free Schools, also known as the "safe schools czar." Jennings, a powerful LGBT rights activist who is himself a gay man, was the founder of the Gay, Lesbian, and Straight Education Network (GLSEN). GLSEN is one of the largest LGBT activist organizations in the nation and is devoted to promoting homosexuality in K-12 schools. Jennings served as "safe schools czar" from 2009-2011.

Given his connection with the organization, we should not be shocked to discover that GLSEN received a grant from the Centers for Disease Control in 2011 for $1.425 million over five years to promote the LGBT agenda in public schools at taxpayers' expense.[71] Through these publicly funded in-school programs, kids are being bombarded with the message that same-sex attraction and gender-identity confusion are innate and therefore not changeable.

Those who design these programs probably believe that they are offering hope to children who may feel different, flawed, or unlovable. They believe that if they affirm children's LGBT identities as something positive, something that makes up the core of who they are, the children will fare better.

This is not the case. No matter what well-intentioned teachers and administrators believe, these programs ultimately entail an agenda that hurts kids. The messages these programs send do nothing to combat the tragically high suicide rates among the LGBT community. Data indicate that kids are actually put at risk when schools encourage them to identify themselves as gay or transgender at an early age. For each year children delay labeling themselves as LGBT, their suicide risk is reduced by 20 percent.[72]

---

[71] http://www.wnd.com/2011/07/328521/

[72] http://www.ncbi.nlm.nih.gov/pubmed/2034492

I'm passionate about this issue because I was a trans-kid myself. I know how easy it was for my grandma to manipulate me into thinking I should change genders. Young trans-kids need to know they were not born that way, and that most will no longer have a desire to change genders once they grow into adulthood. Parents need to know that up to 94 percent of school-age kids who identify as transgender will grow out of their desire to change genders as adults—if parents and schools stop encouraging them to internalize and publicize their LGBT identities.[73]

The Power of Childhood Influences

I'm not sure we truly understand how easily young people's thinking about gender identity can be influenced by parents, television shows, and teachers who encourage them to explore new genders. During early childhood development, kids learn gender roles from observation within the family setting, peers, television, and school. They use their imagination, actions, and language to play-act what they see.[74]

GLSEN capitalizes on the impressionable, imaginative nature of young children by designing and implementing programs for children as young as kindergarten. Consider their toolkit for elementary educations, *Ready, Set, Respect!* GLSEN knows that the elementary years are a prime opportunity to encourage kids to reject the values of their parents. The handbook outlines a variety of activities that gradually introduce and reinforce the messages that gender is a social construct, that moms and dads are interchangeable, and that anyone who says otherwise is hateful and prejudiced.[75]

Along with lessons designed to help kindergarten through fifth-graders to "explore the definition of a family and to understand that there are a variety of family structures" and to "challenge their own and other's [sic] assumptions about gender and gender roles," the guide recommends a variety of books and videos to help cement the lessons. *Asha's Mums*, for example, teaches third- through fifth-graders that "having two mums is no big deal." An additional discussion guide goes into greater detail about books such as *And Tango Makes Three*, which is recommended for pre-kindergarten through third-graders:

> This book talk is designed to help students realize that there are different family structures including families led by LGBT parents. This is the true story of Roy and Silo, two male penguins who share a nest like other penguin couples, and who are given an egg in need of nurturing...[76]
>
> Conclude by telling students that Tango's family is just one kind of family. Ask them if they think there is a certain number of kinds of families and how they know that. Let students know that through your life you have discovered and met and continue to meet different kinds of families and that you're not sure there is a certain number of possibilities.

---

[73] http://www.ncbi.nlm.nih.gov/pubmed/25231780

[74] http://www.childrennatureandyou.org/Imaginative%20Play%20in%20 Early%20Childhood.pdf

[75] http://www.glsen.org/sites/default/files/Ready%2C%20Set%2C%20 Respect%21%20GLSEN%27s%20Elementary%20School%20Toolkit.pdf

[76] http://www.glsen.org/sites/default/files/ readacrossamericadiscussionguidesonly.pdf

Other books, such as *10,000 Dresses* and *My Princess Boy*, are listed as resources to help children who are "Exploring Non-Traditional Gender Roles." While parts of the lesson plans are correct and even healthy (yes, girls can climb trees and boys can play with dolls), encouraging cross-gender identification at such a young age can have painful, long-lasting consequences. Inadvertently manipulating the minds of young people by suggesting that their "real" gender might not match their body can shape how they think, feel, and behave for years to come.

As someone whose grandmother lavished me with affirmations as she cross-dressed me as a girl, I am concerned by the growing trend in schools of encouraging kids to change genders. The activists have convinced the parents this will do no harm. I have traveled this path, and I can tell you: childhood influences matter.

Events and "Research"

GLSEN website provides an LGBT inclusive curriculum to help educators develop lessons that include "positive representations of lesbian, gay, bisexual and transgender (LGBT) people, history, and events."[77]

The GLSEN student calendar for grades six through twelve is full of events and suggestions for how to celebrate them: LGBT History Month, LGBT Pride Month, National Coming Out Day, and Ally Week, which is touted as "a week where we can have vital conversations to move the movement forward toward our collective queer liberation!"[78]

What other external organizations are granted access to shaping school curricula and activities? I would venture to say that GLSEN is one of the most provocative. Parents take note: the organization aided by taxpayer funds and influencing schools is the one devoted to the LGBT cause.

In order to justify the need for LGBT curricula, clubs, and programs to be included in the classroom, GLSEN often cites the National School Climate Survey[79], which they conduct every two years. References to the survey are peppered throughout their educator's guides, student programs and campaigns, and press releases, with such phrases as "Research shows . . . " The problem is: the sampling is flawed.

Basic principles of statistics and probability state that generalizations about a population from a sample are valid only if the sample is representative of that population.[80] Random sampling is the best way to do that. Read the survey and it's obvious that the sampling is not random and not representative of US students. In fact, it is a "self-selected" sample, which means that anyone can elect to take the survey, which is freely available on their website.[81] For example, a transgender man in his seventies can fill out the survey posing as a student, which I did to illustrate how flawed the selection process is. The problem of self-selection is that such polls are biased toward people with strong opinions.

---

[77] http://www.glsen.org/sites/default/files/LGBT%20inclus%20 curriculum%202014_0.pdf
[78] http://www.glsen.org/allyweek
[79] http://www.glsen.org/sites/default/files/NSCS_ExecSumm_2013_ DESIGN_FINAL.pdf
[80] http://www.corestandards.org/Math/Content/7/SP/
[81] http://www.glsen.org/survey

Politics, Bullying, and the Science of Sexual Orientation

These problematic school programs are both a symptom and a cause of our culture's continuing confusion about gender and sexuality. When it comes to the nature of sexual identity and orientation, scientific studies with findings that run contrary to the party line are squelched or dismissed out of hand. Researchers who dare to follow where the data lead and to question existing premises are lambasted and risk being professionally marginalized.

One example of this is the bullying of Dr. Robert Spitzer, a leading figure in the study of homosexuality. Spitzer's work was embraced and celebrated by LGBT rights activists until he authored a study in 2003 called "Can Some Gay Men and Lesbians Change Their Sexual Orientation? 200 Participants Reporting a Change from Homosexual to Heterosexual Orientation." The study abstract finishes with the line: "Thus, there is evidence that change in sexual orientation following some form of reparative therapy does occur in some gay men and lesbians."[82]

Here was a case of a prominent scientist following his curiosity, challenging position statements about reparative therapy (also known disparagingly as "conversion therapy") made by major mental health organizations in the United States, and publishing the objective results of what he found. For this, he was attacked mercilessly. After nearly a decade of public, personal, and professional assault, eighty-year-old Spitzer recanted his views in May 2012 and issued a letter of apology to the gay community.[83]

Now, President Obama is advocating a ban on psychotherapy that suggests sexual orientation and the desire to change genders are themselves changeable. His administration has issued this statement: "As part of our dedication to protecting America's youth, this Administration supports efforts to ban the use of conversion therapy for minors."[84]

More research needs to be done into the nature of sexual orientation and sexual identity. However, current research suggests that by intervention and encouragement, school programs designed by LGBT rights activists are encouraging children to self-identify in ways that are harmful to their psychological well-being. Rather than allowing the scientific community the space to objectively study these issues, and giving members of the psychiatric profession room to respond to the freely stated needs of the children who come to them, politicians who are hungry for public approval are zealously working to outlaw appropriate and effective psychotherapies for kids who want them.

It's Time to Protect Our Kids

I understand the impulse that probably motivates many people to encourage young children to embrace an LGBT identity. After a lifetime of feeling like "a woman trapped in a man's body," I underwent gender reassignment surgery and lived as a woman for years. I was convinced that this was the right decision, and that this was an option that everyone should have for the sake of their happiness and psychological well-being.

---

[82] http://link.springer.com/article/10.1023%2FA%3A1025647527010

[83] http://www.mercatornet.com/articles/view/frail_and_aged_a_giant_apologizes

[84] https://petitions.whitehouse.gov/petition/enact-leelahs-law-ban-all-lgbtq-conversion-therapy

I was wrong. My gender change only brought temporary relief; it did nothing to combat my underlying psychological disorder. My suffering brought me close to suicide. Years after my gender change, I underwent traditional therapy and successfully restored my masculinity and my sanity. Effective psychotherapy and my faith proved to me that changing genders is not a medical necessity.

I have written extensively about the lack of evidence that changing genders is medically necessary. What I didn't expect was for the State of California to agree with me. On May 5, California officials asked a federal court to block a judge's order that the state provide sex-reassignment surgery for a prisoner. The state officials argued that "no treating physician has ever determined that reassignment surgery is medically necessary [for the prisoner in question]."[85]

The State of California is willing to argue for protecting a prisoner from unnecessary surgery, but the same state is unwilling to step in and protect the personal privacy of non-transgender school children in restrooms and locker rooms. With Assembly Bill 1266, California became the first state in the nation to require public schools to allow transgender students to use restrooms and participate on sports teams matching the gender with which they identify, rather than their biological sex.[86]

Homosexuals and transgendered people, like all other citizens, should be protected by law from violence and abuse. But that doesn't change the principle that parents should have access to public education for their children that does not push an ideological sexual and political agenda based on a vision of the human person that many parents deeply disagree with, especially when significant evidence suggests that the messages embedded in these school programs can be harmful to children.

Control of schools should belong to parents, not to the federal government and activist organizations such as GLSEN.

---

[85] http://www.foxnews.com/us/2015/05/05/california-seeks-to-block-inmate-sex-reassignment-surgery/
[86] http://leginfo.legislature.ca.gov/faces/billNavClient.xhtml?bill_id=201320140AB1266

A Nine-Year-Old Boy is Spreading a "Contagion of Mass Delusion"

National Geographic's cover photo is exploitation. The health and well-being of a child are being sacrificed to advance a political and cultural crusade.

BY WALT HEYER
PUBLIC DISCOURSE, JANUARY 5, 2017
WWW.THEPUBLICDISCOURSE.COM/2017/01/18465/

Psychiatrist Richard Corradi calls transgenderism a "contagion of mass delusion."[87] As a former transgender, I can tell you that Dr. Corradi is correct. Yet *National Geographic* magazine selected a trans-activist boy named Avery Jackson for the cover of its special January "Gender Revolution" issue[88]—an image and publication that will only help promote this "contagion of mass delusion" around the globe.

Like it or not, there are two sexes: male and female. Man and woman join to form the foundation of family. *National Geographic* apparently felt the need to give the LGBTQ movement a helping hand in redefining gender and family.

If you're an LGBTQ loyalist, you will love the "in your face" cover photo of the boy Avery. But for me, one who was restored after living for eight years as a female transgender, the cover photo is a sad and painful reminder of a lost childhood, a family ripped apart, and a marriage that did not survive. To me, the cover is a glossy reminder of the brokenness of transgender ideology.

The cover photo of Avery, like all photos, shows one moment in time. What it does not give us is a long-range perspective of the consequences of Avery's choices and those of his parents. It cannot show us his future.

I lived "the life," just like Avery. I was a cross-dressing boy at age nine, but—after years of pain and self-delusion—my cross-dressing stopped decades later, when I realized that the idea of changing sexes is pure fantasy. Cross-dressing initially felt zany, fun, exhilarating, and wonderfully affirming of my belief that I should have been born a girl. But after many decades of trying to comprehend the gender confusion that persisted even after my sex transition, I came to understand that my grandmother's cross-dressing of me was emotional child abuse. The psychological harm grew as years went by.

---

[87] https://thefederalist.com/2016/11/17/psychiatry-professor-transgenderism-mass-hysteria-similar-1980s-era-junk-science/

[88] https://shop.nationalgeographic.com/product/magazines/special-issues/national-geographic-gender-revolution-special-issue---u.s.?code=NG2N10003

Suicide

The transgender promotional cover photo of Avery fails to address the 41 percent of the transgender population who will at some point attempt suicide.[89] Even when affirmed, accepted, and loved, transgender individuals attempt suicide, which indicates that the issues they struggle with run deeper than a change in gender identity can rectify. Sex reassignment has not proven to be effective in resolving gender dysphoria for nearly half of this diverse population of gender-troubled individuals.

A review of 100 research findings concludes that sex changes are not effective, and many transgender people after surgery remain traumatized to the point of suicide.[90]

This *National Geographic* cover is slick work, as it attempts to legitimize cross-dressing. Calling it "transgenderism" sounds more current than "cross-dressing," but the reality remains the same.

Avery is simply a cross-dressing boy. Cross-dressing affects outward appearance only; what you do not see are the deeper long-term psychological consequences. No sex is changed; no biological transformation takes place.

Interestingly, in the glossary of the "Gender Revolution" issue, no mention is made of cross-dressing.[91]

Yet, to promote their misguided ideological mission to deconstruct gender norms, the author-activists include the recently invented term for all of us non-transgender people, who number about 99.7 percent of the population: "cisgender." In this way, the sexual activists are engaging in nihilism—dismissing human nature and observable reality itself.

Fantasy and Delusion: What "Feels Right" Isn't Always Right

Transgenderism is interesting in theory, but slicing up bodies and injecting hormones is pure Frankenstein 2.0. To treat gender dysphoria, a surgeon operates on a man and makes a "woman." To keep up the façade, cross-gender hormones are prescribed for life.

Is the surgeon's transgender female equivalent to a biological female? This argument requires some intellectual parallels.

Let's compare a real diamond with a manmade cubic zirconia. Which one is a real gem? Or take a 20-dollar bill printed by Treasury Department of the United States and compare it with a counterfeit $20 made in the back room of Lefty's bar. Which one is genuine?

Surgically created sex changes and cross-dressing boys are as fake as a counterfeit twenty-dollar bill or a cubic zirconia. Yet, if we are to be politically correct, we should call a cubic zirconia a diamond and accept a counterfeit twenty-dollar bill as legal tender. We don't want the zirconia or the counterfeit currency to feel sad because we call them fake.

With the extreme emphasis on political correctness and safeguarding people's feelings, we are abandoning all ability to call what is fake "fake" and what is real "real."

---

[89] https://calculators.io/national-transgender-discrimination-survey/
[90] https://www.theguardian.com/society/2004/jul/30/health.mentalhealth
[91] http://www.nationalgeographic.com/magazine/2017/01/explore-gender-glossary-terminology/

Yes, I enjoyed cross-dressing. Yes, the cross-dressing feelings were strong, delighting me when I slipped on that soft, full-flowing purple chiffon evening dress Grandma made especially for me. Yes, strong feelings of wanting to be a girl grew from seeing myself in the mirror. I believed I should have been born a girl and desired to be one. As a young person, I did not doubt I should have been a girl.

My delusional pursuit progressed over forty years from cross-dressing to cross-gender hormone therapy to surgery. I sought out a gender therapist who specialized in diagnosing gender dysphoria and approving people for gender reassignment surgery. But seeking him out was a mistake, because a gender therapist's vision of treatment is narrowly focused on one destructive path: sex change.

In hindsight, I can see more clearly today than ever before.

I can see from my experience that transgenderism is fantasy motivated by strong feelings. When it comes to gender, people can change clothing and other aspects of the public persona, but biological sex will always remain fixed.

There are no lab tests or medical findings that can even prove the existence of transgenderism. The only way to diagnose it is when someone self-identifies as transgender. No amount of hormones or cosmetic surgery can effect a biological change of sex. Feelings, no matter how strong, cannot change sex. To pretend anything else is only a masquerade. At best, transgenderism is Mardi Gras, not reality.

Child Exploitation

Even if young Avery is willing to be used in this way, *National Geographic*'s cover photo is exploitation. The health and well-being of this child are being sacrificed to advance a political and cultural crusade.

Avery may not realize that his feelings and photos are a revenue source for *National Geographic* and a strategic tool for the LGBTQ lobby. Yes, the bright lights are squarely on Avery. He is today's poster child—a hero, at least for now. But Avery's male sex is unchangeable, while feelings do change. What will surface eight, ten, or even thirty years from now? Anyone who thinks that affirming his transgenderism can undo Avery's innate male sex has caught the contagion of mass delusion.

Avery's mom surely thinks she is helping her son, just as my grandmother thought she was "helping" me. Today, my body bears the scars from all the unnecessary surgeries I endured because as a young boy I was enabled, encouraged, and provided opportunity to act out such a fantasy.

It is naïve to believe there are no negative outcomes from using this young boy as a symbol and presenting him as an activist. *National Geographic*'s irresponsible imagery of a cross-dressing boy on the cover will no doubt ratchet up the spread of the contagion that is transgenderism.

Notably, the magazine does not include any interviews with individuals who have had their lives destroyed by the long-term consequences of cross-dressing and gender confusion. Cross-dressing eroded my true gender which in turn ruined my teen years, ripped apart my marriage, and ended my career.

There Is a Way Back

Avery and I have something in common: the strong belief starting in childhood of being a girl.

What makes me different from Avery is seventy years of life experience dealing with the transgender fantasy. Experience is a great teacher. I learned that sex-change surgery and living the life of transgender female didn't deliver the serenity I was promised. Instead it complicated matters. Every day I had to confront the reality that I was not a real woman.

Many do not have the desire or courage to admit that transgenderism is delusional and was never required medically to resolve their gender conflict. I, on the other hand, wanted my sanity restored. Admitting my regret made me rare in trans-land.

I turned to Christ and away from transgenderism. I wanted to be obedient to the Lord. Obedience is giving up what I want, in order to live the life Christ wants. I had to stop living in defiance of God and stop demanding that the church, God, and everyone else make accommodations for my delusions. Demanding that people use my preferred female pronoun was childish.

I must have been right about obedience, because once I gave up what I wanted, He drew me to a new level of sanity. Through prayer and counseling, I was unshackled from my transgender female life and restored to life as male.

One passage that guided my steps and gave me hope comes from the book of Matthew, where Jesus says, "Enter through the narrow gate; for the gate is wide and the way is broad that leads to destruction, and there are many who enter through it. For the gate is small and the way is narrow that leads to life, and there are few who find it."[92]

The LGBTQ movement and their co-conspirator, *National Geographic*, throw open the wide gate that leads to transgenderism and seeks the destruction of gender persona. But gender acquired through hormones and surgery is a delusional pursuit, and the delusion is contagious. Promoting Avery's situation as a success story will hurt others who are struggling, because it advances the false idea that embracing transgenderism will solve the issues they face and heal the pain they feel.

I determined to be one of the few who find the narrow way that leads to a redeemed life. My faith was rewarded with a redeemed life in my male gender, far better than transgenderism. Yes, that makes me very different—and very richly blessed.

---

[92] https://www.biblegateway.com/passage/?search=Matthew+7%3A13-14&version=NASB

Chapter 3.
No Scientific Basis

Politicians' Response To Transgenders Is Likely To Increase Suicides

A December 2015 study shows no evidence of cross-gender brain in transgenders. What they did find suggests a link to mental disorders, which are in turn linked to suicide.

BY WALT HEYER
THE FEDERALIST, JANUARY 6, 2016
THEFEDERALIST.COM/2016/01/06/POLITICIANS-
RESPONSE-TO-TRANSGENDERS-IS-LIKELY-TO-INCREASE-SUICIDES/

It's nearly a year after the suicide of Josh Alcorn (who called himself Leelah), the 17-year-old Ohio transgender who stood in front of a moving tractor-trailer. Alcorn's death was a tragic failure on so many levels.

Who knows what caused the teenager such deep depression? According to Suicide.org, untreated mental illness is the key factor in 90 percent of all suicides, with depression being the leading cause.[93]

The findings of two recent studies help to explain the cause of transgender gender depression, known as gender dysphoria. The findings offer a reason why transgenders claim their cross-gender thoughts and emotions cannot be controlled and why they feel the need for cross-gender behavior and social interactions.

As Debra Soh wrote on Monday in the *Wall Street Journal*, "Of the boys and girls seen in clinics like Dr. Zucker's, a high percentage—up to 80% in a study of 44 gender-dysphoric boys—grow up to be not transgender, but bisexual, gay or lesbian adults. Thus, helping prepubescent children feel comfortable in their birth sex makes more sense than starting a lifetime of hormonal treatments and surgeries that will in all likelihood turn out to be unnecessary and unwanted."[94]

Politics, Soh says, is keeping doctors like Kenneth Zucker from carrying out the best-known treatments for those afflicted with transgender thoughts. This means activists are inflicting more suffering on afflicted people, including children, rather than acknowledging all the available research and experience that can help alleviate their pain.

Links to Mental Disorders, Not Cross-Sex Attributes

A December 2015 study suggests transgender brains have a marker for the existence of mental illness. The researchers attempted to find support for the idea that transsexuals have a brain that corresponds to their wished-for gender, but they found no evidence of cross-gender brains. Instead, they found an

---

[93] http://www.suicide.org/suicide-causes.html

[94] http://www.wsj.com/articles/the-transgender-battle-line-childhood-1451952794?mod=djemMER

abnormality that suggests a link to psychological and behavioral dysfunction and mental disorders in the brains of transgenders.[95]

These findings support the results of another study released in August 2014 that found 62.7 percent of those diagnosed with gender dysphoria suffer from psychiatric axis 1 comorbid disorders, or mental illness.[96]

The presence of mental disorders has monumental implications for transgender treatment and should be taken seriously because of the link between some mental disorders and suicide. How can transgenders be properly treated when the transgender power brokers deny that psychological disorders may be a contributing factor?

Failure to provide psychotherapy for co-existing mental issues will keep the transgender suicides on the front page. With the backing of the White House, states and cities are criminalizing psychotherapy that explores and treats comorbid disorders in transgender and homosexual youth. The advocates have used the tragic death of a teen transgender to pass unnecessary laws to keep youngsters from getting sound psychotherapy that could prevent suicide.

Please Help Us, Don't Enable Us

I was a young person who had an undiagnosed comorbid disorder that drove me to unnecessary gender reassignment surgery, a surgery authorized by a homosexual activist. I lived as a transgender female for eight years, but gender reassignment wasn't the answer for me. I was still suicidal. I recovered through psychotherapy to uncover the underlying disorder and through my faith that gave me hope for the journey.

It's been 30 years since my surgery, and unfortunately the treatment protocol hasn't changed: gender dysphoric individuals continue to be shuttled toward hormones and surgery with no concern for detecting and treating comorbid disorders. If anything, opposition to the notion that psychological illness might exist in transgenders has become more strident, with a heaping dose of political correctness added in.

Powerful activists, lawmakers, and school administrators should use Alcorn's death to push for psychotherapy guidelines to uncover the mental disorders that lead to the depression that leads to suicide. Instead, denial has reached new heights and lawmakers are taking steps to outlaw therapy.

Therapy Outlawed in Four States

California, New Jersey, Oregon, Illinois, and the District of Columbia have banned conversion therapy. In Ohio, openly gay Cincinnati city councilman Chris Seelbach proposed an ordinance at the city council's law and public safety committee in December that would make it illegal for licensed counselors working with minors struggling with same-sex attraction or gender confusion to provide therapy whose goal is to overcome it, even if the teenager requests the therapy.

---

[95] http://www.ncbi.nlm.nih.gov/pubmed/26637450
[96] http://www.ncbi.nlm.nih.gov/pubmed/25180172

The city council passed the ordinance to levy a $200-a-day, $6,000-a-month fine on any counselor who tries to help a sexually confused teen. A family group has asked the council to overturn the ordinance, the first in the country of its kind at the city level.[97]

Lawmakers in four states, with others likely to follow, have made it illegal to provide youth with therapy that would uncover and treat co-existing illness. Even if the teenager wants therapy and the parents agree, therapy is not allowed to treat their gender confusion.

The government is overstepping. No one with common sense can look at the evidence of mental illness and the high suicide attempt rate and not see a link between the two, much less go ahead and pass laws to make it illegal to provide treatment that could save lives.

Do We Want More Suicides?

Assemble the evidence and it's easy to see that the laws barring therapy are a recipe for more transgender youth suicide. Here are results from a survey of 6,450 transgenders conducted by the National Center for Transgender Equality and National Gay and Lesbian Task Force,[98] and a World Health Organization report compiled from 15 countries:[99]

- 50 percent of transgender youth attempt suicide
- The core cause of suicide is untreated mental illness
- Studies point to the existence of mental disorders in transgenders
- Transgenders themselves report their "wonderful" confused life includes extreme poverty; misuse of drugs and alcohol; incomes four times lower than non-transgenders; unemployment twice the rate of the general population; homelessness at twice the rate of the general population
- Transgender women are 49 times more likely to contract HIV/AIDS than the general population

Suicides are the direct result of untreated psychological disorders, and transgenders need treatment to help reduce the staggering number of suicides. Lawmakers are interfering with recovery by withholding sound psychotherapies from a population in dire need of effective treatment.

My transgender life could be described using the list above. Thanks to effective psychotherapy, I recovered from a transgender life, ill-advised gender reassignment surgery, gender dysphoria, and from the childhood comorbid disorder that was ultimately diagnosed. I have lived free from the transgender madness for more than 20 years. Today's transgenders must have open and free access to any and all psychotherapies at any age.

---

[97] http://www.wlwt.com/news/group-asking-for-repeal-of-cincinnatis-lgbt-conversion-therapy-ban/37030170
[98] http://www.thetaskforce.org/downloads/reports/reports/ntds_full.pdf
[99] http://www.who.int/hiv/mediacentre/news/transgender-hiv-policy-feature/en/

Research Claiming Sex-Change Benefits Is Based On Junk Science

Sex-change studies base their conclusions on as few as 10 percent of study subjects. The truth is, many people who follow Caitlyn Jenner's path will deeply regret it.

BY WALT HEYER
THE FEDERALIST, APRIL 13, 2017
THEFEDERALIST.COM/2017/04/13/RESEARCH-
CLAIMING-SEX-CHANGE-BENEFITS-BASED-JUNK-SCIENCE/

Caitlyn Jenner has perfected the art of cashing in on each step of gender transition. A few short weeks before the release of his new book, Jenner acknowledges the boys are now gone. Adios to his life-long companions in gender reassignment surgery (known as bottom surgery).

Jenner is wealthy and can cash in on celebrity, but a large portion of the transgender population remains lost and unaccounted for. Did they die, detransition, or commit suicide? All we know is the attempted suicide rate for transgender people has remained above 40 percent for many years.

Doctors jam trans kids with puberty blockers and trans adults with cross-gender hormones, then recommend irreversible genital surgery, all without having long-term systematic studies of the effectiveness of such invasive treatment. Parents of trans kids don't have the benefit of trustworthy information on the probable outcomes of up to 90 percent of gender changers.

Research about transgender people is biased toward reporting success. Studies lose track of many participants, often the majority, and there is no mechanism for tracking those who are dissatisfied after gender-change treatment.[100] My transition back to male hasn't been tallied in the negative column of any study. Ditto for the trans people who reach out to me.

Huge Numbers of Study Subjects Are Lost to Follow-Up

One limitation of long-term transgender research is that many participants who were present at the beginning of the study can't be located at its end. In medical parlance, they are "lost to follow-up." A 2007 textbook titled "Principles of Transgender Medicine and Surgery" explains the limitations of the studies: "A large proportion of patients (up to 90%) are lost to follow up… [which]…complicates efforts to systematically study the long-term effects of gender reassignment surgery."[101]

Another review of more than 100 international medical studies of post-operative transsexuals conducted in 2004 by the University of Birmingham's aggressive research facility, Arif, warned "the results of many gender reassignment studies are unsound because researchers lost track of more than

---

[100] https://www.theguardian.com/society/2004/jul/30/health.mentalhealth
[101] https://www.amazon.com/Principles-Transgender-Medicine-Sexuality-Hardcover/dp/0789032686

half of the participants. For example, in a five-year study of 727 post-operative transsexuals published last year, 495 people dropped out for unknown reasons."[102]

Since the scientific community reports up to 90 percent of transsexuals are lost to follow-up and therefore not counted in study results, I'm skeptical when I hear the LGBT soundbite that says only a tiny percentage are dissatisfied after changing gender. The missing 90 percent could have given up on gender change and gone back to their birth gender or even committed suicide. No one knows, because they dropped out of sight. Too many hormones, too much surgery, and too many are lost.

Media reports about transgender outcomes is also biased positive because the research is also. Arif found "most of the medical research on gender reassignment was poorly designed, which skewed the results to suggest that sex change operations are beneficial." Arif also reported "no robust scientific evidence that gender reassignment surgery is clinically effective."

None of the people who have contacted me over the past 11 years about going back to their birth gender will be counted as having undesirable outcomes. That's because the LGBTQ studies purposefully exclude anything that would reflect badly on their overblown trans agenda.

Sex Changes Have Been Unsound Since Their Inception

From the start, the effectiveness of treating transgender people by affirming their non-biological identity was based on falsified evidence. Dr. Harry Benjamin will be known as the founder of transsexualism, but the real madness we see today reflects the legacy of Dr. John Money, a psychologist. During his time at Johns Hopkins University Hospital in the 1960s and '70s, Mooney launched the tragic trajectory of surgical transgenders, suicides, and regrettable outcomes.

Money made a name for himself with research on a set of twin boys, one of whom had his penis ruined in a botched circumcision. When the boy's distressed parents contacted Money for help, he saw an opportunity to conduct research on the cultural versus biological determinants of gender. Money recommended that doctors remove the remnants of David's injured genitalia and his parents raise him as a girl. They followed Money's advice, and at the age of two David Reimer became Brenda.

Over the years, Money met with the Reimer twins and wrote articles touting the success of his gender experiment and how well Brenda was adapting. His results fueled the acceptance of gender reassignment in the medical community.

The problem was, Money fabricated the results. The truth didn't come out until the twins were in their 30s. David had been suffering for most of his life from severe depression, followed by financial instability and a troubled marriage. Money withheld information the medical community and public needed to know about gender reassignment, and replaced it with lies.

When David Reimer and his twin brother broke their silence, they exposed Money as a fraud and pedophile. They told how Money had taken photos of them together naked in sexual poses when they were only seven years of age. Money did not stop with snapping photos. The twins described sexual abuse, saying Money forced them to engage in incestuous sex play with each other while he watched.

---

[102] https://www.theguardian.com/society/2004/jul/30/health.mentalhealth

The twins' outcome was grim. David died of suicide at age 38, and his brother died a few years later of a drug overdose. This foundation of gender reassignment surgery was based on fraudulent, fabricated research, and this form of treatment all too frequently ends in suicide or suicide attempts.

When a High-Profile Trans Person De-Transitions

Once in a while, a high-profile trans person reveals discontent with life after changing genders. Alexis Arquette, of Hollywood's famous Arquette family, began life as Robert and achieved fame as a transgender actress. In the media tributes that followed his death at age 47 last September, few mentioned that Alexis had detransitioned and stopped living as a woman. However, *The Hollywood Reporter* did write of Arquette's view of gender change:[103]

> In 2013, amid increasing health complications, Alexis began presenting herself as a man again, telling [close friend] Ibrahim that 'gender is bullshit.' That 'putting on a dress doesn't biologically change anything. Nor does a sex-change.' She said that 'sex-reassignment is physically impossible. All you can do is adopt these superficial characteristics but the biology will never change.' That realization, Ibrahim suspects, was the likely source of her deep wells of emotional torment.

Clearly, even a well-known and talented transgender individual who is embraced and accepted in his chosen identity can struggle and decide to return to his birth sex. But he is not counted in any study.

As one who transitioned, lived as a woman for eight years, and returned to life as a male, I hope more people will speak publicly about the reality of life after changing gender—the doubts and questioning, the fatigue of living a masquerade, and the desire to go back to one's birth gender. Transgender people write to me confidentially, yet frankly, about their gender struggles and the desire to de-transition, but they find the idea of once again changing their appearance and identity daunting.

When People Speak Openly About Their Sex Change

People who write to me aren't counted in any ongoing studies, but they give insight into the minds of those who undergo gender transition. Here are two stories from folks I corresponded with in 2010.

Regret arrived quickly for a male who transitioned to female and wrote to me four months post-op:

> I recently had the sex change surgery, and although I thought I was completely sure of what I was doing, I began to regret the decision a mere three weeks after the operation.
>
> Some might say I was experiencing post-op depression, but it was definitely more than that. I also suspect that many of the other patients at the hospital who had the same operation experienced similar feelings based on my discussions with them.
>
> What really drove the point home for me was the realization that it required eight hours on an operating table to make my genitalia appear to be female.
>
> That pretty much tells me that I'm NOT female at all. If I were female, why wasn't I born with female genitalia? Sure, there are some intersexed people with ambiguous genitals,

---

[103] http://www.hollywoodreporter.com/news/final-days-alexis-arquette-a-928507

but I'm not at all intersexed. My chromosomes are the normal male XY, with absolutely no abnormalities.

The reality is that I'm male, and no amount of surgery changes that fact. I'm now four months post-op, and I've begun to transition to live as a male again. I feel it's the only way to be honest with myself and with society.

If you are considering this surgery, think very carefully about the consequences. Make sure that the doctor or counselor that's approving you for the surgery is qualified to evaluate whether you need the operation or not.

The second email comes from a man who regretted his gender transition a mere year and a half after surgery. It shares a father's painful revelation of wanting to return to being a man and father again.

I am 46 and 1.5 years post op MTF [male to female]. I struggled with my gender identity most of my life. I am so miserable and every day I struggle to get thru the next minute. I have to pray for the strength not to go to the gun store. Every minute is filled with suicidal thoughts. I can't live like this anymore. Please help me. Guide me what to do medically, surgically to fix this mess.

I am so glad I came across your website. After 10 months of post-op psychotherapy, I know sadly now my problems were great depression, unresolved issues as you said (I was sexually abused by my grandfather at 3 years old, father was killed in the line of duty when I was 5, grew up thinking I must be gay, had sex with men and was disgusted, and cross dressed most of my life.) My new therapist is calling it a transvestic fetish that went terribly wrong, coupled with GID.

Why couldn't we get to this pre-op? It's just a sick money making industry as I see it. I have already removed the breast implants, and will be restarting testosterone soon. I have destroyed my career, my finances and my marriage and alienated my family.

The pain as you know is so great! It feels like a knife in my heart. I can't sleep. I am so disgusted with myself. How could a smart, successful guy get so lost? I had it all. Now I'm watching it slowly fade away. You and all the people that give me words of encouragement are the only thing keeping me going. I have rope, and I know when and where all the next guns shows are; I don't want to live like this. My therapist is going to recommend me to gender therapists; to get a surgical solution I can live with. At 46 years of age I just hope I have the strength to get there; my batteries are drained. I have not read your book; but I am willing to listen to your thoughts and ideas.[104]

Red flags against gender-change surgery abound. Up to 90 percent of gender changers in studies cannot be located for follow-up, lowering the quality and credibility of the activist trans agenda. Scientific evidence showing that gender reassignment surgery is clinically effective is lacking.

---

[104] "Gender, Lies and Suicide," by Walt Heyer. p. 73-76

A founder of the modern surgical gender change model of treatment, Dr. John Money, falsely reported success to promote himself and advocate for transgender surgery. Performer Alexis Arquette de-transitioned back to Robert, said "Gender is bullshit," and blew the whistle on the madness and futility of gender change.

Letters in my inbox relate first-person accounts that the LGBTQ lobby will not even acknowledge exist and that poke holes in the often-told myth that regret is rare. Jenner has said adios to his boys, while far too many transgender people have said adios to family and friends and cannot be found.

One can only hope people considering a sex change or who regret their sex change have a "come to Jesus" meeting like I did, or risk becoming one of the 90 percent lost in the wilderness of transgenderism.

Diagnosis of Gender Dysphoria—Too General and Too Much Harm

The diagnosis of gender dysphoria prematurely puts people on a path to transition while trivializing and dismissing contributing factors such as alcohol and drug abuse, sexual fetishes and co-existing psychological disorders. The trans "treatment" being idolized today should meet the same fate as lobotomies, tooth pulling and colon removal—tossed on the historical rubbish heap of debunked horrific experiments perpetrated on innocent, hurting people.

BY WALT HEYER
PUBLIC DISCOURSE, AUGUST 7, 2019
WWW.THEPUBLICDISCOURSE.COM/2019/08/55621/

The diagnosis of gender dysphoria—defined as a conflict between a person's physical sex and the one with which he/she identifies[105]—is so general that it can embrace any of a multitude of other ailments. But once gender specialists decide on the diagnosis of gender dysphoria, they stop looking further. If a concerned patient or parent reveals something such as abuse or mental illness that seemed to be a trigger, the specialists consider it less pertinent. Even ongoing drug or alcohol abuse is ignored. Swept up by the broad diagnosis of gender dysphoria, innocent people receive non-reversible, gender-affirming treatment.

Diverse Disorders

By exhuming what has been buried beneath the diagnosis of gender dysphoria, we can form a theory concerning why so many people regret sex change and contact me for help undoing the damage. Perhaps gender dysphoria in some cases is a *symptom*, not a diagnosis, that points to other conditions that could benefit from a treatment other than cross-sex hormones and surgeries.

People in distress about their gender usually seek help from gender specialists who have a blind spot. They hear "gender distress" and conclude, often quickly, that transgender-affirming treatment is the *only* option for *every* patient. But a look at the variety of types of gender distress—none of which benefit from cross-sex hormones and surgery—shows how wrong that assumption is.

Transvestism, or crossdressing, is when a man likes to dress in women's clothes but doesn't want to be a woman and otherwise lives typically as a male. The APA doesn't consider crossdressing a *transvestic disorder* until it is accompanied by sexual excitement.[106]

Drag queens, a.k.a. female impersonators, are male and predominantly homosexual. When dressed up, they present as caricatures of women in flamboyant style.

---

[105] https://www.psychiatry.org/patients-families/gender-dysphoria/what-is-gender-dysphoria
[106] https://www.psychiatry.org/patients-families/gender-dysphoria/expert-q-and-a

Autogynephilia is when men experience erotic arousal at the thought or image of themselves as women.

Psychological conditions present in almost 70 percent of people with gender dysphoria[107] include anxiety disorders (panic disorder, social anxiety disorder, post-traumatic stress disorder), mood disorders (major depression, bipolar disorder, etc.), eating disorders (anorexia nervosa, bulimia nervosa, etc.), psychotic disorders, dissociative disorders, and substance abuse disorders.[108] Dissociative disorder was found in 29.6 percent of those with gender dysphoria and 45.8 percent had a high prevalence of lifetime major depressive episodes.[109]

Rapid Onset Gender Dysphoria (ROGD), is a relatively recent phenomenon observed in previously normal teens, primarily girls, who suddenly announce their desire to transition to the opposite sex. Initial research suggests that it may be a social contagion, brought on by angst about puberty and the influence of social media and sympathetic depictions of transgenderism.[110]

So, then who is truly transgender? Some would argue it is all of the above, but I would argue that it remains an open question with no answer. But this much is clear: patients deserve to receive better diagnoses and less invasive treatment plans than simply being thrown onto the fast track to transition.

From My Inbox

People write to me asking for advice on how to detransition, that is, to stop identifying as transgender and go back to living as their biological sex. Every single one of them, after some discussion and personal reflection, has pointed to something in his or her history, such as childhood abuse, trauma, mental disorders, or family issues, that caused each one to want to abandon the reality of his or her sex and adopt an alternate identity. These could be the cases where gender dysphoria is a *symptom*, not a diagnosis, and could benefit from a treatment other than cross-sex hormones and surgeries.

For example, a person who has been sexually abused might desire to become a member of the opposite sex in an unconscious attempt to shield himself from more abuse. Or, an adolescent may experience body dysmorphia—an obsession about some aspect of his or her appearance—that results in the flawed idea that his or her sex is wrong and the body needs to be changed.

Through their own life experience, and unfortunately often only in hindsight, people with regret see clearly that the cross-gender hormones and surgeries did not fix what ailed them and instead, harmed them. These are the cases where the therapists rushed to recommend hormones—powerful drugs with known and unknown side effects[111]—before ruling out the presence of other issues that respond to less radical therapies. Most say they wish the gender therapists had addressed the other issues before providing any gender affirming therapy that did more harm than good.

I prefer to see a "slow down and look deeper" approach, especially for young people (whose parents need to have input and not be cut out of the process). Some trans activists disparage this approach as

---

[107] https://www.researchgate.net/publication/250920575_Psychiatric_
characteristics_in_transsexual_individuals_Multicentre_study_in_four_European_countries

[108] https://www.verywellmind.com/axis-i-disorders-2797271

[109] https://www.sciencedirect.com/science/article/abs/pii/S0165178115000050

[110] https://journals.plos.org/plosone/article?id=10.1371/journal.pone.0202330

[111] https://www.acpeds.org/the-college-speaks/position-statements/gender-dysphoria-in-children

"gatekeeping." But medicine is supposed to enforce standards and restrictions to protect patients from harm and work for their flourishing, not simply be a dispensary for whatever the patients request.

Two examples: Sexual Fetish and Psychological Disorders

James Shupe's story is an example of how generalizing the diagnosis of gender dysphoria fails to address autogynophelia, a sexual fetish where men who cross dress are sexually attracted to their own image as a woman.

Shupe explains it this way in his *Daily Signal* essay:[112]

> Dr. Ray Blanchard has an unpopular theory that explains why someone like me may have been drawn to transgenderism. He claims there are two types of transgender women: homosexuals that are attracted to men, and men who are attracted to the thought or image of themselves as females.
>
> It's a tough thing to admit, but I belong to the latter group. We are classified as having autogynephilia.
>
> After having watched pornography for years while in the Army and being married to a woman who resisted my demands to become the ideal female, I became that female instead. At least in my head.

Like so many others who came to identify themselves as transgender persons and later regretted it, Shupe was sexually abused as a child but never properly diagnosed or treated for it. The therapists failed Shupe by looking at the symptom and not looking deeper for the cause.

A second example is Blair Logsdon, whose story shows how the generalized diagnosis of gender dysphoria ignores underlying psychological issues. In his quest to relieve gender distress, he requested, and received, 167 unnecessary gender-affirming surgeries from 1987 to 2005, earning him a place in the Guinness Book of World Records.

In 1987, at the age of 26, Logsdon underwent the first of many cosmetic surgeries to change his appearance from male to trans-female. Within a few months, he said he deeply regretted becoming a trans-woman, but continued for decades to plead for more surgeries, both feminizing and masculinizing. The doctors and surgeons complied, failing him in their responsibility to "first do no harm" while profiting from performing the 167 disfiguring surgeries.[113]

Historical Context

Performing surgery to cure psychological ills didn't start with sex reassignment surgery.

Starting in 1913, Dr. Henry Cotton became famous for treating psychologically distressed patients with radical, experimental, irreversible surgery. In the time before the discovery of bacteria and antibiotics, Dr. Cotton removed various body parts of the patients, such as teeth, colons, and even testicles to prove his theory that all mental illness was the result of infections. When some patients

[112] https://www.dailysignal.com/2019/03/10/i-was-americas-first-non-binary-person-it-was-all-a-sham/
[113] https://www.dailysignal.com/2018/01/12/man-received-167-sex-change-surgeries-lives-world-regret/

inevitably died from complications of Dr. Cotton's "treatment," he counted them in the success column because they were no longer suffering.[114]

For decades, starting in the 1930s, Drs. Walter Freeman and James Watts made their mark in medicine by treating psychological distress with the frontal lobotomy, a barbaric experimental practice that used an ice pick to indiscriminately scramble the brains of patients. Like Cotton's patients, after the procedure Freeman's patients were "no longer suffering" but dramatically changed.[115]

Today's Treatments for Gender Dysphoria

The mistaken idea of treating psychological distress by cutting body parts continues with so-called "gender affirmation" treatments (really they're *trans*gender affirmation) that remove or add breasts, rearrange genitals and administer powerful cross-sex hormones to masculinize or feminize appearances—with lifelong physical and psychological consequences[116] for the innocent casualties.[117]

For fifty years, the experiment of providing cross-sex hormones and surgery to treat gender distress has resulted in surgical mistakes, unhappiness, regret and suicide.[118] A large study in Sweden, a transgender-affirming society, shows that the suicide-completion rate for people after gender-affirming treatment was nineteen times that of the general population.[119]

> Over the last ten years people have expressed to me their bewilderment
> about how this genital mutilation surgery is even legal.

Several men who have written to me recently used the phrase "open wound" to describe their surgically created pseudo-vaginas.

My Story

My position on this subject has been shaped by my own experience with gender dysphoria before and after sex-reassignment surgery, and by years of receiving emails from other regretters.

When my gender therapist, Dr. Paul Walker, told me the only effective treatment for my severe gender distress was hormones and surgery, I regrettably followed his recommendation.

I was happy as a trans woman at first, but within a few years, I felt worse off than before. Counselors were divided in their assessment. Some said I had dissociative disorder and some disagreed. Regardless of the label, what I know is that living in my adopted female persona for eight years didn't solve my troubles, but instead made them worse. I became suicidal.

---

[114] *Paper Genders*, Walt Heyer

[115] Ibid.

[116] https://www.thepublicdiscourse.com/2018/11/42698/

[117] https://www.thepublicdiscourse.com/2018/01/20810/

[118] https://www.thepublicdiscourse.com/2016/02/16376/

[119] https://journals.plos.org/plosone/article?id=10.1371/journal.pone.0016885

So-called "gender-affirming" therapy almost caused me to end my life. I thank God it didn't. Years of heart-wrenching counseling under multiple therapists, faithfully pursuing sobriety, and an encounter with Jesus Christ restored my sanity. I detransitioned, got married to a (real) woman, and now tell my story as a cautionary tale to others. I live with the scars and effects of unnecessary surgery and the long-lasting consequences.

My detractors say I was never transgender. They say a diagnosis of dissociative disorder nullifies my experience. If that's the criterion, then according to the study cited before, almost 30 percent of the trans population would be disqualified as transgender. Besides being intolerant and non-compassionate, that argument aims to silence anybody who has been harmed by transgender-affirming treatment. People can hold opposite viewpoints on an issue, but saying that someone's experience of harm at the hand of gender professionals is invalid or "hate speech" because it differs from that of others has no place in public discourse.

The Diagnosis is Harming People

In today's climate, where sound, scientific facts of medical practice are abandoned in favor of political correctness, people of all ages are being swept up in the diagnosis of gender dysphoria and cannot escape being improperly treated with transgender-affirming therapies.

The diagnosis of gender dysphoria prematurely puts people on a path to transition while trivializing and dismissing contributing factors such as alcohol and drug abuse, sexual fetishes and co-existing psychological disorders. It pathologizes children who innocently experiment with gender roles or who exhibit various anxieties. The result is physical and psychological harm, unhappiness, regret, and a significant rise in suicide.

Like the discredited procedures of Drs. Cotton, Watts and Freeman, the trans "treatment" being idolized today should meet the same fate as lobotomies, tooth pulling and colon removal—tossed on the historical rubbish heap of debunked horrific experiments perpetrated on innocent, hurting people.

As I wrote in my book, *Paper Genders*, cutting off breasts, filling patients with cross-sex hormones, cutting off or refashioning male genitalia, installing a pseudo penis on a female—all of today's transgender treatments are barbaric and need to stop. Someday these matters will be decided in the courts and hopefully the harmful practices will be curtailed, but "someday" is too late for those being ensnared into the trans ideology today.

The wave of regretters is coming. I'm already seeing it.

I Wish I Had Been Told About These Risks Before I Had Gender Surgery

---

True compassion is acknowledging the mental disorders and providing effective, sound treatment in an effort to slow the staggering number of suicides, before rushing to perform irreversible surgeries.

BY WALT HEYER
THE DAILY SIGNAL, JUNE 9, 2016
WWW.DAILYSIGNAL.COM/2016/06/09/I-WISH-I-
HAD-BEEN-TOLD-ABOUT-THESE-RISKS-BEFORE-I-HAD-GENDER-SURGERY/

Many Americans are unaware of the serious problems that face transgender persons.

For instance, a 2016 study comparing 20 Lebanese transgender participants to 20 control subjects reported that transgender individuals suffer from more psychiatric pathologies compared to the general population.

More than 50 percent had active suicidal thoughts and 45 percent had had a major depressive episode.[120]

While it may not be politically correct to link psychological disorders with the transgender population, the researchers see the evidence that a link exists. As a former transgender person, I wish the guy who approved me for gender surgery would have told me about the risks.

Quick to Diagnose

The experience of many gender-confused individuals is that medical professionals are quick to reach a diagnosis of gender dysphoria and recommend immediate cross-gender hormone therapy and irreversible reassignment surgery without investigating and treating the coexisting issues. Research has found that powerful psychological issues, such as anxiety disorder, post-traumatic stress disorder, or alcohol or drug dependence often accompany gender dysphoria.

A study published in JAMA Pediatrics in March 2016 shows a high prevalence of psychiatric diagnoses in a sample of 298 young transgender women aged 16 through 29 years old.

More than 40 percent had coexisting mental health or substance dependence diagnoses. One in five had two or more psychiatric diagnoses. The most commonly occurring disorders were major depressive episodes and non-alcohol psychoactive substance use dependence.[121]

---

[120] http://www.ncbi.nlm.nih.gov/pubmed/27017319
[121] http://www.ncbi.nlm.nih.gov/pubmed/26999485

Yet, transgender individuals are never required to undergo any objective test to prove their gender dysphoria—because no diagnostic objective test exists.

The cause of this condition can't be verified through lab results, a brain scan, or review of the DNA make-up.

Research studies from 2013 and 2009 looking for a "transgender gene" showed not a smidgeon of abnormality in the genetic make-up that causes someone to be transgender.[122] [123]

No alterations in the main sex-determining genes in male-to-female transsexual individuals were found, suggesting strongly that male-born transgender persons are normal males biologically.

Psychological Care Urgently Needed

The study concluded that improved access to medical and psychological care "are urgently needed to address mental health and substance dependence disorders in this population."

On the contrary, it did not conclude that improved access to bathrooms, hormones, or surgery are urgently needed.

A 2015 study of 118 individuals diagnosed with gender dysphoria found that 29.6 percent were also found to have dissociative disorders and a high prevalence of lifetime major depressive episodes (45.8 percent), suicide attempts (21.2 percent), and childhood trauma (45.8 percent).

It also remarked that differentiating between a diagnosis of dissociative disorder and gender dysphoria is difficult because the two can closely resemble each other.[124]

Another study found a "surprisingly high prevalence of emotional maltreatment" in the 41 transsexuals studied. It called for further investigation to clarify the effects of traumatic childhood experiences and the correlation between transsexualism and dissociative identity.[125]

That finding tracks with what I experienced in my transgender life. In my life and in the lives of those whose families contact me, traumatic childhood experiences are present 100 percent of the time.

Childhood Gender Dysphoria

One area where medical professionals should tread lightly is in the diagnosis and treatment of children who have gender identity issues.

A 2015 study aimed to gather input from pediatric endocrinologists, psychologists, psychiatrists, and ethicists—both those in favor and those opposed to early treatment—to further the ethical debate.

The results showed no consensus on many basic topics of childhood gender dysphoria and insufficient research to support any recommendations for childhood treatments,[126] including the currently

---

[122] http://www.ncbi.nlm.nih.gov/pubmed/23324476

[123] http://www.sciencedirect.com/science/article/pii/S027858460900222X

[124] http://www.ncbi.nlm.nih.gov/pubmed/25656174

[125] http://www.ncbi.nlm.nih.gov/pubmed/12637845

[126] http://www.ncbi.nlm.nih.gov/pubmed/26119518

published guidelines that recommend suppressing puberty with drugs until age 16, after which cross-sex hormones may be given.[127]

An analysis of the 38 youth referrals for gender dysphoria to the Pediatric Endocrinology Clinic at the University School of Medicine in Indianapolis showed that more than half had psychiatric and/or developmental comorbidities.[128]

Without sufficient research and consensus on treatment of children diagnosed with gender dysphoria, and knowing over half have coexisting disorders, any invasive treatment, even if recommended by the current guidelines, is simply an experiment.

It's time to stop using children as experiments.

Transgender Persons Are Struggling Psychologically

Transgender individuals need psychotherapy not access to cross-sex restrooms, showers, and dressing areas. Blaming society for the ills of transgender persons will not improve their diagnosis and treatment.

Reckless disregard for the mental disorders in favor of enforcing preferred pronouns is madness. It's time to show compassion by telling the truth and stop pretending they are born that way.

True compassion is acknowledging the mental disorders and providing effective, sound treatment in an effort to slow the staggering number of suicides, before rushing to perform irreversible surgeries.

---

[127] http://press.endocrine.org/doi/full/10.1210/jc.2009-0345
[128] http://www.ncbi.nlm.nih.gov/pubmed/26903434

Chapter 4.
Therapy Is Lifesaving

If California's LGBT Therapy Ban Had Been Law 30 Years Ago, I Might Have Killed Myself

If I had been prevented from having access to helpful people and materials, as Assembly Bill 2943 proposes, the bill would have been a 'stay trans and die' bill for me.

BY WALT HEYER
THE FEDERALIST, APRIL 25, 2018
THEFEDERALIST.COM/2018/04/25/CALIFORNIAS-
LGBT-THERAPY-BAN-LAW-30-YEARS-AGO-MIGHT-KILLED/

While living in California more than 30 years ago, I had access to sound, effective, time-tested psychotherapy. Because of it, I walked away from the transgender life I had lived as Laura Jensen for eight years in San Francisco.

Yet if I had been prevented from having access to such people and materials, as Assembly Bill 2943[129] proposes, the bill would have been a "stay trans and die" bill for me. I wanted to have access to restoration and redemption from my transgender life, but AB 2943 would make that illegal. The bill intends to prevent any access to what is potentially lifesaving psychotherapy for people who identify as transgender, like I did.

California Family Council points out that AB 2943 prevents counselors from helping adult clients deal with unwanted same-sex attraction or gender confusion, and prohibits authors from selling a book, or even a church from hosting a ticketed conference, addressing these topics.[130]

I started my journey toward redemption and the restoration of my male gender on April 7, 1990, with the help of two outstanding Christian therapists to whom I owe my life. The healing psychotherapy provided me has resulted in 32 years of sobriety, complete restoration of my male gender for 28 years, and marriage to a wonderful woman for 21 years. I speak out for the others who feel hopeless and stuck in a lifestyle that doesn't fit them anymore.

If AB 2943 were in place back in the 1990s, most likely I would have died from suicide or, as this bill proposes, once I embraced my life as a trans-woman, I was sentenced for life. The bill's authors want to make sure the gender-dysphoric people they claim to be "helping" have no way out, even if that's what they desperately want. Only an uncaring legislature would sign such a draconian bill into law.

People Detransition All the Time

If you think detransitions are rare, just Google "detransition" and see the multitude of videos from courageous formerly trans people who tell of the peace they have found with their God-given gender

---

[129] https://legiscan.com/CA/text/AB2943/2017
[130] http://www.californiafamily.org/

through a combination of counseling and faith. If this bill becomes law, these people will no longer have access to help they choose, because apparently some in California's government think no one should be allowed to change his or her mind about what constitutes being at peace with one's sex.

"People have the right to seek the counsel of their choice, but this bill substitutes the government for personal choice," says Liberty Counsel founder Mat Staver.[131] People entering into psychotherapy for gender dysphoria would no longer have the freedom of setting their treatment goals if those goals differ from the government-mandated one.

AB 2943 prevents access guaranteed under the U.S. Constitution to all opinions, no matter if opposing voices disagree. AB2943 is an affront to Americans' civil rights, religious rights, and Constitution-guaranteed freedom of speech. This state law would impose one viewpoint and outlaw all others. The only viewpoint it would permit is that people who express a different gender must be affirmed and guided toward transition to the fake gender. No alternative path is allowed, regardless of the person's wishes. Once someone considers a gender change, he or she must pursue it or else.

AB 2932 has teeth. It proposes to financially ruin those who provide information contrary to the LGBT ideology on gender and sex. Anyone who sells books, counseling services, or anything else that helps someone overcome unwanted transgender identity can be charged with engaging in "unfair or deceptive acts or practices" and be obligated to pay punitive damages, court costs, and attorney's fees.

Included in the wide net of "unfair or deceptive acts or practices" is the sale of memoirs and personal stories featuring people who left the trans-world and how. Evidence that people return to living happily in their birth gender, like I did, would be suppressed

AB 2943 says "advertising, offering to engage in, or engaging in" efforts to change sexual behaviors or gender expressions would be illegal under the California's Consumers Legal Remedies Act. It specifically outlaws telling a client about poor outcomes that can arise from gender change or suggesting that psychological counseling is helpful in resolving gender confusion.

While I still have the freedom to speak without fear of punishment, I will tell you what the authors of this bill don't want you to know.

The Science On Gender Isn't Settled

When an individual self-identifies as being the other gender, this is not objectively provable through science, medicine, or biological truth. It is simply an idea some people have. It can be a strongly held idea, but it is a fantasy that has serious consequences.

This diverse population has a need to act out their cross-gender masquerade. This should strongly suggest that something much deeper sexually, emotionally, or psychologically is causing this unusual behavior. For some I know personally, deep inside remains unresolved grief and pain that just will not go away. Unresolved pathologies need to be discovered and treated before cross-gender hormones are taken and any gender surgeries are performed, to ensure these drastic alterations to one's body are actually addressing the real needs of the person.

---

[131] http://libertycounsel.com/ca-bill-to-censor-counseling/

I hear from those whose lives have been broken because gender-change treatment was the only option provided. Years afterward, when they find themselves discontent or depressed even though they are accepted as the other gender, the lucky ones seek access to effective psychotherapy. The unfortunate ones live a despondent life, or fall prey to suicide ideation. Some quietly return to their birth gender, wondering "What happened?"

We do not know enough to say for certain that gender-change surgery and hormones are the right choices for every person who considers them. Significant gaps in scientific knowledge and research exist regarding transgender health. A review of 2,405 articles published through June 2016 focused on transgender health and concludes that "most of the published work that exists is not primary research, and there are very few studies that look at long-term outcomes."[132]

California AB 2943 would prevent me from sharing that self-identified transgender people largely suffer psychiatric, psychological, or sexual disorders that are not effectively treated as prescribed by the standards of care issued by the politically driven World Professional Association for Transgender Health (WPATH). A 2014 study showed that 62.7 percent have co-existing psychiatric disorders such as depression, phobias, adjustment disorders, and extreme anxiety.[133]

People Deserve the Freedom to Consider All Options

Gender dysphoria or cross-gender expression can evolve from difficult family situations where children are caught between battling parents, placed in foster care, or live in other types of unsettling environments that result in the child feeling depressed and anxious over a long period.

A 2016 study shows a high prevalence of psychiatric diagnoses in a community-recruited sample of young transgender women. Forty-one percent of participants had one or more mental health or substance dependence diagnoses. The researchers concluded: "Improving access to routine primary care, diagnostic screening, psychotherapy, and pharmacologic treatments, and retention in care in clinical community-based, pediatric, and adolescent medicine settings are urgently needed to address mental health and substance dependence disorders in this population."[134]

When I ask the individuals who contact me about having difficulty in their chosen gender, 100 percent of the time they can pinpoint a situation in their childhood that strongly contributed to development of gender incongruence. California is outlawing access to information and counseling that would help this population recover from the effects of childhood events.

> People would not be allowed to hear about the failure of sex change to resolve gender confusion or about the high rate of attempted suicide *after* taking cross-gender hormones and undergoing gender change surgeries.

---

[132] https://www.ncbi.nlm.nih.gov/pmc/articles/PMC5627669/
[133] https://www.ncbi.nlm.nih.gov/pubmed/25180172
[134] https://www.ncbi.nlm.nih.gov/pmc/articles/PMC4882090/

It is important to understand that transgender suicide is not caused by discrimination or family or societal rejection. According to suicide.org, 90 percent of all people who die by their own hand, including those who identify as transgender, have untreated mental illness.

AB 2943 would not allow me to share that autogynephilia, an erotic or affection phenomenon, can lead to a misguided request for gender-change surgery. Autogynephilic men fall in love with the idea of themselves as women. They will seek sex reassignment because they are sexually aroused by the idea of having breast implants and other cosmetic surgery to feminize their appearance.[135] They are the object of their own affection.

From my observations in speaking with people with this condition, they realize after surgery, often years after, that the clinicians who approved and supported their surgical gender changes are clueless about diagnosing autogynephilia. For them, cross-gender hormone therapy and gender surgeries weren't appropriate treatment. Because the clinicians affirmed their misplaced desire to become women, their lives were upended and severely impacted.

Consumer fraud is serious business, and that's why California's Consumers Legal Remedies Act exists. But to use it to mandate state-determined psychotherapy goals and to call public debate a "false and deceptive practice" is a mistake. The state has overstepped. Cross-gender expression is too complex a subject to be legislated. This bill would harm the very individuals it proposes to help and protect.

---

[135] https://www.ncbi.nlm.nih.gov/pubmed/17951885

Freedom to Change Your Life: Why the Government Shouldn't Ban "Reparative Therapy"

The Southern Poverty Law Center and other LGBT organizations seek to end civil rights for people with same-sex attractions who freely desire therapy rather than to continue in their current lifestyle. Equality in civil rights demands that no one should be unjustly stripped of their lawful, rightful access to effective therapies.

BY WALT HEYER
PUBLIC DISCOURSE, APRIL 5, 2016
WWW.THEPUBLICDISCOURSE.COM/2016/04/16625/

The freedom of people with same-sex attractions to exercise their civil rights is under siege by legal bullies who hate redeemed and restored lives. The Southern Poverty Law Center (SPLC) and two other groups are out to crush the civil rights of those who desperately desire therapy.

On February 24, the SPLC and other LGBT organizations filed a formal complaint with the Federal Trade Commission designed to silence People Can Change (PCC), an organization whose clients seek help in dealing with their same-sex attractions. Four liberal lawmakers added their names to the complaint in an all-out effort to penalize anyone who would offer therapies called "reparative therapy" or "conversion therapy" to anyone who freely asks for it.

The legal filing demonstrates a visceral hatred not only toward these therapies but also toward people who don't want to act on their same-sex attractions, and want to minimize or perhaps even change them. The legal filing aims to take away the freedom, civil rights, and human rights of people who desire to engage in therapies rather than in same-sex relationships. The SPLC tactic is to harass organizations that offer therapy with which they do not agree. Having achieved success in a case filed in New Jersey state court against Jews Offering New Alternatives for Healing (JONAH), they are emboldened to go after People Can Change by filing with the United States Federal Trade Commission.

The complaint asks that PCC be barred from displaying the firsthand testimonies of courageous and compassionate people who want to share their experience of freedom and peace.

Why they're doing it: to destroy any evidence that change is possible

If people want to resist acting on, minimize, or perhaps even change their same-sex attractions, why would anyone want to stop them from trying? This stubborn blocking of free choice seems to indicate another agenda at work.

Why do these groups so despise the notion that people can make choices about the actions they engage in and even change their attractions? Why do they want to silence any evidence that it has happened? The answer seems obvious: These advocates have the goal of stopping any therapy that proves people can change when it comes to sexual attractions.

The agenda is abundantly clear. Because the linchpin of the Lesbian, Gay, Bisexual, and Transgender civil rights deception rests squarely on the misleading narrative that people "are born that way," *anything* that threatens their storyline must be discredited and destroyed:

- Anyone who wants not to act on same-sex attractions, or seeks to minimize and even eliminate them, will be blocked from finding help.
- Anyone who has successfully lived out chastity will be ostracized and marginalized.
- Any organization that dares to point to objective results from people who have made progress with their sexual attractions will be silenced and financially destroyed.
- Any evidence that shows that a person is not born homosexual, or that a person is not born transgender, will be banished and outlawed.

Clearly, the testimonies of numerous same-sex attracted and transgender people like myself[136] who live out our new, changed lives are the evidence that invalidates the LGBT narrative of "born that way."

Restored lives are living proof that change is possible.

The targeting of PCC is only the beginning. For activist groups like the SPLC, each small victory builds on the previous win and is used as "evidence" in the next case filed against the next pro-counseling group. For example, the SPLC pulls in gender-identity counseling in its complaint, even though PCC focuses on same-sex attraction. The SPLC is conflating sexual attraction counseling with gender-identity counseling, saying that transgender people can't change back to their birth gender, in order to set up the target for their next complaint.

What's the danger in the therapy?

If conversion therapy didn't work, it would die away naturally. There would be no demand. There would be no need for the Southern Poverty Law Center to seek to prevent such therapies from being offered to those who wish to try it. Their complaint is all the proof any court needs to understand that today's "reparative therapy" is actually effective.

Techniques done in the name of "reparative therapy" in the past, such as using aversion methods based on Pavlov's theory of rewards and punishments, or imposing involuntary and coercive intervention, were found to be harmful and are not being used today. Today, the same cognitive therapy traditionally used by psychotherapists for every other psychological issue is used for unwanted same-sex attraction. In fact, it was through traditional therapy that I was able to walk out of my transgender life. The irony of the Southern Poverty Law Center targeting People Can Change for offering reparative therapy is that PCC doesn't offer it or any other kind of therapy. According to Rich Wyler, founder of PCC, PCC is a self-help, peer-support organization for men who are seeking help with unwanted same-sex attraction.

---

[136] https://www.thepublicdiscourse.com/2015/04/14688/

> The truth is that some homosexual and transgender people change. The complaint filed with the Federal Trade Commission is hateful toward us who live new lives.

Apparently the SPLC does not want the nation to know that recovery from the transgender and homosexual lifestyles is actually possible. We who tour the nation speaking about our transformed lives are living, breathing proof that recovery is possible. By exercising the freedom to choose which therapies we wanted to try, we found a new life apart from homosexuality and transgenderism.

We who have come out of the lesbian, gay, or transgender lifestyle found the serenity and satisfaction we had desired all our lives. Our lives should be celebrated, not condemned or dismissed. Our lives are proof of the effectiveness of therapy for some individuals, regardless of what the detractors do to disparage or ban it.

The People Can Change website contains numerous testimonies of men who affirm that, under PCC's program, they have "experienced profound change in our sexual identity, behavior, interests and desires—change that has brought us great peace and satisfaction." The founder himself is "a man who had personally experienced enormous transformation from unwanted homosexual attractions." The organization only seeks to help those men who freely choose to try the therapy that has worked for others. For stating these things publicly, PCC is the subject of a consumer complaint from LGBT advocacy groups and supporters.

Our stories show the success of reparative therapy

I was diagnosed with gender dysphoria by a homosexual gender therapist. He advised me to undergo gender reassignment surgery. Because I trusted his expertise, I followed his advice, and it was a big mistake. Even though I lived the transgender life for eight years as Laura Jensen, a female, my gender issues were not resolved. The surgery was so therapeutically disastrous in my case that I attempted suicide as a way out. I was one of the 41 percent of transgender people reported in the National Transgender Discrimination survey that suffer from significant depression and attempt suicide.[137] The lifesaving solution for me was therapy and restoration of my birth gender.

Now I share the story of "coming out" of that life. Along the way I have met others who were gay, lesbian, or transgender who share the same changed life experience I have come to love. Years of pain had turned many of our lives upside down. By turning to therapies, we healed the shame and deep hurt so that the pain no longer drives us to unwanted behaviors.

The actions of groups like the SPLC are an attempt to disparage our changed lives, to insist that we don't exist—but that doesn't change the reality that we do exist and we did change. Who is to say whether a specific person can change or not? If some persons have a deep desire to rid themselves of same-sex attractions, shouldn't they be allowed to try?

Of course, not all therapy is always effective for every person. No one in the psychology field would ever claim that counseling will help every person, every time. Counseling doesn't work that way.

---

[137] http://www.thetaskforce.org/static_html/downloads/reports/reports/ ntds_full.pdf

The claims in the complaint are false and misleading

The SPLC complaint against People Can Change is a jumble of misinformation. It charges that conversion therapy methods "constitute deceptive, false, and misleading practices," yet the charge itself is misleading. The American Psychological Association (APA) task force couldn't say definitively whether the therapy helped or harmed: "There are no scientifically rigorous studies of recent SOCE [Sexual Orientation Change Efforts] that would enable us to make a definitive statement about whether recent SOCE is safe or harmful and for whom."[138]

The SPLC states that the therapies are "abusive and harmful to children" but the programs at PCC do not allow participation by children under the age of 18 and the average age of the men seen by PCC is 36 years of age, according to Rich Wyler, founder of PCC.

Ironically, the treatment that was recommended for me, gender change, caused substantial harm in my life and many other people's lives, yet the Southern Poverty Law Center has not filed to eliminate all gender-change surgeries—quite the opposite, in fact. Their efforts are directed at silencing anyone who holds the opinion that encouraging four-year-old trans-kids to cross-dress at school, at home, and in public, and to use the bathroom of their preferred gender, is harmful.

New Jersey has enacted a ban on gay-to-straight conversion therapy for minors. The law signed by Governor Chris Christie prevents any licensed therapist, psychologist, social worker, or counselor from using sexual orientation change efforts with a child under age 18. In California, Governor Jerry Brown signed a similar bill that makes any therapy that doesn't affirm same-sex attraction or gender transition illegal for children.

In these states, therapists can help children go through gender transition by affirming them in the other gender and recommending puberty blockers or cross-gender hormones or even surgery to transition, but talk therapy to avoid such invasive and permanent body-damaging measures is deemed "harmful" and outlawed.

According to a PhD counselor friend of mine in California, the law puts a chill on offering any therapy, even when requested, for children under the age of 18 who struggle with unwanted gender confusion or same-sex attraction.

I was personally offended and appalled when the Southern Poverty Law Center interjected kids into their complaint against PCC. I was a four-year-old trans-kid, and I can tell you there is nothing normal about it. Gender transition is being pushed today as the only treatment for gender issues, and that is a flat-out lie. Studies show that the majority of transgender people have co-existing mental disorders that go untreated.[139]

Those of us who have willingly sought talk therapy and found it to work know we were not born that way and that the effects of traumatic childhood events can be overcome. It was only after engaging with skilled therapists to deal with the emotional trauma that we no longer needed to live in an unwanted lifestyle.

---

[138] http://www.apa.org/pi/lgbc/publications/
[139] https://www.thepublicdiscourse.com/2016/02/16376/

Outlawing effective treatments is unjust

Outlawing the therapies that help some people with same-sex attractions or gender-identity conflicts is, at its very heart, unjust. The civil liberty of individuals to choose therapies should be protected and preserved, not crushed by lawyers.

We need to make sure that LGBT organizations such as the Southern Poverty Law Center do not crush human and civil rights under the weight of their hatred for those who defect from the LGBT lifestyle. Even as many people are celebrating the Supreme Court's redefinition of marriage, other people who want to get rid of their same-sex attraction are being stripped of their lawful, rightful access to effective therapies.

People who choose to not embrace their same-sex attractions should be afforded the same equal rights as those who embrace them. Laws should not take away their dignity and their free right to rid themselves of same-sex attractions. I have lived free of transgenderism for over twenty years, and I am just one of many examples showing that change is possible. The law should not prevent access to therapy that may save lives just because LGBT supporters want to silence the individuals who chose an alternative path.

Outlawing Psychotherapy For Trans-Kids Will Not Prevent Suicides

The Obama White House is backing a move to end some psychotherapies for transgender children. This is risky and could lead to more suicides.

BY WALT HEYER
THE FEDERALIST, APRIL 16, 2015
THEFEDERALIST.COM/2015/04/16/
OUTLAWING-PSYCHOTHERAPY-FOR-TRANS-KIDS-WILL-NOT-PREVENT-SUICIDES/

Psychologically healthy people do not commit suicide. Changing genders is an outward expression of some form of depression that started long before the suicide.

Studies have shown conclusively that suicide is the result of mental illness and untreated depression, but the elite who push for gender change ignore the evidence. Gender-change advocates blame lack of support from parents and society for the suicides of transgender people. Advocates blame bullying, discrimination, and inequality in society—anything but mental illness or depression.

In the 1970s, Dr. Charles Ihlenfeld administered hormone therapy to hundreds of transgenders over six years in his practice as an internist and colleague of Dr. Harry Benjamin. His conclusion? He saw too much unhappiness and too many suicides. Not much has changed since the 1970s. Hormone therapy is still administered to transgenders. Suicide still occurs with far too much frequency, and 41 percent of transgenders attempt suicide. Affirming the false belief that changing genders is a cure for depression has not changed the outcome.

According to those who study suicide, "Over 90 percent of people who die by suicide have a mental illness at the time of their death. Untreated depression is the number one cause for suicide."[140]

When transgenders realize sometime later—after a few months, a few years or, in some cases, a few decades—that gender change didn't resolve their unhappiness, discouragement and depression follow. They experience first-hand that no amount of surgical manipulation of body parts, cross-gender behaviors, or cosmetic changes to appearance will ever medically change a person from one gender to the other.

Gender Does Not Change

I know; I lived the "transgender life" for eight years. I followed all the prescribed steps to change my gender and I was surrounded by affirming friends. I totally invested myself physically, psychologically, financially, and emotionally into the promise of a future free from gender dysphoria. But I was also one of those 41 percent who attempted suicide out of despair.

---

[140] http://www.suicide.org/suicide-causes.html

All my life I had looked forward to changing genders. All the steps in the transition process added to the anticipation: gender-affirming clothing and hairstyle, a new gender-affirming name, cross-gender hormones or hormone blockers, and surgeries for gender-enhancing appearance. All these activities reinforced the false belief and unrealistic expectation that, by following this process, I could change my gender.

Several years into my new life, I found that I was depressed. Changing genders was a temporary diversion. It offered no permanent solution to my mental distress and, in fact, created new problems. I felt ashamed, broken, and beyond hope.

For me, the first step to walking out of the grip of depression was letting go of the unrealistic expectation that boys can magically change into girls, or girls into boys. The next step was exploring the possibility that I might have some mental illness beyond gender dysphoria.

Transgenderism Means Rejecting the Self

When a person wishes to change his or her gender, her or she is in every sense rejecting his or her core gender self-identity. The avalanche of affirmation for the opposite gender encourages them in their self-rejection and inspires an unachievable hope that happiness is waiting for them on the other side of transition.

In the National Transgender Discrimination Survey, 41 percent of more than 6,000 transgenders surveyed reported they had attempted suicide at some time. How high does the number have to go before the foolishness of denying the role of mental illness stops? The advocates refuse to acknowledge a link between transgender suicide and mental illness ,and by doing so they keep transgenders from receiving appropriate treatment that could prevent suicides.

The enlightened elite blame lack of affirmation and acceptance for transgender suicide. They say that transition and cross-gender hormones are the answers to transgender happiness and suicide prevention. Perhaps you agree with them. Think again.

It's Time to Focus on Preventing Suicide

Kyle Scanlon, a female-to-male transgender, lived the life that activists claim will prevent suicide. Fully integrated, supported, and loved, Scanlon was the executive director of the Lesbian Gay Bi Youth Line, and a well-known and well-respected valued leader and mentor in the trans community in Toronto, Canada. He was committed to improving the quality of life for others. Yet, he turned to suicide on July 3, 2012. His friends said he suffered from depression before and after his transition.[141] Not a smidgeon of discrimination or inequality existed in this transgender's life; no society to blame. He chose to die, even after changing genders.

Scanlon, with every possible support for being transgender, still took his life. That should be a lesson for us. You can blame society, but it's the unresolved mental disorders causing suicide.

The time has come to focus first on preventing suicide, not changing genders. We know untreated depression is the leading cause of suicide, but when people tell their doctors they dislike their birth

---

[141] http://torontoist.com/2012/07/toronto's-trans-community-grieves-loss-of-kyle-scanlon/

gender and hate their bodies, that fact seems to go out the window. Doctors treat the gender-confused by assisting them toward changing their genders. Perhaps the recklessness of doctors in not identifying mental disorders is causing suicides. For kids, perhaps add in parents and school boards who encourage living the trans life, which places undue psychological pressure on kids who can't deal with it.

Adult and kid suicides will continue as long as doctors fail to effectively diagnose and treat their mental disorders. Kyle's suicide is the factual evidence, an unfortunate consequence of focusing on the outward appearance when psychological issues run deep inside. Some day we will learn that no amount of change—including all the surgeries to "look good"—will ever be enough to heal the ache inside.

Transgender People Need Help

In 2008 the National Gay and Lesbian Task Force joined with the National Center for Transgender Equality to conduct a survey of more than 6,000 transgenders in the United States. Their findings show the stark reality of the transgender life:[142]

1. Transgenders suffer four times the national average of HIV infections.
2. 70 percent of transgenders misuse drugs and alcohol.
3. Transgenders are twice as likely to be homeless as the general U.S. population.
4. Transgenders are twice as likely to be unemployed as the general U.S. population.
5. Transgenders live in extreme poverty and are more likely to have incomes under $10,000 a year.
6. 41 percent of transgenders report attempting suicide.

In my view, this sad list makes the case for the prevalence of transgender psychological issues, especially depression, which leads to suicide. The survey results point to the failure to provide effective treatment to individuals who struggle with their gender identity.

Psychologically healthy people do not commit suicide. Changing genders is an outward expression of some form of depression that started long before the suicide.

---

[142] http://www.thetaskforce.org/downloads/reports/reports/ ntds_multiracial_respondents.pdf

Childhood Sexual Abuse, Gender Dysphoria, and Transition Regret: Billy's Story

Billy is not the first who turned to a transgender identity to escape pain and trauma. It's time for psychotherapists to seriously address the unique causes of each individual's gender dysphoria before encouraging them to pursue hormones and surgery.

BY WALT HEYER
PUBLIC DISCOURSE, MARCH 26, 2018
WWW.THEPUBLICDISCOURSE.COM/2018/03/21178/

Billy B.'s story is not exceptional or unique. Childhood sexual abuse is an experience common to many of those who write me with regret about changing genders. Stories like his have filled my email inbox for the last ten years. That's precisely why I asked him if I could share it.

Billy remembers, as a young child, being curious about the differences between boys and girls, between him and his sister. In the first grade, as he looked around his classroom, he wondered where he belonged: with the boys or with the girls? Billy says his body told him he belonged with the boys, but his thoughts were telling him he belonged with the girls.

Billy says the question arose for him because he had been dressing up as a girl at home, putting on his sister's makeup and earrings out of curiosity. This can be benign behavior that children grow out of, but in some situations, it can evolve into an escape into a fantasy world.

Billy was a small skinny boy with a speech impediment. He was often teased by the other children. They would taunt him, saying "What did you say?" and "I can't understand you" when he would try to speak. Billy was too physically small and verbally challenged to fight back, so he swallowed his emotions and withdrew.

Billy longed to escape from his skinny body and speech difficulty. In his nightly bedtime prayers, he begged God to change him into a girl so that the other kids wouldn't make fun of him. But no one should conclude that Billy's choice of emotional hiding place made him a girl—or a "transgender child" as the experts now say; he was only a bullied little boy trying to cope.

Abuse, Shame, and Pain

In the summer after sixth grade, Billy's world came crashing down. At summer swimming league, Billy's new diving instructor targeted Billy for sexual abuse—abusers have a knack for picking on the weakest kids. Billy says, "The coach played with me." In other words, the diving coach perpetrated a horrific crime against a vulnerable child.

Like the hundreds of female gymnasts who reluctantly came forward recently about the sexual abuse suffered years before at the hands of their sports doctor Larry Nassar,[143] Billy was so traumatized that he did not tell anyone for a very long time. Billy pushed the emotions away with strenuous physical activity—bicycling, swimming, and running. Billy says he would do this "until the pain in my body was greater than the pain in my mind." He also escaped by using his sister's makeup and earrings. He says that after the sexual abuse "I so very much hated my appendage"—that is, his male genitalia.

Billy is not the first who turned to a transgender identity to escape pain and trauma. In fact, Billy's story is not all that different than my own. And in the stories I receive from other regretful people who attempted transition, childhood sexual abuse abounds.

The shame and pain of being used by a sexual predator is beyond the imagination. Most abused kids push the feelings deep inside and shut out the memories. The pain, shame, guilt, and fear often keep them from telling anyone about the abuse until much later in life, if they ever do. Many sexual abuse victims—like Billy, me, and others who write to me—get swept up by LGBT therapists who suggest that the proper treatment is to start on powerful sex hormones followed by gender "affirming" surgery. The problem is that hormones and surgery will not be effective in providing long-term treatment for depression or other ailments caused by sexual trauma. Too many therapists rush to prescribe radical hormonal and surgical measures before diagnosing and treating the psychiatric disorders shown to coexist in the majority of gender dysphoric clients: depression, phobias, and adjustment disorders.[144] Billy's story illustrates the importance of digging into why a person wants to surgically alter his or her body and not assuming that cross-dressing or role-playing as the opposite sex means that children need a sex change.

Like many men who identify as women and want their genitalia surgically removed, Billy was still attracted to women. In college, he fell in love with a woman, and the intensity of the feelings blew the hinges off the doors that had held his emotions locked up inside him. Overwhelmed, he asked his sister for advice, and she helped him find a sexuality therapist. Billy says, "I spent the first of many years trying to find out why I was this way."

Unraveling the how and why of behavior shaped by traumatic events is never quick or easy work, especially early in the process. Billy told his therapist about the sexual abuse, but it wasn't a topic that they explored in depth. The emphasis was on Billy's feeling like a female. Billy read all the books he could find on the topic, and he became convinced that once he transitioned all would be okay. Affirmed by his therapists and confident in knowing what he had to do, he decided to surgically alter his male genitalia to a facsimile of a female's.

Billy's therapist referred him to a doctor in New Orleans who would provide hormone therapy to start the transition. Then came feminizing cosmetic and genital surgeries, dieting to lose muscle mass, and changing his name from Billy to Billie. He kept his employment, but it was not an easy transition. Billie had a high-flying career as an engineer.

---

[143] https://apnews.com/dbdd84931d444e5f8263e2e869e96096/Nassar-accuser:-%27Larry-was-a-master-manipulator%27

[144] http://www.hindawi.com/journals/psychiatry/2014/971814/

But, in Billy's words, "All of the effort, pain and expense was for naught." After living seven to eight years as a female, Billy started attending church. As he grew in his faith in God, he realized his trans-life was a lie he could not live any longer. Billy started thinking in earnest about detransitioning back to the man God had originally intended him to be.

So, after prayer, Billie approached the managers at work about becoming Billy. They were sympathetic, understanding, and supportive. Later, when the male hormones started making Billie look more male than female, the manager had to tell his co-workers about Billie's change back to Billy. Incredibly and wonderfully, they were supportive and several gave words of encouragement right there in the meeting. As Billy says, "God made the way!"

Billie successfully detransitioned back to Billy and met a beautiful lady who had two daughters from a previous marriage. They became friends, fell in love and got married in 2011.

"I'm Another"

When Billy first emailed me, his subject line was "I'm another," meaning another of the growing number of people, young and old, who formerly identified as transgender and who have detransitioned back to living as their original sex. He is also "another" of the people diagnosed with gender dysphoria who were sexually abused at a young age and falsely assured by medical practitioners that their problems would go away with cross-sex hormones and surgery.

It's commendable to see the recent media attention on the "me too" movement for women who were sexually abused, but that's only half the story. Boys like Billy who were sexually abused by older males need to be included, too. Perhaps it is time for a new movement—"I'm another"—for people who suffered the double harm of being sexually abused and then surgically mutilated. They learn the hard way, as Billy puts it, that it was "all for naught," after convincing everyone else to use the right names and pronouns and getting access to cross-gender bathrooms.

Billy says, "I do have problems, but it's my choice of living a happy and productive life or let my problems get the best of me." Billy says he has chosen to get his strength, comfort, and forgiveness from God through Jesus Christ and live with joy.

I work with people who contact me because they regret attempting to change their sex. With impressive self-awareness, they clearly articulate what triggered their identification as transgender. They can always point to some situation—often but not always sexual abuse—in their past that caused them to want to escape who they were and become someone else instead.

Most people who identify as transgender are suffering from any of a wide variety of undiagnosed comorbid disorders. Unfortunately, gender therapists too often affirm a trans identity by providing access to hormones and surgery while ignoring the underlying causes, which should be treated with sound, effective psychotherapy.

It's time for psychotherapists to seriously address the unique causes of each individual's gender dysphoria *before* encouraging them to pursue hormones and surgery.

The National Geographic Transgender Cover Champions Child Abuse And Junk Science

Cross-dressing a young boy is emotional and psychological child abuse and should be stopped, not celebrated on the cover of magazines like National Geographic.

BY WALT HEYER

THE FEDERALIST, JANUARY 3, 2017

THEFEDERALIST.COM/2017/01/03/NATIONAL-GEOGRAPHIC-
TRANSGENDER-COVER-CHAMPIONS-CHILD-ABUSE-JUNK-SCIENCE/

The *National Geographic* staff chose a cover story of nine-year-old-boy who says he's a girl for the January 2017 special issue, entitled "Gender Revolution." Transgenderism is today's popular social delusion which, contrary to the publicity surrounding it, affects a miniscule portion of the population.

Young Avery Jackson, whether deliberately or not, is an LGBTQ activist whose image is being used to promote transgender politics and raise money for a transgender house in Kansas. Now *National Geographic* is participating in the activism by spreading the progressive ideology of fluid genders and providing an easy rallying point for future LGBTQ fundraising campaigns.

The activists' theory of gender fluidity, or gender spectrum, suggests that God-designated genders of male and female indicated by biology is too limiting. Their theory separates gender from sex and says that gender is determined by how people feel or think, not by the objective evidence of body parts, chromosomes, and other distinct biological markers.

Why is the boy's picture so disturbing to me? Because, like Avery Jackson, I was a cross-dressing boy at the age of nine. I can tell you that crossdressing a young boy is emotional and psychological child abuse and should be stopped, not celebrated on the cover of magazines. I started wearing female clothing at the age of four. My grandma encouraged me by providing clothing and affirmation over a prolonged period. I was sure I wanted to become a female.

Eventually, I did become a female transgender. I was approved and underwent the full range of hormone therapy and surgeries and legally changed my identity. I lived life as a female, Laura Jensen, for eight years. All too late I realized transgenderism was all "B.S."—a surgical masquerade to superficially project a change of gender. Like others who elect to live the transgender life, I painfully discovered it was only a temporary fix to deeper pain.

Sexing Up Lies that Lead Children Astray

A cover photo is visually exciting and can persuade young people that male and female gender models are not fixed, when they are. Photos like the one on the cover of *National Geographic* can encourage a child to question his or her gender and sex and act out accordingly.

Not all boys who cross-dress will develop gender confusion, but disturbing to me is how easily gender distress can become an unwanted reality for unsuspecting children when changing gender is encouraged, nurtured, and celebrated seemingly everywhere. Encouraging boys to cross-dress can encourage various disturbing behaviors and anxieties, such as sexual fetishes and gender confusion.

Young people are told transgender feelings are permanent, immutable, physically deep-seated in the brain, and can never change. That's simply not true. Anyone past age 25 knows that even very strong feelings can change.

During my time of gender distress, I consulted with the leading gender experts to find relief. I was told that the only way I would ever find peace was to change my gender. Yet me and many other former transgenders have discovered the truth: the peace that comes from changing genders is temporary. Feelings change. At some point, which may take years, reality penetrates the fog and living as a superficial female no longer "feels" right. I hear from transgender people who write, "I feel duped. How can I undo this and return to living in my birth gender?"

Real Journalism and Science Investigates Dissent

If *National Geographic* truly wanted to explore the complexities of gender change, they would have included stories of people who discovered that living the transgender life was an empty promise.

A case in point is that of Alexis (born Robert) Arquette, a transgender pioneer and actor who died last September at the age of 47. Arquette's decision to stop living as a woman was done silently. A posthumous *Hollywood Reporter* article tells of Arquette's struggles:

> In 2013, amid increasing health complications, Alexis began presenting herself as a man again, telling Ibrahim [a close friend] that 'gender is bullshit.' That 'putting on a dress doesn't biologically change anything. Nor does a sex-change.' She said that 'sex-reassignment is physically impossible. All you can do is adopt these superficial characteristics but the biology will never change.'[145]

Dr. Richard B. Corradi, a professor of psychiatry at Case Western Reserve University School of Medicine, calls transgenderism a "Contagion of Mass Delusion" similar to the hysterias of the 1980s and '90s, "junk science" that reinforced hysterical, false stories of satanic ritual abuse and recovered memories.[146]

The very people who should know better have bought into the hysteria. Just as "mental health professionals" a generation ago supported the child abuse delusions, and even participated in prosecuting the unjustly accused, so too have they fueled the fire of the transgender delusion.

National Geographic should know better than to buy into these kinds of hysterias. Susan Goldberg, the editorial director of National Geographic Partners and editor-in-chief of the magazine, is

---

[145] http://www.hollywoodreporter.com/news/final-days-alexis-arquette-a-928507
[146] https://thefederalist.com/2016/11/17/psychiatry-professor-transgenderism-mass-hysteria-similar-1980s-era-junk-science/

recklessly using the magazine and this child to promote gender questioning and the theory of gender as a spectrum. The magazine cover is designed to change minds and influence gender transition.

National Geographic gives no balanced discussion, magazine cover shot, or special edition for the many people who have been harmed by gender transition when the change failed to resolve our much deeper psychological issues. No mention is made of those who detransitioned, regretted changing genders, or died. The magazine makes no exploration of the many underlying illnesses that can cause the desire to change gender, and the fact that treating these illnesses can alleviate the feelings of gender confusion.

Why Can't a Woman Be More Like a Man

Goldberg told NBC Out, NBC's digital portal targeted at LGBT people, that "We wanted to look at how traditional gender roles play out all over the world, but also look into gender as a spectrum."[147] The young boy's picture on the cover should spark a national discussion about Goldberg and *National Geographic.*

In answer to the question "Why did you focus on children—and put one on the cover?" *National Geographic* staff responded:

> The worst thing about being a girl is that you just can't do things that boys can do," Tomee War Bonnett, a nine-year-old living on the Pine Ridge Reservation in South Dakota, told us. This sentiment was expressed by girls worldwide—using different words and in different languages, but bound by the same constraints. We put Avery on the cover because she symbolized a lot of the complex and current conversation occurring around gender.[148]

Let me see if I am understanding correctly. Girls worldwide expressed that the worst thing about being a girl is not being allowed to do the things boys do, and *National Geographic* decided that a boy who thinks he is a girl is the appropriate symbol of this conversation. It requires amazing mental gymnastics to arrive at this conclusion. Avery, a boy, symbolizes none of the complex conversation about gender constraints girls have expressed worldwide. Using him to illustrate the concerns of biological females is a slap in the face, again elevating male concerns and profiles over theirs.

The *Nat Geo* staff has conflated the issue of females feeling constrained by being female with a completely unrelated topic: the transgender population experiencing severe distress with gender identity. These are hardly the same issues and definitely don't have the same impact: females number about 50 percent of the population, while people who identify as transgender number a scarce 0.3 percent of the world's population, at best.

In tandem with the magazine issue, *National Geographic* produced a two-hour documentary also called "Gender Revolution," featuring trans kids and their parents. It completely abandons any

---

[147] http://www.nbcnews.com/feature/nbc-out/national-geographic-explores-gender-through-new-issue-documentary-n695966

[148] http://www.nationalgeographic.com/magazine/2017/01/gender-issue-reader-comments-faq/

pretense of covering male-female gender inequality. Like the special issue of the magazine, the "documentary" is an indoctrination for the activist transgender point of view. It endorses cross-gender affirmation and transition for children to the exclusion of any other less-invasive treatment.

This Is Child Abuse

Studies have shown that childhood gender dysphoria does not inevitably continue into adulthood. An overwhelming 77 to 94 percent of gender dysphoric children do *not* become adults with gender dysphoria.[149] Given this, it's social, medical, and psychological malpractice to push young children to lop off or sew on body parts and take highly charged cross-sex hormones that can further destabilize their prepubescent bodies and minds, especially when they are highly likely to regret what grown adults pushed them into before they were able to sort through such life-altering decisions.

It's distressing to me as a former transgender to see the lopsided media coverage, even outright promotion, presented by what formerly had been a respected, apolitical publication. Imagery has a powerful influence on the minds of children and young adults. Just like the infamous *Vanity Fair* cover of Olympian Bruce Jenner in women's clothing, this cover and documentary will cause gender questioning in susceptible individuals and lead them into further heartbreak. I know from my own experience and the experiences of those who write me that gender change is a temporary reprieve that makes authentic healing even more difficult later.

It's distressing to see male and female binary genders being debased and replaced by gender transition and "gender spectrum," because I know first-hand that restoration from gender distress begins with acknowledging the truth of biology: only male and female exist, and no one can change from one to the other, no matter how strong the feelings are.

---

[149] https://www.ncbi.nlm.nih.gov/pubmed/25231780

Chapter 5.
Regrettable Outcomes

Doctors Pushed Her to Get Sex Reassignment Surgery. Now, She Knows It Was a Mistake.

True compassion is acknowledging the mental disorders and providing effective, sound treatment in an effort to slow the staggering number of suicides, before rushing to perform irreversible surgeries.

BY WALT HEYER
THE DAILY SIGNAL, FEBRUARY 1, 2019
WWW.DAILYSIGNAL.COM/2019/02/01/DOCTORS-PUSHED-HER-
TO-GET-SEX-REASSIGNMENT-SURGERY-NOW-SHE-KNOWS-IT-WAS-A-MISTAKE/

Every week, I receive at least one heartbreaking letter of regret from someone who was sexually abused as a young person and later underwent a "sex change" in a misguided attempt to heal the pain.

The sex-change cheerleaders in the medical profession routinely diagnose these people with gender dysphoria and rush to administer cross-gender hormones and recommend surgery.

I myself was sexually abused as a young person and diagnosed with gender dysphoria over 35 years ago. The diagnosis of gender dysphoria is not the problem. The tragedy is failing to recognize and treat the deeper wounds of sexual abuse.

Many struggling individuals who request a change of gender are looking for an escape, a hiding place, or as one teenager confided to her mother who wrote to me for advice, a way to "erase" her troubled past. Caught in the grips of pain, they see a transgender identity as an appealing portal to a happier new life.

Stories like mine and 30 others in my new book "Trans Life Survivors" provide testimony that, for far too many, changing genders is not a life-long solution to the trauma of a difficult or abusive childhood. We discovered after surgery that the sex-change promoters had used us in a grand social and medical experiment.

Treating childhood abuse with cross-sex hormone therapies and surgeries is absurd, and deeply damaging.

A case in point is a lady named Deborah from Dorset, England, who contacted me recently and consented for me to share her story.

Deborah was sexually abused when she was only 2 years old by her father, whom her mother later divorced. In the years that followed, her older brother physically and verbally abused her while her mother looked the other way.

When Deborah was 14, her father came back into her life and seemed to be the model of an attentive dad—taking her on outings, lavishing her with gifts, and acting nice. So, when he invited her to spend a weekend with him, Deborah, feeling comfortable and happy about having her dad back in her life, accepted.

After his 14-year-old daughter was inside his home and secure in her bed, he did the unthinkable again.

Due to the intense trauma and emotional stress this caused, Deborah couldn't focus on her studies or pursue the education that would lead to a good career. In adulthood, she barely eked out a living and made bad choices in relationships.

The pain from sexual abuse doesn't go away on its own, and the victim often copes by escaping psychologically.[150]

Deborah shares that at age 44, she was watching a television program whose topic quickly captured her attention: transgender men. She recalls thinking, "Wow, this must be me."

She sought a doctor who specialized in the treatment of gender identity disorders, particularly transsexualism, and scheduled an appointment with a well-known British psychiatrist, Dr. Russell Reid with the National Health Service's main gender clinic at Charing Cross Hospital in London.

Gender specialists typically have a major blind spot in discerning the influence child abuse has had on a patient's desire to identify as the opposite gender. Deborah's experience with Reid in 2002 illustrates this thoroughly.

She writes:

> I told him about my life, how abusive it was, he didn't really seem concerned at all. He said, 'I am sure you're transgender. Let's not waste any time,' and injected me right there with Sustanon 250 mg, an anabolic testosterone steroid.

At the time, Deborah said she was happy. But upon reflection, she realized alarm bells should have been ringing, because Reid didn't consider any of her horribly traumatic sexually-abusive life experiences as relevant to her gender distress. Instead, he hastily and recklessly gave her testosterone, a powerful male hormone.

She went on to receive surgeries to shape her body into that of a man, and lived as Lee, a trans man. She now says she realizes she never had gender dysphoria, but was suffering from "body dysmorphia." As she sees it, she hated her body because it caused her to be sexually abused.

Gender change was the tragic result of a misdiagnosis, not gender dysphoria.

Lee now wants to return to living as a female. Unfortunately, she is sporting a full beard and other male-identified characteristics. She's on a waiting list for reversal procedures at The Laurels, the National Health Service gender clinic in Exeter, and has questions for her caregivers: Who in the U.K. will accept the consequences of this failed diagnosis? Will the National Health Service allow her

---

[150] https://www.omicsonline.org/open-access/trauma-and-treatment-of-child-sexual-abuse-2167-1222-S4-024.php?aid=61080

to have the reversal procedures? Who will pay for the extensive electrolysis needed to remove her facial hair?

Out of all the people who have written me over the years wanting to undo the effects of gender transition, about half say childhood abuse was the key factor in wanting to erase and escape their past. They all say it worked for a while, but over the long term, it was not a solution for the pain of an abusive childhood.

Let's all pray the clinic will do the right thing and help Deborah restore the life that was recklessly derailed in 2002.

More importantly, let's demand that gender clinics everywhere stop this insanity of providing sex change for everyone who asks, without treating the contributing factors first.

Transgender Identities Are Not Always Permanent

Transgenderism is based on feelings that can change over time.

BY WALT HEYER
PUBLIC DISCOURSE, SEPTEMBER 27, 2016
WWW.THEPUBLICDISCOURSE.COM/2016/09/17753/

All too abruptly, another bright life has ended. Alexis Arquette (formerly Robert Arquette), a transgender performer and activist, returned to living as a man before his death on September 11, 2016, at the age of 47. Arquette appeared in the movies *Pulp Fiction* and *The Wedding Singer* and was a force for transgender rights.

Although there were many media tributes after his death, few mention his decision to stop living as a woman. However, one piece in *The Hollywood Reporter* does speak of Arquette's struggles after transitioning. Clearly, even well-known and talented transgender individuals who are embraced and accepted in their chosen gender can continue to struggle and may decide to return to their birth sex.

> In 2013, amid increasing health complications, Alexis … began presenting herself as a man again, telling [her close friend] Ibrahim that "'gender is bullshit.' That 'putting on a dress doesn't biologically change anything. Nor does a sex-change.' She said that 'sex-reassignment is physically impossible. All you can do is adopt these superficial characteristics but the biology will never change.'" That realization, Ibrahim suspects, was the likely source of her deep wells of emotional torment. [151]

The process of abandoning the transgender life and reverting back to one's innate gender/sex is called detransitioning. As someone who has detransitioned myself, I only wish more would speak up about the reality of what life is like after transitioning to the other gender and why some people eventually decide to embrace their birth sex.

Why Would a Trans Person Detransition?

People are not born transgender. The indisputable evidence that transgenderism is not innate is the existence of people who wholeheartedly believe that they need a sex change and then later—often many years later—change their mind and go back. People who have detransitioned, as I have, write to me and tell me their stories and their struggles. They don't want too many people to know who they are and what they have lived through. They want to live quietly and keep a low profile because they are filled with shame and regret. They are unable to bring themselves to disclose publicly that the transgender life didn't work out as they had hoped. The shame, I can tell you, is unimaginable.

---

[151] http://www.hollywoodreporter.com/news/final-days-alexis-arquette-a-928507

How do they get to the point of detransitioning?

Based on strongly held feelings, a transgender individual will take hormones and undergo surgery to align the appearance of the body with what is thought to be one's true gender. I did it myself.

> People, especially young people, think strong feelings will never change, but over time they can and do.

Many of us who have gone through this "transformation" realized too late that it was not a medical necessity or required treatment for our problems. Regret often comes years later when the realization sets in that falsely claiming to be an alternate gender persona did not resolve the deep issues with which we struggled. At best, transition was a short-lived reprieve from the agony of feeling that one's biological sex is incorrect.

Dave's Story

A first-person example came in an email to me about a month ago. This young adult—I'll call him "Dave"—tells his heart-wrenching story in his own words, echoing the same words spoken by other regretful transgender individuals over many years:

> I transitioned to female beginning in my late teens and changed my name in my early 20s, over ten years ago. But it wasn't right for me; I feel only discontent now in the female role. I was told that my transgender feelings were permanent, immutable, physically deep-seated in my brain and could NEVER change, and that the only way I would ever find peace was to become female. The problem is, I don't have those feelings anymore. When I began seeing a psychologist a few years ago to help overcome some childhood trauma issues, my depression and anxiety began to wane but so did my transgender feelings. So two years ago I began contemplating going back to my birth gender, and it feels right to do so. I have no doubts—I want to be male!

We learn from this man what I learned in my own life: the transgender feelings are not permanent, immutable, or deep-seated in the brain. Feelings, no matter how powerful, do not justify taking hormones and undergoing surgery.

Warnings have been sounded by doctors for nearly forty years, and yet the regret, unhappiness, suicide, and detransitioning continue. For me, like Dave, psychotherapy did what surgery could never do: it cured me of the desire to become someone I could never biologically be. The application of sound psychotherapy ended my transgender feelings.

When their products fail, auto companies are compelled to issue recalls and to pay for the repairs. Not so with the surgeons or psychologists who have popularized and enabled gender transitioning. They escape all consequences, while ex-transgender people are left to foot the bill financially, emotionally, physically, and personally.

Physically Detransitioning

The process to physically detransition depends on what steps the individual took to alter his or her appearance.

Some who transition do not undergo radical genital surgeries. A case in point is the former Olympic star Jenner. The highly public transition to female did not include genitalia surgery so his parts remain as he was born—male sex. Chaz Bono is another case of a highly publicized transition from female to male, and at this point Chaz's genitalia remain all innate female sex.

Women who transition to male typically take testosterone, the male hormone, which causes facial-hair growth, masculine-appearing muscle, and body-mass changes. They also undergo mastectomy to remove their breasts. As to changing the genitalia, the surgery to construct a male penis is costly and risky, and the result is often not worth the investment. The few who have contacted me did not alter their genitalia or undergo hysterectomies.

The major challenges for the female-to-male transgender person who detransitions back to female are electrolysis treatments to remove the facial hair, which can be expensive and painful, and considering what to do about the now-missing breasts. Reverting back to female may or may not include breast implants. In making that decision, like all detransition decisions, it is up to the individual to weigh the pros and cons.

For men who transitioned to women with full genitalia surgery, their original equipment is no longer available. When they wish to return to the male gender, one option is to have a phalloplasty procedure (the construction of a penis). But in practice, many men who detransition opt not to have it done due to the high cost and risk. Besides, the resulting appendage often does not function at the level of the original male genitalia. Therefore, if detransition statistics include only those who have surgical phalloplasty, the number will be missing the majority of those who detransition.

Unfortunately, not all of what the surgeons do to change gender can be undone. Body parts that were sacrificed, reshaped, or removed will never function the same way again.

Like many of the nearly 20 percent who report regret after surgical gender change,[152] I first needed to come to terms with the truth that no amount of surgery or hormones can ever change innate, biological sex. Armed with the factual knowledge that my sex—male—had never changed, I started to take steps to detransition.

Reasons for Detransitioning

The reasons for detransitioning are vast. Some people go back to their innate sex after a suicide attempt. Some simply conclude, "It just wasn't for me." Some have said it was too difficult to play dress-up as the opposite sex every day; it became too much trouble to keep the trans-life going. Some say they realized they were not real women and never would be. For others, medical problems caused by the surgery spark the desire to detransition.

For me, it was learning about the psychological factors that can cause someone to wrongly identify as a transgender. Early childhood sexual abuse is the leading cause reported to me, but there are often

---

[152] https://www.theguardian.com/society/2004/jul/30/health.mentalhealth

other factors. Studies have shown a multitude of other disorders coexist among transgender people and that experiences other than abuse can cause gender identity difficulty.

My eyes were opened when I entered a Certificate Study Program in the late 1980s that included courses in psychology relevant to destructive behaviors and addictions. I started to realize the transgender condition could be a developmental disorder that evolved over time, not something innate at birth.

At that time, the Diagnostic and Statistical Manual of Mental Disorders (DSM) identified transgenderism as Gender Identity Disorder, a psychological disorder that caused a mismatch of one's gender identity. The latest edition, the DSM V, removed the word "disorder" and revised the name of transgenderism to Gender Dysphoria.

But the name change did not help reduce the number of people who have regrets or attempt suicide. The new name for the same condition has not resolved what causes the desire to identify as transgender.

The medical community does a major disservice to this population by failing to advocate improved diagnosis of the coexisting psychological disorders, and failing to provide treatment that could prevent unnecessary sex-reassignment surgeries.

The Silent Ones

Transitioning is an attempt to escape into a surgically fabricated and hormonally induced transgender world. My transition was the result of years of cross-dressing starting at the hands of my grandmother at age four, after which I was molested by my uncle. Deep psychological pain caused me to want to be female. My transgenderism was a hiding place until I received proper psychotherapy, then set my sights on God. Slowly but steadily, God's love redeemed my life. I no longer needed a hiding place. I have been restored to a new life that is better and brighter than ever. Now, over twenty years after detransitioning, I'm living the dream—married and restored, unshackled by all the transgender madness.

It's important to understand that people of all walks of life, all ages, with or without a faith-based foundation, detransition. We who detransition are the silent, mostly unaccounted-for, witnesses of the brevity of the reprieve.

I stayed silent long enough.

It is painful to watch advocacy groups try to refashion men and women with cosmetic sex-change surgery. The consequence, tragically, will be a trail of more broken lives. What we see in Dave's story and mine is that this grand experiment has not proven to be effective in treating everyone with gender identity issues. When someone says "I'm transgender" it is likely a day will come, perhaps years later, when he or she will also say, "The transgender life is not for me."

> We need to understand: transgender feelings *can change* and detransition *does happen*. Gender persona can change, but biological sex remains.

Regret Isn't Rare: The Dangerous Lie of Sex Change Surgery's Success

Stop enabling the delusion that transition is the only answer. Allow scientific research to flourish, no matter what the results show. Look at the evidence and facts and encourage treatment options that address dangerous psychiatric conditions first.

BY WALT HEYER
PUBLIC DISCOURSE, JUNE 17, 2016
WWW.THEPUBLICDISCOURSE.COM/2016/06/17166/

We have been told sex reassignment surgery is successful. The advocates say that regret is rare, and that 98 percent of surgeries are successful. While that figure might be true for surgical complications, before we accept a narrative of surgical success we should consider the evidence. To evaluate success or failure, we need to go beyond the mechanical skill of the surgeon to examine the emotional and psychological wholeness of the patient afterwards—and not just in the first few months, but in the years to come.

Transgender advocates have worked to create a false narrative, hoodwinking the world into believing that no one ever has regrets from a surgical change of gender. They say the transgender ideology they promote is harmless, safe, even beneficial. But what happens when we dismiss the rhetoric, look at the research, and apply basic critical thinking? We see the reports of success fade and those of regret rise.

Twelve years ago, *The Guardian* reported that a review of more than 100 international medical studies of post-operative transgender patients by the University of Birmingham Aggressive Research Intelligence Facility found "no robust scientific evidence that gender reassignment surgery is clinically effective . . . Research from the US and Holland suggests that up to a fifth of patients regret changing sex."[153]

Shortly after undergoing sex change surgery, most people report feeling better. Over time, however, the initial euphoria wears off. The distress returns, but this time it is exacerbated by having a body that is irrevocably molded to look like the opposite gender. That's what happened to me, and that's what the people with regret who write to me say happened to them.

A Tale of Tragic, Preventable Regret

Recently I received an email that blows the lid off the idea of sex change success and illustrates the truth about damaged lives. This man's story of transition started in his teens. He explains:

> I transitioned to female beginning in my late teens and changed my name in my early 20s, over ten years ago. But it wasn't right for me; I feel only discontent now in the female

---

[153] http://www.theguardian.com/society/2004/jul/30/health.mentalhealth

role. I was told that my transgender feelings were permanent, immutable, physically deep-seated in my brain and could NEVER change, and that the only way I would ever find peace was to become female. The problem is, I don't have those feelings anymore. When I began seeing a psychologist a few years ago to help overcome some childhood trauma issues, my depression and anxiety began to wane but so did my transgender feelings. So two years ago I began contemplating going back to my birth gender, and it feels right to do so. I have no doubts–I want to be male!

I did have orchiectomy [the removal of one or both testicles], and that happened before my male puberty had completed, so I have a bit of facial hair which I never bothered to get electrolysis or laser for, and so the one blessing about all this is that with male hormone treatment I can still resume my male puberty where it was interrupted and grow a full beard and deep voice like I would have had if transgender feelings hadn't intruded upon my childhood. My breasts are difficult to hide though, so I'll need surgery to get rid of them. And saddest of all, I can never have children, which I pray God will give me the strength to withstand that sadness.

When this man's childhood trauma was treated appropriately, his transgender feelings waned. But sadly, he lost ten years of his life and the ability to father biological children.

This young man's story could have been foreseen and prevented if only transgender advocates had embraced the early findings of Dr. Charles Ihlenfeld. In 1979, Dr. Ihlenfeld warned his colleagues about unsuccessful outcomes. Based on six years of experience treating over 500 people with cross-gender hormones, Dr. Ihlenfeld sounded a warning on gender transition. He found that there was simply too much unhappiness among patients after changing genders, and that too many people who had sex change surgery later took their own lives. In his medical opinion, 80 percent of those who want a sex change should not do it. And for the remaining 20 percent, he found that that the sex change would only provide a temporary reprieve, not a lifelong solution.[154]

When so many post-operative transgender individuals remain distressed, even suicidal, then a reasonable conclusion is that surgery is not sufficient to eliminate the depression.

Dangerous Levels of Psychiatric Disorders

People with a diagnosis of gender dysphoria are encouraged to undergo sex transition as treatment. But according to studies, over half of this population is likely to have one or more coexisting psychiatric disorders, such as depression, phobias, and adjustment disorders,[155] which influence the outcomes, as we saw in the letter earlier.

The coexisting psychiatric disorders should be treated first before
undergoing irreversible, life-changing sex change surgeries.

---

[154] http://lvtgw.jadephoenix.org/Info_htm/Herbal_G/ginko_b2.htm
[155] http://www.ncbi.nlm.nih.gov/pmc/articles/PMC4142737/

A staggering 41 percent of people who identify as transgender reported in a national survey that they had attempted suicide.[156] That's over *twenty-five* times the rate of suicide attempts (1.6 percent) among the general population. Clearly, this is a group at high risk for dangerous levels of depression—and, as the work of Dr. Ihlenfeld attests, sex change surgery is not the way to help keep them safe.

Yet any report of psychiatric issues among transgenders is seen as too negative to the social justice narrative. Individuals with gender dysphoria are discouraged from seeking treatment for their depression, phobias, and adjustment disorders. Instead, it is assumed that their psychiatric difficulties are due to their "not being true to themselves," and they are fast-tracked to transition. To my knowledge, transgender advocates have never made a point to warn the transgender community to look for other treatable disorders or to lobby the medical community for better diagnosis and care for coexisting disorders, which are present in over half the group.

I will readily admit that I have skin in the game on this topic. I was diagnosed with gender dysphoria and approved for sex reassignment surgery by the pre-eminent authority at the time, Paul Walker, PhD. He chaired the committee that authored the original Harry Benjamin International Standards of Care, which are similar to the guidelines in use today. He quickly approved me for hormone therapy and surgery without considering the comorbid disorders that might have fueled the gender dysphoria. Like the person whose story I shared above, after male-to-female surgery didn't permanently heal my gender discomfort, I sought counseling.

> Amazingly, the feelings of gender discomfort I had for a lifetime died out
> after extensive counseling resolved the issues.

The majority of transgender people (62.7 percent, according to one study[157]) have at least one comorbid psychiatric disorder. Many people think transgenders are homosexual and that changing genders is about sexual relations. That wasn't the case for me, nor for the people who have written me over the last ten years. Every single one of them had unwanted pain caused by sexual abuse, deep trauma, mental disorders, horrible loss, or terrible family circumstances in early life. Often the parents were not aware that any abuse or trauma had occurred. Treating psychological pain with sex change surgery doesn't work.

Regret Is Not Rare

Most people don't realize that the outcomes of sex transition are not tracked over time. That is, no one knows how many people are happy, how many have regrets, how many return to their birth sex, or how many have died as a result of suicide. Even when studies are conducted, the results are often based on a minority of the participants because, as *The Guardian* reported: "the results of many gender reassignment studies are unsound because researchers lost track of more than half of the participants. For example, in a five-year study of 727 post-operative transsexuals published, 495 people dropped out for unknown reasons."

---

[156] http://www.thetaskforce.org/static_html/downloads/reports/reports/ntds_report_on_health.pdf
[157] http://www.ncbi.nlm.nih.gov/pmc/articles/PMC4142737/

In addition, many studies may report misleading outcomes because they look at results over too short a period of time.

Feelings of regret or suicide may not surface for ten to fifteen years after the transition, but studies don't track patients that long.

People with regret have contacted me as far out as thirty years after transition.

Today, we are told that those with gender dysphoria—whether they are four-year-old children[158] or Olympic athletes[159]—are better off living as the opposite sex. Putting blind trust in those who use bullying tactics to discourage debate or scientific challenge has traumatic and sometimes deadly consequences for the innocent victims. Consider the harm that occurs today as a result of this propaganda:

- Unbiased medical information and treatment is simply not available to those considering sex change. Only one course of treatment is provided: hormone treatment and sex reassignment surgery.
- Hurting people who regret transitioning are bullied into silence.
- Researchers can be run out of their profession if their results challenge the transgender activists' narrative. The freedom to pursue scientific evidence is in jeopardy.

Let's stop enabling the delusion that transition is the only answer.

Let's allow scientific research to flourish, no matter what the results show.

Let's look at the evidence and facts and encourage treatment options that address dangerous psychiatric conditions first.

In that way, we can ensure the best outcomes for those who have gender dysphoria.

---

[158] http://www.telegraph.co.uk/women/family/transgender-children-my-son-told-me-he-was-a-girl/
[159] https://www.thepublicdiscourse.com/2015/04/14905/

University Refuses Research On Growing Numbers Of Trans People Who Want To Go Back

---

All expressed they were convinced by trans activists that transition was the answer and now they live with the negative consequences of that decision.

BY WALT HEYER
THE FEDERALIST, OCTOBER 4, 2017
THEFEDERALIST.COM/2017/10/04/UNIVERSITY-
REFUSES-RESEARCH-GROWING-NUMBERS-TRANS-PEOPLE-WANT-GO-BACK/

In late September, the United Kingdom's Bath Spa University turned down an application by James Caspian, a psychotherapist who specializes in working with transgender people, to conduct research on gender reassignment reversals.[160] The university deemed the subject "potentially politically incorrect."[161]

Caspian is hardly someone to be considered against gender change. Since 2001, Caspian has worked extensively with gender variant people and has been a trustee of a UK charity "dedicated to education about and support of transgendered, transsexual and cross-dressing individuals."[162]

Caspian's interest in reversals germinated in a conversation in 2014 with Dr. Miroslav Djordjevic, a leading genital reconstructive surgeon based in Belgrade with years of experience in gender reassignment surgery.[163] Djordjevic told Caspian of the uptick in requests to his clinic for reversal surgery from men who had previously transitioned to female (known as "transwomen"). Djordjevic received his first request to undo the previous male-to-female surgery and recreate male genitalia in 2012. Within six months, six more transwomen had sought out his expertise for surgical reversal of gender reassignment.

Djordjevic, an award-winning researcher with several hundred papers published in peer-reviewed journals, books, and abstracts,[164] and a professor of urology and surgery,[165] lamented to Caspian about the lack of academic study on the subject of reversal. So Caspian decided to take up such a study. The university approved Caspian's research project at first, and he began preliminary investigation.

---

[160] https://www.theguardian.com/education/2017/sep/25/bath-spa-university-transgender-gender-reassignment-reversal-research

[161] http://www.dailymail.co.uk/news/article-4916026/University-bars-non-PC-study-transgender-operations.html

[162] http://transgenderawareness.co.uk/about-me/

[163] http://www.telegraph.co.uk/health-fitness/body/gender-reversal-surgery-rise-arent-talking/

[164] http://www.genitalsurgerybelgrade.com/about_tim.php?Bibliography-Publications-2

[165] http://www.genitalsurgerybelgrade.com/about_tim.php?Biography-Curriculum-vitae-3

"I found it very difficult to get people willing to talk openly about the experience of reversing surgery," Caspian said. "They said they felt too traumatized to talk about it, which made me think we really need to do the research even more."[166]

Caspian's preliminary findings suggested a growing number of young people—particularly young women transitioning to men—were having regrets. When he provided a detailed proposal to the university, he was told that it must be submitted to the ethics committee. The committee rejected his research proposal, citing concerns over potential criticism towards the university. The university is currently investigating the matter.[167]

I Feel Vindicated in Highlighting Trans Regret

As a former transwoman whose life was devastated by gender transition, I have been interested in research about gender change regret for years. In fact, I wrote a book, *Paper Genders*, that investigated where the research was pointing and how research was stifled or results skewed. I've been told that either I don't exist or was never "really" transgender.

Over the past 12 years of running the website sexchangeregret.com, I've heard many stories of the rush to surgery and the regret that sets in later. It's been an uphill battle to debunk the myth that "gender change is the answer to all gender dysphoria" and to interest people in acknowledging that those who don't want to continue living as the opposite gender deserve compassion, treatment and support.

Djordjevic is a refreshing exception in the world of gender change surgeons.

First, he enforces strict guidelines for gender dysphoric patients who desire a gender change, in a process that can take two years and includes psychiatric evaluations. He then applies the same strict guidelines to those requesting reversal. I am particularly impressed by what The Sava Perovic Foundation, of which Djordjevic is chairman and surgical team leader, says on its website:[168]

> Gender reassignment reversal requires strong, convincing, explicit, psychiatric evaluations from two or more experts in gender dysphoria. They must both approve the reversal surgery.
>
> Of course, the evaluations CANNOT be from the incompetent mental health professional who approved the totally wrong initial surgery.
>
> Strong, convincing, explicit, psychiatric evaluations from two or more experts in gender dysphoria is required.
>
> The new evaluations MUST address the issue of how such a terrible mistake was made in the first place.
>
> The new evaluations should explain how World Professional Association for Transgender Health (WPATH) Standards of Care, carefully developed over decades by many highly

---

[166] http://www.bbc.com/news/uk-41384473

[167] https://www.theguardian.com/education/2017/sep/25/bath-spa-university-transgender-gender-reassignment-reversal-research

[168] https://www.savaperovic.com/sex-change-reversal.htm

qualified professionals, failed to protect the patient from mistaken and inappropriate gender change.

The second way in which Djordjevic is an exception in the world of gender-change surgeons is that he is genuinely concerned about the stories of crippling depression he hears from those who request reversal surgery.

Third, Djordjevic advocates for rigorous academic research into the phenomenon of detransition.[169]

James Caspian Deserves Praise, Too

Caspian also gets my applause because of his willingness, even in the face of being called politically incorrect, to follow the evidence about gender-change reversals and his desire to investigate further and shed much-needed light on why some people are so devastated. I sent a note to him, urging him to persevere. He wrote back that the research is so needed and thanks for the encouragement.

Like Caspian, I have heard the same stories from people who want to detransition: they are traumatized by the prospects. I've written about their struggles and shared their stories, and I'm gratified to see that I'm not the only one realizing that this population does, in fact, exist.

"Tranzformed" is the name of a recently released documentary featuring 15 detransitioners, both male and female, myself included. We speak candidly of how we arrived at the place where gender change seemed to be the answer to our confusion, and how and why we chose to reverse, or detransition.[170]

In late September, six of us who have detransitioned or are in the process met around a table for a day and shared our lives and stories. The difficulty of detransition arose time and again. Several participants used nicknames, not their real names, even in this presumably safe environment, because of shame and concern for backlash from transgender activists. All expressed a similar story: they were convinced by the trans activists that transition was the answer and now they live with the negative consequences of that decision. The pain, fear, and frustration of those still in the process of detransition were evident.

It's Hard to Get Your Body Back Again

Detransition is a difficult and lengthy process: physically, emotionally, psychologically, and legally. Friendships become strained. Family relationships are stressed. Restoring legal documents is tedious and draining.

It is vital to point out that very few of those who detransition will undergo genital surgery to attach a recreated penis. Any interest that transwomen initially have in the surgery usually fades after considering the surgical risks, costs, time invested, and outcomes. Most will decide that having reversal genital surgery is not worth the time and money.

---

[169] http://www.telegraph.co.uk/health-fitness/body/gender-reversal-surgery-rise-arent-talking/
[170] http://www.tranzformed.org/

Australia's "60 Minutes" recently aired a story[171] about a youngster who began transitioning from a boy to a girl at age 12, but now two years later, has changed his mind. From an early age, Patrick Mitchell felt uncomfortable in his own skin and didn't feel like he fit in. He remembers first hearing about the concept of "trans" at age seven. From that point on, he wanted the doctors to make him a girl.

At age 12, he was diagnosed with gender dysphoria. He begged his mother to let him transition into a girl and, with her support, began taking estrogen and presenting socially as a girl.

But now, two years later, he finds his feelings have changed.

As he told Australian "60 Minutes," "I began to realise I was actually comfortable in my body. Every day I just felt better." With the support of his mother, Patrick is planning to stop his transition and to have surgery to remove the breasts that developed due to the estrogen.

I hear from young adults who transitioned as teens and want to go back but are facing lifelong consequences.

Not all children can have the self-awareness to know that transitioning no longer feels right or to admit they changed their mind. Some feel locked in or trapped. I hear from young adults who transitioned as teens and want to go back but are facing lifelong consequences.

The effects of taking cross-gender hormones can be irreversible, even though the person stops taking them. Doctors report infertility can result.

For example, I've heard from young women who must undergo painful electrolysis to remove facial hair that sprouted from taking testosterone, and I've heard from men who continue to look feminine. Some surgeries cannot be undone, such as altered genitalia or facial changes. Fortunately for Patrick, he can have surgery to change the appearance of his chest, but even then, scars are inevitable.

I have been vocal about regret and detransition with my books and website, sexchangregret.com, for over 10 years now. The well-respected surgeon Dr. Miroslav Djordjevic and the psychotherapist James Caspian are discovering what I have known all along: regret and detransitions are on the rise because too many "gender affirming" surgeries are performed on people who don't need them.

---

[171] http://www.news.com.au/entertainment/tv/current-affairs/patricks-pain-i-didnt-know-who-the-person-staring-back-at-me-was/news-story/65ff86c8bfe269109f1b28cbeb93ab7a

Ex-Transgenders And -Homosexuals Come Out Of The Closet

For the first time, former transgenders and homosexuals and those who love them will gather to discuss bringing hope to troubled lives.

BY WALT HEYER
THE FEDERALIST, OCTOBER 26, 2015
THEFEDERALIST.COM/2015/10/26/
EX-TRANSGENDERS-AND-HOMOSEXUALS-COME-OUT-OF-THE-CLOSET/

Standing for Truth is a first-time gathering of national experts, therapists, doctors, attorneys, religious leaders, former homosexuals, parents and friends of former homosexuals, children of homosexual parents, and those with transgender surgery regret who dare to speak the truth.

About 20 speakers will be contributing to the day-long conference October 26 in Salt Lake City. I'm that last one in the list above: the one with transgender surgery regret. Detractors have called me a pseudo-celebrity but I find that preferable to living out my life as a pseudo-female or pseudo-female transsexual.

No matter how uncomfortable or inconvenient it may be to LGBT people and their supporters, the rates of transgender regret and suicide remain high and therefore cannot be dismissed as unimportant. Research has shown that more than 60 percent of transgenders suffer from comorbid disorders. To me, that proves transgenders are misdiagnosed a majority of the time. Comorbid disorders are a direct cause for the staggering and shameful attempted suicide rate among transgenders of 41 percent.

Don't Confuse Transgender and Gay People

I have some hopes for the outcome of the conference and for the people who will be joining me in speaking truth.

First, let me clear up a common misconception. The stated focus of the conference is understanding homosexuality. The funny thing about having me participate is that I was never homosexual, and in my work with regretful transsexuals none of them has been homosexual.

> The politically incorrect truth is that the vast majority of transgender regretters with whom I'm familiar are, in fact, not homosexual.

The transgenders I work with are individuals who suffer from powerful feelings of gender identity confusion but are not dealing with same-sex attraction or homosexuality issues.

Throughout my life, uninformed individuals have assumed I was homosexual. Perhaps that is why I was invited to participate in this conference. I cannot help but wonder how many of the speakers and attendees will be disappointed that I'm not homosexual and never have been.

While I'm on the subject of homosexuality, I'd like to clear up another misconception people have about me and my viewpoint. Some people say I must be anti-homosexual. I'm not. My Alcoholics Anonymous sponsor of last 30 years is a homosexual. I have dinner and spend time with him and other homosexual friends from time to time. So when someone says I'm anti-gay, it shows how little they know about transgenders in general, and about me specifically.

In fact, my homosexual friends encourage me to speak out about the regret they see among transgenders and transsexuals after gender change. LGBT supporters, however, like to blast me as being rabidly anti-LGBT. The truth is, I'm rabidly anti-suicide for transsexuals and transgenders, and I don't support the many unnecessary gender reassignment surgeries performed on hurting individuals that often result in deep regret.

Where There's a Will, There's a Way

Some of the therapists presenting at this conference will be touting the effectiveness of controversial reparative therapies. I have found two truths about therapy and its effectiveness.

- The first is that no therapy of any kind will be effective if the client is unwilling to participate.
- The flipside is if someone truly wants help and has a real desire to stop troublesome behaviors, the type of therapy doesn't matter: Change can and will happen.

If someone truly wants to change, no one can stop him. On the other hand, if someone does not want to change, no one can influence him to change his behavior.

The conference presenters include religious participants who may talk about how LGBT is transforming the church. Some homosexuals, in defiance of the King James Bible, have prepared their own, called The Queen James Bible, which omits or rewrites all references to homosexuality as a sin.

But I have always felt uneasy when religious leaders focus on the sins of homosexuals and transgenders as if they themselves are free of sin. Scriptures calls all of us sinners in the book of Romans: "For all have sinned and fall short of the glory of God (Romans 3:23)."

Scripture does not give religious leaders any high road over anyone else regarding sin.

> We are all sinners and fall short of God's glory: religious leaders and
> homosexuals are alike in that regard.

Church leadership might reject homosexuals outright, thinking they are beyond Christ's redemption. I found out firsthand how some religious leaders want nothing to do with transgenders. While I was living as Laura Jensen, my transgender persona, I attended a church one Sunday. Later that day, the pastor delivered the harsh news: "We don't want your kind in our church." Thankfully, that wasn't the end of the story.

Another church leader welcomed me and allowed me to become a part of the church. Because of this church, whose members and leadership loved and prayed for me, a transgender, I was eventually redeemed and restored. Pastors need to trust God that Christ's power and grace can, and often does, redeem transsexuals and homosexuals.

A Desperate Need for Legal Beagles

What major conference would be complete without attorneys addressing the legal ramifications of the LGBT agenda? I have a personal interest in the legalities of gender designation on birth records. I hope the lawyers at this conference will speak the truth about the roadblocks regretters encounter in restoring original gender markers on their birth records.

From the legal viewpoint, my life has been destroyed twice. The first destruction came in 1983. After the surgeons feminized my appearance with their knives, the courts agreed that my gender changed and my birth record could be legally revised from male to female. The second devastation has been courts' repeated denial of my petitions since 1989 to restore my male gender designation on my birth record. Lawyers have helped me prepare a strategy and the paperwork several times, but judges so far have not allowed my birth record to be restored to male.

My last attempt to restore my male gender marker on my birth certificate was in 2011, after California changed its law to allow anyone to change his or her legal gender without having to have surgery. (Previously, gender change surgery was a legal requirement for this.) A California Superior Court judge denied my right to legally restore my gender to male. After all these years of being restored to life as a male, my birth record still has the wrong gender.

It is crazy how easily newly-minted transgenders can change their gender in the courts. But for those who regret undergoing gender change, the door slams shut. Like me, they are sentenced to pay for their regretful decision by having the wrong gender specified on their birth certificate, with no legal recourse.

Medical Truth Tellers

Physicians will speak at the conference, and I know some of them will address the obvious fact that is biologically impossible to change anyone's gender. Sure, the cosmetic surgeries can make it look that way, but it is all an elaborate surgical masquerade. Cosmetic changes are incapable of producing a biological change of gender. Some regretters have told me how tiring it was to keep up the masquerade.

Perhaps the most amazing truth during the conference will come from the stories of Janet Boynes, a former homosexual; Regina Griggs, parent of a former homosexual; Andrew Graham, a former homosexual; Dawn Stefanowicz, who was raised by a gay parent; and even myself, a transgender regretter.

I hope an open forum across various disciplines like what is being presented at this conference helps people better understand both sides of the social issue. Keep your eye on this first-of-its kind conference, and pray. Pray that it will breathe truth into those who struggle with gender identity issues or same-sex attraction and the families who love them.

'Batwoman' Actress Ruby Rose Is Happy She Didn't Transition to a Man

Actress Ruby Rose experienced childhood trauma before she desired to transition to a boy.

BY WALT HEYER
THE DAILY SIGNAL, OCTOBER 16, 2019
WWW.DAILYSIGNAL.COM/2019/10/16/BATWOMAN-
ACTRESS-RUBY-ROSE-IS-HAPPY-SHE-DIDNT-TRANSITION-TO-A-MAN/

On the occasion of World Mental Health Day last week, actress Ruby Rose opened up about her early childhood trauma, mental disorders, and attempted suicides in an Instagram post.

Rose, 33, who currently stars in the TV series "Batwoman" as the title character, wrote:[172]

> Today is world mental health day. This photo is from right before I started OITNB. I've struggled with mental health my entire life. I was first diagnosed with depression at 13, then major depressive disorder at 16. When I was 18 I found out I had Dissociative amnesia . I had a few years entirely erased from my memory and a chance run in with my best friend from primary school was the first I learned about it. She remembered me but I didn't recognize her at all. She remembered our teachers, things we did and my monkey backpack.. things I didn't remember even when she said them with such innocent conviction. I went home and asked my mum "Did i have a monkey backpack at school?" That is when it all started to unravel and my life changed…I started asking questions. I found out I went from a smiling laughing child to a quiet mute who sat alone and stared off to the distance during recess after one of many traumatic events that I didn't remember. One that my mum had to tell me about but hadn't for so many years because the doctors at the time said I was too young to process what had happened and that it was for the best. I was also diagnosed with Bipolar for a long time until it turned out I just had depression.. the pure sad depression without the fun and not so fun parts of mania, it was an overactive thyroid that created that misdiagnosis. Cut to many dark times. On medication, off medication, on and off and on and off per each wrong diagnoses. There were hospitalizations, suicide attempts as young as 12. Cut to therapy and meditation, cut to seeing me at ever self-help section of every bookstore. Cut to a brain scan which showed I had severe PTSD… cut to more therapy and tests that led me to my final diagnosis… C-PTSD. Complex PTSD. What I have learned from the struggles of mental health is just how strong I am. It's how amazing people are because they love me and support me and yet you can't judge those who don't understand and don't know how to do that either. It's that you cannot judge people at all because you

---

[172] https://www.instagram.com/p/B3diEE0n0ys/

can never know what they have been through. It's that self love and self care is more important than anything else.

A post shared by Ruby Rose (@rubyrose) on Oct 10, 2019 at 7:38pm PDT

The trauma and resulting mental health issues experienced by the Australian model and actress typify one of the quintessential causes of gender distress and confusion.

Unfortunately for adolescents and young adults with gender distress today who seek help, therapists often single-mindedly diagnose them with gender dysphoria [like happened to Sydney[173]] and recommend life-altering gender transition that won't suffice as treatment for mental disorders.

Rose has admitted that as a child, she felt like she had been born into the wrong body and longed to become a boy. But in a 2015 interview, she said she's glad she didn't opt for gender reassignment surgery.

"I started to change the way that I dressed and talked, and realized that I didn't want to transition. I just wanted to be more comfortable in my own skin," she said. [174]

She later said, "I'm a woman. I want to have babies one day, so I'm glad I didn't make changes earlier in my life."[175]

A Message Many Need to Hear

I applaud Rose for her openness about her childhood struggles and how her desire to become male at a young age later changed. She was brilliant to realize she would be happy to not transition.

In a day when children are increasingly pushed toward gender transition, Rose serves as a "public service announcement" for not acting on the desire to transition, but instead for getting more comfortable in one's skin. Her story also shows how early childhood trauma, mental disorders, and attempted suicides can contribute to a desire to transition.

That's why she's a hero for speaking out.

> Rose's story should encourage others to apply the brakes and examine their own childhood rather than jumping into a transition.

Sex Change Regret Is Escalating

Based on the emails I have received, the number of people who deeply regret their gender transition is escalating, especially as young people rush to take cross-gender hormones and undergo surgery.

---

[173] https://www.dailysignal.com/2019/10/07/i-spent-a-year-as-a-trans-man-doctors-failed-me-at-every-turn/

[174] https://www.accessonline.com/articles/exclusive-ruby-rose-talks-intense-fame-celebrity-crushes-caitlyn-jenner-163054

[175] https://people.com/bodies/ruby-rose-glad-didnt-get-gender-reassignment-surgery/

In fact, just a few days ago I published an article about hundreds who regretted transitioning both in the U.S. and the United Kingdom.[176] Rose wisely avoided further trauma by choosing not to transition—but so many have not.

I've openly share my story of cross-dressing at age 4 and experiencing other childhood trauma that resulted in multiple misdiagnoses, finally leading to a diagnosis of dissociative disorder. In many ways, my story resembles Rose's.

I often get emails from people who tell me how childhood trauma, abuse, and severe loss in their lives directly link to their desire to transition.

My first published article nearly five years ago, which warned about this, was titled "What Parents of Transgender Kids Need to Know."[177] In the article, I point out that studies indicate "two-thirds of transgenders suffer from multiple disorders at the same time," a phenomenon called "comorbidity." The top three disorders evidenced in transgenders are depression (33%), specific phobia (20%), and adjustment disorder (15%).

> In addition, a child who says they want to identify as the opposite sex has a two-thirds chance of having a co-existing disorder.

Like Rose, I was once a young child hurt by trauma. But unlike her, I didn't dodge transition. I wish I had escaped, as do the many others who write me.

That's why I wrote my book, *Trans Life Survivors,* to highlight these regrettable outcomes, and it's why I'm so happy Rose is speaking out about childhood trauma. Her painful, but powerful story is a message of hope to people who think they have no choice but transition.

Unlike Rose, when I told my story I was highly criticized for suggesting early childhood trauma and abuse, and the mental disorders that follow, can provoke the onset of gender distress that is diagnosed as gender dysphoria.

I am pleased Rose has not been criticized, but instead celebrated for her important "coming out" about childhood trauma and mental health struggles.

Please, no matter what side of this issue you are on…

> let's stand together to stop the rush to put children on puberty blockers, cross-gender hormones, and permanent sterilization…

without first looking back at their childhood history.

If we look, we'll often find that it's filled with trauma and abuse.

We should treat that first rather than recommending gender transition that a child will likely regret years later.

---

[176] https://www.premierchristianity.com/Blog/I-regretted-my-transition-to-female.-Hundreds-of-other-trans-people-feel-the-same
[177] https://thefederalist.com/2015/01/09/heres-what-parents-of-transgender-kids-need-to-know/

Chapter 6.
"Save James"
Texas Custody Case

Mom Dresses Six-Year-Old Son As Girl, Threatens Dad With Losing His Son For Disagreeing

A Texas custody case splits a 6-year-old child's gender identity in two.

BY WALT HEYER
THE FEDERALIST, NOVEMBER 26, 2018
THEFEDERALIST.COM/2018/11/26/MOM-DRESSES-
SIX-YEAR-OLD-SON-GIRL-THREATENS-DAD-LOSING-SON-DISAGREEING/

Six-year-old James is caught in a gender identity nightmare. Under his mom's care in Dallas, Texas, James obediently lives as a trans girl named "Luna." But given the choice when he's with dad, he's all boy — his sex at birth.

In their divorce proceedings, the mother has charged the father with child abuse for not affirming James as transgender, has sought restraining orders against him, [178] and is seeking to terminate his parental rights. [179] She is also seeking to require him to pay for the child's visits to a transgender-affirming therapist and transgender medical alterations, which may include hormonal sterilization starting at age eight.

I learned of James' plight on a recent visit to Plano, Texas, where I spoke to teenagers about my own transgender story. I lived through a similar scenario when I was his age. I was cross-dressed for two-and-a-half years by my grandmother, who made a purple chiffon dress for me. Somewhat like James, my cross-dressing occurred under one adult's care, but away from grandma's I was all boy with my mom and dad. Also, just like James, I found my way into the office of a gender therapist, who quickly started me toward transition.

When his mother, a pediatrician, took James for counseling, she chose a gender transition therapist who diagnosed him with gender dysphoria, a mental conflict between physical sex and perceived gender. James' precious young life hinges purely on the diagnosis of gender dysphoria by a therapist who wraps herself in rainbow colors, affirms the diagnosis of gender dysphoria, and dismisses evidence to the contrary. Remove the "rainbow" from James' diagnosis, and it crumbles under the weight of the criteria for the diagnosis of gender dysphoria.

The diagnosis is critical, because labeling a child with gender dysphoria can trigger a series of physical and mental consequences for the child and has legal ramifications in the ongoing custody case. Get it wrong and young James's life is irrevocably harmed.

---

[178] http://savejames.com/wp-content/uploads/2018/09/Younger-VS-Georgulas.pdf
[179] http://savejames.com/wp-content/uploads/2018/10/Save_James_Dossier-2.pdf

James Does Not Fit the Gender Dysphoria Criteria

The criteria for a diagnosis of childhood gender dysphoria are that a child be persistent, consistent, and insistent about being the opposite sex.[180] James's mom is "all in" on the diagnosis of gender dysphoria and assisting with social transition. She used the name Luna to enroll him as a girl in first grade, and provides only female clothes.

Meanwhile, Dad isn't seeing signs of gender dysphoria. In the father's home, James appears to be a normal boy and doesn't identify as a girl. He has a choice of boy's or girl's clothes there, and he chooses to dress as a boy. The fact that James changes gender identity depending on which parent is present makes the diagnosis of gender dysphoria both dubious and harmful.

The transition therapist has observed that James is not consistent, insistent, or persistent in the desire to become "Luna." For example, a dossier filed with the Dallas court says that, under the skilled eyes of the therapist, the child was presented two pieces of paper, one with the word "James" and one with the word "Luna," and asked to pick the name he preferred. When the appointment only included his mother, James selected Luna, the name and gender he uses at his mother's home and in his first-grade classroom. When the appointment was only with his father, however, James pointed to the boy name James, not the girl name.

The glaring disparity between a child's preferred identity when in the presence of one parent versus the other should cause a therapist to reassess, perhaps nullify the diagnosis of gender dysphoria, and terminate any steps toward transition. But in the case of James, this hasn't happened.

Using a Little Boy as a Weapon of War

When James is away from his mother, he consistently rejects the idea that he is "Luna girl" or that he wants to be a girl. Because the court prohibits dad from dressing James as a boy or from teaching him that he is a boy by sharing religious or science-based teachings on sexuality, dad presents James with male and female clothing options and James always chooses, even insists on, his boy clothes. Dad told me, "James violently refuses to wear girl's clothes at my home." This is not a sign of gender dysphoria.

Eyewitness accounts from friends corroborate dad's observations of James preferring to be a boy. Bill Lovell, the senior pastor of Christ Church Carrollton, wrote: "Based on the three occasions I've spent time with him, I'd say he acts and looks unmistakably like a healthy six-year-old boy. … I am praying for James, an average six-year-old boy, a sweet-natured, intelligent, lovable and at this point particularly vulnerable young man, caught up in a titanic clash of worldviews."[181]

Ellen Grigsby shared in an email her observations after meeting James and his fraternal twin brother for the first time: "They were both 'all boy' and were having a great time. Both boys were absolutely dressed as boys and behaving as boys."

Sarah Scott is a family friend and mother of three boys who frequently play with James and his brother. She and her husband are sensitive to allowing James to lead the way in gender choices such as names, pronouns, and clothing. I asked her the obvious question: "How do you know James does

---

[180] https://www.psychiatry.org/patients-families/gender-dysphoria/what-is-gender-dysphoria

[181] http://christchurchcarrollton.org/circling-the-square/praying-for-james/

not want to be a girl?" Sarah responded in an email with several examples she's seen of James' desire to remain a boy:

> Friday, Sept. 21: We had the boys over. The boys took turns telling stories and James made up a story about five little boys (himself, his brother and my three sons) who were such good friends that they magically turned into pumpkins, so they could stay in the pumpkin patch together forever. He didn't say kids. He specifically and happily referred to himself as a boy.

> Saturday, Oct. 20: We all went on a walk to the park. We had such fun! It had rained the night before. On the walk, James slipped and got his clothes dirty. He asked if he could borrow some of my boys' shorts and if I could wash his clothes. I said sure! — and went to grab something he could wear. While I was looking, he said, 'Guess what Mrs. Sarah? You don't need to find a shirt because boys don't have to wear them if you're hot!' I laughed and told him I guess that's a good thing about being a boy! He said, 'Yes, it is!'

> Saturday, Nov. 3: His mother came to pick up the boys to take them to [his brother's] soccer game. James hugged his dad and said, 'Love you.' He refused to go to the soccer game as a girl with mom and stayed with dad. That evening they came to our house.

James exhibits no desire to be "Luna" the girl except when he is with his mother. The boy's behavior offers a stinging rebuke of the diagnosis of gender dysphoria. This by all accounts is not a true or clinically correct diagnosis of gender dysphoria. Yet the therapist stands by her diagnosis and continues to keep "Luna" on track to gender transition.

Is This Therapy or Manipulation?

Unlike James, I was an adult at the time of my diagnosis. Grandma was gone by then, but the therapist, like so many today, affirmed my cross-gender identity and guided me through gender transition. He provided access to hormones and surgery and I soon had the full gender-affirming surgery and identified as "Laura." I felt that my gender identity and biological sex were at odds, but what the therapist failed to consider were the other factors driving my desire to change gender, which needed to be addressed first.

What this mom is doing to James looks very much like what my grandmother did to me by affirming me in the purple dress. My grandmother didn't intend to harm me, but her actions destroyed my childhood and my family and consumed nearly 50 years of my life.

James has no idea what he is in for or how his gender journey will play out, but with an incorrect diagnosis it will be ugly. I became very concerned about James because he is not exhibiting the diagnostic attributes of gender dysphoria. His gender preferences are not consistent or insistent, but flip back and forth, according to which parent is present.

When James is permitted to relax around friends away from his mom, he seems natural and happy being a boy. If James truly had gender dysphoria, he would demand the proper pronouns, always dress as a girl and insistently, persistently, and consistently claim to be a girl in all situations, not just with mom. Instead, friends say he has done the opposite — he has insisted on being a boy. It is time to consider that the boy is not transgender.

Misdiagnosing People Has Horrific Consequences

Misdiagnosis of gender dysphoria happens around the world, and people's lives are harmed when it does. I wanted people to see what I see, that people of all ages have been incorrectly diagnosed with gender dysphoria, so I wrote a book, *Trans Life Survivors*, that shares many first-hand stories of misdiagnosis of gender dysphoria and the heart-breaking results.

Therapists are taking notice, too, of the increasing prevalence of people detransitioning and going back their birth sex, and suggesting a need for comprehensive psychological assessments, rather than fast-tracking children to transition. An article in The Atlantic shares interviews with Scott Leibowitz, a psychiatrist who treats children and adolescents in Columbus, Ohio, and Laura Edwards-Leeper, a psychologist at Pacific University and Oregon's Transgender Clinic. Both believe as Edwards-Leeper shares, "that comprehensive assessments are crucial to achieving good outcomes for TGNC [transgender and gender non-conforming] young people, especially those seeking physical interventions, in part because some kids who think they are trans at one point in time will not feel that way later on."[182]

Pediatrician Michelle Cretella, executive director of the American College of Pediatricians, describes the pediatric community's encouragement of sex change and hormonal treatments for children as "institutionalized child abuse."[183]

If we do not save James from a misdiagnosis, his next step is chemical castration at age eight, only two years away. James needs a more comprehensive psychological assessment to explore why he identifies as a girl with mom and as a boy with dad. I want to do what I can to "Save James"[184] from his gender nightmare, and to raise awareness about how easily children can be misdiagnosed and labeled as gender dysphoric and the extensive damage that can cause in their young lives.

A questionable diagnosis locks a vulnerable child into an alternate gender identity long before they can understand what is happening or where it might lead. It's up to the adults to observe the child carefully, consider and question the grey areas, and ultimately guard innocent children against hasty diagnoses and conclusions about something so fundamental as their gender identity.

[182] https://www.theatlantic.com/magazine/archive/2018/07/when-a-child-says-shes-trans/561749/

[183] https://www.christianpost.com/voice/dr-michelle-cretella-transgender-ideology-institutionalized-large-scale-child-abuse.html

[184] http://www.savejames.com/

6-Year Old Texas Boy On Track For Repressed Puberty Due To Gender Dysphoria Diagnosis

Little James is comfortable being a boy when he's around his dad and other friends. So why is his mother dressing him as a girl and calling him Luna?

BY WALT HEYER
THE FEDERALIST, JANUARY 15, 2019
THEFEDERALIST.COM/2019/01/29/6-YEAR-OLD-
TEXAS-BOY-TRACK-REPRESSED-PUBERTY-DUE-GENDER-DYSPHORIA-DIAGNOSIS/

As reported in an earlier article[185] concerning a Dallas, Texas, custody case, when in the care of his mother six-year-old James attends first grade obediently dressed as a girl enrolled under the name "Luna." But when with his father, where he's given the choice of boy or girl clothes, James chooses boy clothes and refuses to wear girl clothing. Despite this inconsistent behavior, a gender therapist has given James a diagnosis of gender dysphoria.

In response, heartwarming things have happened in the fight to save James. A team of designers volunteered their services to update the savejames.com website and another caring friend started an online petition directed to Texan representatives to do something to prevent this kind of abuse of children.[186] Generous people donated to the father's legal expense fund, raising half of what is needed.

But the father, Jeff Younger, is still hampered by a shortage of finances to secure expert witnesses and perform a forensic custody evaluation to change the outcome for James.

Follow-Up Visit

After writing the first article about James, I arranged to visit Jeff and his six-year-old twin sons in Texas. We met on a Thursday evening during the boys' usual two hours of visitation with their father. To keep the time casual, Jeff suggested we spend the time with his good friends, the Scott family and their four young children, who always enjoy time together.

Jeff and I drove across town to the mother's home to pick up the boys. As we pulled up, the front door opened, and the two young boys came flying out. James was dressed as a boy, like his brother. Into the backseat they went, saying hi to their dad and to me before they started talking about Ninja Turtles and other things they had done at school. Not one smidgeon of gender dysphoria or "girl talk" appeared during the drive back to the Scott home.

---

[185] https://thefederalist.com/2018/11/26/mom-dresses-six-year-old-son-girl-threatens-dad-losing-son-disagreeing/

[186] https://www.change.org/p/save-6-year-old-james-from-chemical-castration

The next two hours were supervised and playful bedlam. Jeff brought out a toy popular with this bunch of friends—plastic swords and shields. Immediately, all six children were joyfully absorbed in rough-and-tumble swordplay with their fathers and each other. A pleasant dinner followed, and then the children went off to other playtime activities.

I observed James' mannerisms, voice inflections, and interactions, looking for evidence of gender dysphoria. I can emphatically say that during the two hours of the visit I saw no sign of gender dysphoria. James indicated no desire to be a girl, nor did he behave like a girl or talk like a girl during the entire time. Both James and his brother happily engaged with the four Scott children and the adults. Both were talkative, demonstrated strong vocabularies, and eagerly showed off their artwork created during a previous playdate.

I asked Jeff why James was dressed as a boy when he ran out of mom's house. Jeff explained that James prefers to dress as a boy, even at his mother's, except when he goes to school dressed as a girl.

After observing James and his behavior, I cannot see how his counselor at Dallas Rainbow Counseling could have diagnosed James with gender dysphoria. She spent time with James and his father, where James showed a preference for being a boy. Even if James preferred a girl name in sessions with his mother, it is a huge leap to a diagnosis of gender dysphoria. He's only six, after all.

A misdiagnosis cannot be ruled out, and a prudent next step is a comprehensive psychological assessment to explore why he identifies as a girl with mom and as a boy with dad. Per the custody order, the only parent authorized to oversee James' psychological counseling is his mother.

A Single Diagnosis Is Not Enough

A single therapist's diagnosis of gender dysphoria has put James on a life-changing protocol known as the Dutch protocol. (The Dutch protocol lacks scientific basis,[187] yet clinics are adopting it.) The protocol consists of social transition to acting like the opposite sex, and hormone blockers.

Social transition is the first step. James' mother has enrolled him in first grade as a girl with a girl name and dresses him as a girl for school. Social transition for a young child is not harmless. It's grooming. My grandmother dressed me as a girl when I was 4, 5, and 6 years old, which led to my own gender confusion.

The next step is administering drugs to block the necessary and natural process of physical maturity and puberty, as early as age 8.[188] Dr. Michael Laidlaw, an endocrinologist practicing in Rocklin, California, says, "What parents should find truly terrifying is the psychological effect of this medication."

Early evidence shows a troubling effect: All of the children put on blockers continue towards sex changes.[189] The blockers themselves seem to influence children to transition. In vivid contrast, 60 to 90 percent of trans kids who are not reinforced in this desire or put on puberty blockers are no longer

---

[187] https://quadrant.org.au/magazine/2018/07/experimenting-children-gender-dysphoria/
[188] https://thefederalist.com/2018/12/14/puberty-blockers-clear-danger-childrens-health/
[189] https://www.wpath.org/media/cms/Documents/Web Transfer/SOC/Standards of Care V7 - 2011 WPATH.pdf

trans by adulthood.[190] In other words, most trans children naturally grow out of it as they go through puberty, if they are not socially locked into an opposite-sex identity and puberty is not blocked.

Puberty blockers and the following step, cross-sex hormones, are known to cause serious side effects, including infertility.[191] Children are not able to understand these consequences or give informed consent.

James is on track to be given these drugs.

Another opinion is so clearly needed. It's easy to see why this father is alarmed and fights so hard for his boy. An intervention is clearly needed and needed now. A second opinion needs to come from someone who is not a cheerleader for diagnosing gender dysphoria and preparing a child for a sex change. The ideal counselor will explore the family dynamics and other contributing factors.

If the current counselor is solid in her belief the gender dysphoria diagnosis is indisputable and fixed, she should support getting a second opinion in the best interests of the child.

Cross-Dressing Young People Will Influence Their Future

The case of James is very troubling to me because I know how the story unfolds. My grandmother dressed me as a girl when I was 4, 5, and 6 years old. Like James, I was far too young to comprehend the long-term consequences of being encouraged to cross-dress at such a young age, much less fight back. In my child's mind, it felt good to be the center of her attention. Now I call what grandma did to me "child abuse" because her grooming of me as a female negatively affected my entire life.

In adulthood, I was diagnosed with gender dysphoria and underwent unnecessary cross-gender hormone therapy and surgical gender change. I lived eight years as a woman and tried my best to make it work, but after surgery I still had gender dysphoria. Even worse, I was suicidal. Before giving me hormones and surgery, my medical providers should have helped me explore the possible psychological roots of my desire to escape into a female persona, but none did.

I'm not the only one whose life was hurt by the rush to change gender. I have heard from so many trans adults who ask me for advice in going back to their sex at conception that I compiled 30 people's emails into a book, *Trans Life Survivors*. Several people in the book transitioned in their teens but when they hit their twenties, their feelings of gender dysphoria changed. They grew out of it, but only after making irreversible changes to their bodies, including the ability to have children, and losing years of their life to an alternate identity.

Help James From Being Locked In

Jeff and his lawyer are pursing action through the court to save James, but public response is still very much needed. Even after a generous outpouring of support, Jeff is still hampered by a shortage of finances to secure expert witnesses and perform a forensic custody evaluation.

This case is not only about one six-year-old boy, but about all children who will get locked into a trans life by a gender dysphoria diagnosis and a parent's endorsement of social transition and hormone

---

[190] http://www.sexologytoday.org/2016/01/do-trans-kids-stay-trans-when-they-grow_99.html
[191] https://www.thepublicdiscourse.com/2018/01/20810/

blockers. If Younger can prevail in proving the diagnosis of gender dysphoria and the resulting treatment is misguided, this Texas case has the potential to save other young children from similar gender identity nightmares.

Texas Court Gives 7-Year-Old Boy A Reprieve From Transgender Treatments

---

The mother no longer has unfettered authority to manipulate her 7-year old boy into gender transition. Instead both mother and father will share equally in decision-making for him and his twin brother.

BY WALT HEYER
THE FEDERALIST, OCTOBER 25, 2019
THEFEDERALIST.COM/2019/10/25/TEXAS-COURT-
GIVES-7-YEAR-OLD-BOY-A-REPRIEVE-FROM-TRANSGENDER-TREATMENTS/

In a closely watched Dallas, Texas, child custody case, Judge Kim Cooks put aside the disappointing jury's verdict of Monday against the father and ruled Thursday that Jeffrey Younger now has equal joint conservatorship with the mother, Dr. Anne Georgulas, of their twin boys.

The mother no longer has unfettered authority to manipulate her 7-year old boy into gender transition. Instead both mother and father will share equally in medical, psychological, and other decision-making for the boys. Additionally, the judge changed the custody terms to give Younger an equal amount of visitation time with his sons, something that had been severely limited.

This week has been tumultuous for Younger. He had requested that a jury grant him sole main conservatory. On October 21, the day of the jury's decision, Younger told me the jury voted 11-1 that while yes, the boys should have a sole main conservatory, they didn't agree that it should be him.

The public outcry and nationwide media attention were significant. Texas Republican Gov. Greg Abbott announced state child protection agencies would investigate[192] and Texas Sen. Ted Cruz encouraged Texas lawmakers to act to keep children from being given surgeries and hormones to make them appear more as their opposite sex.[193]

A Boy His Mother Wants to Be a Girl

I first became involved with little James' situation in 2018 when I met his father at a conference in Texas. I immediately felt a connection because I was just a boy when the seed of gender distress was planted in my young psyche by an adult family member who cross-dressed me and affirmed how good I looked. Now in my seventies, I have the benefit of hindsight to know how badly this can play

---

[192] https://twitter.com/GregAbbott_TX/status/1187156266449330176
[193] https://twitter.com/SenTedCruz/status/1187157175250149376

out, with years lost in the transgender mix-master. I've written two articles to raise awareness about Younger's situation, here[194] and here.[195]

For those who need a little background, here's a recap from my November 26, 2018 Federalist article, "Mom Dresses Six-Year-Old Son As Girl, Threatens Dad With Losing His Son For Disagreeing."[196]

> Six-year-old James is caught in a gender identity nightmare. Under his mom's care in Dallas, Texas, James obediently lives as a trans girl named 'Luna.' But given the choice when he's with dad, he's all boy—his sex from conception.
>
> In their divorce proceedings, the mother has charged the father with child abuse for not affirming James as transgender, has sought restraining orders against him, and is seeking to terminate his parental rights. She is also seeking to require him to pay for the child's visits to a transgender-affirming therapist and transgender medical alterations, which may include hormonal sterilization starting at age eight."

All the evidence points to a boy torn between pleasing two parents, not an overwhelming preference to be a girl.

What Happened When I Met James

I visited Younger in Texas a year ago and met his sons, James and his fraternal twin brother. The two-hour court-ordained visitation time we shared was casual, held, as it occasionally is, at the home of close family friends and their children.

I took the opportunity to jump in the car with Younger as he drove across town to pick up the boys at his ex-wife's home. As we pulled up, the front door opened, and the two young boys came flying out. James was dressed as a boy, like his brother. Into the backseat they went, saying hi to their dad and to me before they started talking about Ninja Turtles and other things they had done at school. Not one smidgeon of gender dysphoria or "girl talk" appeared during the drive or the subsequent playtime and dinner.

This week, I asked Younger how his sons were doing. Younger says James' fraternal twin brother is confused and "tells everyone he wants to live with his dad." As to James, on a recent visitation time with his father, James dressed himself as a classy young man with creased pants and necktie all day and chose to stay dressed that way to go back to his mother's. It seemed to be a powerful nonverbal way for James to defy his mother's wishes.

---

[194] https://thefederalist.com/2018/11/26/mom-dresses-six-year-old-son-girl-threatens-dad-losing-son-disagreeing/

[195] https://thefederalist.com/2019/01/29/6-year-old-texas-boy-track-repressed-puberty-due-gender-dysphoria-diagnosis/

[196] https://thefederalist.com/2018/11/26/mom-dresses-six-year-old-son-girl-threatens-dad-losing-son-disagreeing/

Experts Agree James Needs Protection

Younger said at the trial he was painted as paranoid and in need of several years of psychotherapy because he doesn't believe his young son wants to be a girl. But many experts agree that transgendering young children is hazardous.

At the trial, Younger's expert witnesses testified about these dangers and provided supporting evidence. Dr. Stephen Levine, a psychiatrist renowned for his work on human sexuality, testified that social transition—treating them as the opposite sex—increases the chance that a child will remain gender dysphoric. Dr. Paul W. Hruz, a pediatric endocrinologist and professor of pediatrics and cellular biology at Washington University School of Medicine in Saint Louis, testified that the risks of social transition are so great that the "treatment" cannot be recommended at all.

Are these doctors paranoid, too? Disagreement based on scientific evidence is now considered paranoia requiring "thought reprogramming." That's scary stuff when enforced by the courts.

The Research Is Still Wide Open On This

As I've written, researchers don't know the long-term outcomes from the radical approach of social and medical transgenderism for children. They do know that most children, if they aren't socially transitioned, will desist from the desire to transition, but unfortunately, they don't know which ones.

Research psychologist Kristina Olson at the University of Washington, a proponent of transition, puts it this way: "We just don't have definitive data one way or another." That's why Olson is leading a study of 300 trans children that will track outcomes over 20 years, "to be able to, hopefully, answer which children should or should not transition," she said.[197]

In other words, we simply don't know right now, yet parents and children are herded in one direction as if we do. And the risks along each step of the path to full transition are enormous.

Why It's Risky to Treat a Boy Like a Girl

The first step, social transitioning, as the mother has done to James, carries many risks. One is that it becomes self-fulfilling. "The Parent Resource Guide: Responding to the Transgender Issue," a collaboration between organizations with very diverse political opinions, says: "When children socially transition, studies show that they are less likely to become comfortable with their biological sex and they end up on a fast-moving conveyor belt towards hormones and surgery."[198]

On the other hand, the scientific and clinical evidence collected over decades by neutral clinicians shows that if *not* affirmed and allowed to go through natural puberty, as many as 98 percent of gender-confused boys and 88 percent of gender-confused girls eventually accept their biological sex.[199]

---

[197] http://www.nbcbayarea.com/investigations/Transgender-Kids-Eligible-for-Earlier-Medical-Intervention-Under-New-Guidelines-423082734.html
[198] https://genderresourceguide.com/
[199] https://www.acpeds.org/the-college-speaks/position-statements/gender-ideology-harms-children

> In other words, going through puberty is the ultimate cure for the majority
> of children with gender confusion; social and medical transition are not.

The next step on transition for children is administering drugs to suppress puberty suppression, which can start as early as age eight. That's why Younger fought so hard to have a say in medical decisions for James. The full effects of these drugs—emotionally, neurologically and physically—when given to healthy children has not been studied. That's right: this use is *experimental and not Food and Drug Administration -approved.*

The drugs have an approved medical purpose—to delay puberty for children who started too young and then resume puberty at a more appropriate age. People who took them as children show evidence of neurological and bodily harms as adults: lower IQ, increased depression symptoms, and harm to bone development (see page 14 of the "Parent Resource Guide").

> Blocking puberty with drugs also seems to lock children into their gender
> confusion, not resolve it.

Data show that as many as 100 percent of gender-confused children who use puberty blockers go on to take cross-sex hormones.[200] That's alarming because we'd expect to see at least *some* children get comfortable in their bodies. But most children taking puberty blockers continued on the path to hormonal and surgical transition, which means they will be left infertile and permanently, irrevocably sterile.

It's Not the Father Who Needs Psychotherapy

Richard B. Corradi, M.D., former professor of psychiatry at Case Western Reserve University School of Medicine, Cleveland, Ohio, wrote, "Just as 'mental health professionals' a generation ago supported the child abuse delusions, and even participated in prosecuting the unjustly accused, so too have they fueled the fire of the transgender delusion…Historically, contagious popular delusions that deny common sense and fly in the face of reality eventually run their course. This will likely be the fate of the transgender craze. But before it collapses under its own weight, many people will suffer irreparable harm."[201]

Little James is one who has suffered harm. My hope is that his father, by having joint decision-making authority for James' medical and psychological care, can prevail so that James will be spared further social transition and find joy in being a boy at school and at home, that he won't have his natural puberty process disrupted by experimental use of powerful drugs, and that he'll keep his genitalia and the ability to father children of his own someday.

---

[200] https://www.jsm.jsexmed.org/article/S1743-6095(15)33617-1/fulltext
[201] https://thefederalist.com/2016/11/17/psychiatry-professor-transgenderism-mass-hysteria-similar-1980s-era-junk-science/

The jury's 11-1 vote to keep sole managing conservatorship from the father shows how invasive and acceptable this idea of confusing children and transitioning them has become.

It's like we are watching a bad movie where scientific evidence is ignored and believing the natural truth of male and female biology is considered paranoia. I can testify from my life experience the trans-life movie ends in unhappiness, regret, detransitions, or sadly, suicide.

So many good people over the last year prayed for James and for his best interests to be served. Bringing the case to court was expensive and many people generously donated through the SaveJames website (which is no longer active as a condition of the court ruling) to allow Younger to hire the best experts and attorneys. Thank you to all who signed petitions, lobbied lawmakers, and participated in various ways.

Don't stop now. I'm asking all fair-minded parents and adults to continue to pray for James and his family, and to...

...lobby lawmakers everywhere to pass legislation that would protect all children from being given experimental, ideologically corrupted treatments that will harm them for life.

Pushing Kids Into Transgenderism Is Medical Malpractice

It is sadistic to use the public school system, which holds a captive audience, to engage in a social gender identity experiment with the nation's young people.

BY WALT HEYER
THE FEDERALIST, SEPTEMBER 21, 2016
THEFEDERALIST.COM/2016/09/21/
PUSHING-KIDS-TRANSGENDERISM-MEDICAL-MALPRACTICE/

Socially indoctrinating young children toward accepting transgenderism is rampant today in public schools. In Washington state, public schools will begin teaching gender expression to kindergarteners in fall 2017, under newly approved health education learning standards.[202] The gay advocacy network GLSEN received a grant from the federal Centers for Disease Control in 2011 for $1.425 million over five years to promote the LGBT agenda in public schools at taxpayers' expense.[203]

By infiltrating the curriculum in our nation's public schools, LGBT activists can groom the next generation of participants. Young people are questioning their gender identity at an alarming rate that seems to be increasing,[204] and are encouraged by educators and medical professionals to experiment with gender transition. Unfortunately, experimentation can cause even more confusion.

Feelings Change, Bodies Don't

The problem with taking the steps to transition physically—cross-gender hormones and surgeries—is that physical changes are likely permanent, but the feelings driving the desire may change, especially for young people. I recently received an email from a man now in his thirties that demonstrates this reality:

> I transitioned to female beginning in my late teens and changed my name in my early 20s, over ten years ago. But it wasn't right for me; I feel only discontent now in the female role. I was told that my transgender feelings were permanent, immutable, physically deep-seated in my brain and could NEVER change, and that the only way I would ever find peace was to become female. The problem is, I don't have those feelings anymore.
>
> When I began seeing a psychologist a few years ago to help overcome some childhood trauma issues, my depression and anxiety began to wane but so did my transgender feelings. So two years ago I began contemplating going back to my birth gender, and it feels right to do so. I have no doubts—I want to be male!

---

[202] http://www.dailycaller.com/2016/0601/Washington-state-to-teach-transgederism-to-kindergartners/

[203203] http://www.thepublicdiscourse/2015/06/15118

[204] https://thefederalist.com/2016/09/20/cbss-jonbenet-ramsey-documentary-was-complete-garbage/

Feelings can change. For this man, feelings that were overwhelming in his teens changed after he went to counseling to deal with childhood trauma.

My story is similar. Changing my gender was an empty promise, a temporary reprieve that didn't fix anything. After much psychological counseling, I came to see that my dream of becoming a girl had simply been an escape to cope with deep pain from childhood events. Unfortunately, the so-called earlier treatment of cross-gender hormones and surgery was destructive for my family, marriage, and career, and nearly caused me to take my own life.

Ignoring Science to Push a Political Agenda

Now children in Washington state will be taught starting in kindergarten about the normalcy of wanting to be the other sex. Public schools should not be the breeding ground for any sexual activism by any group at any time. The public school system is holding kids hostage as activists groom the next generation of transgender activists, despite serious harm this poses to children.

For example, the Charlotte-Mecklenburg Schools in North Carolina has eliminated the use of the terms "boys" and "girls," requiring that teachers call their pupils sex-neutered terms such as "students" or "scholars." They also require educators to keep parents in the dark about their child's request for a different name or pronoun.[205]

The activists who push this agenda in public school studies ignore the science regarding innate sex. An August 2016 review of the scientific literature[206] finds no definitive evidence in research to suggest that transgender people are born that way. This 143-page report from two distinguished doctors from Johns Hopkins University finds there is not enough definitive scientific evidence to suggest gay, lesbian, and transgender people are born as such. More importantly, they affirmed that innate biological sex is fixed and unchangeable. Only gender persona—appearance and behavior—can be changed.

I was a kid who started cross-dressing with my grandmother at the age of four. I can tell you from first-hand knowledge that cross-dressing is a psychological indoctrination. It is sadistic to use the public school system, which holds a captive audience, to engage in a social gender identity experiment with the nation's young people.

Medical Experimentation Can Devastate People

We have known changing genders leads to suicides from reports in the late 1970s that provide a telltale glimpse into the consequences of ignoring the science. Endocrinologist Dr. Charles Ihlenfeld warned about the suicides and unhappiness of transgender clients based on his experience treating more than 500 transgender patients with hormones over a six-year period at colleague Dr. Harry Benjamin's gender clinic.

---

[205] http://www.charlottestories.com/wp-content/uploads/2016/08/CMS-Supporting-Transgender-Students-Training-FINAL.pdf

[206] http://www.thenewatlantis.com/publications/number-50-fall-2016

Ihlenfeld observed that the gender change led to poor outcomes, and concluded that 80 percent of the patients who want to change their physical appearance this way shouldn't do it. Ihlenfeld blew the whistle a little louder when he said, "There is too much unhappiness among people who have had the surgery. Too many of them end as suicides."[207] You wonder why a doctor like this, who was an insider on early gender change experiments, was ignored.

Medicine has a long history of failing to properly and effectively help people who struggle with unusual emotional and psychological issues. Experimenting with surgery as treatment for psychological disorders is not new. My book, *Paper Genders*, gives a 100-year history of these kinds of failures.

This includes psychologist Dr. Henry Cotton. In the early part of the 1900s, Cotton was the head of the main New Jersey state mental hospital in Trenton. He theorized that infections caused mental illness, and was zealous in his effort to cure mental illness by removing the suspected source of infection. He started with removing infected teeth. When that failed, he pulled the remaining teeth and tonsils, then moved on to removing sections of the colon, the stomach, gallbladders, and testicles and ovaries.

Cotton reported a success rate of 85 percent. *The New York Times* lauded Cotton as a scientific genius whose investigations gave "high hope" for the future, and Cotton became famous in the United States and Europe. Desperate people brought their suffering loved ones to the Trenton hospital for the breakthrough treatment. Kept out of public view were the chilling mortality statistics: 30 to 40 percent of his surgical patients died from his so-called treatment.[208]

I find striking similarities between Cotton and the gender-change surgeons of today. The media celebrate those like Caitlyn Jenner who "bravely" change genders. Desperate people who feel they should be the opposite sex seek treatment from sympathetic surgeons, who will cut away male and female body parts, and from endocrinologists, who will inject cross-gender hormones. It sounds barbaric and crazy—and it is.

From Body Chopping to Brain Blending

The surgical insanity did not end with Cotton. Starting in the mid-1930s, neurologist Dr. Walter Freeman partnered with Dr. Watts, a neurosurgeon, to perform lobotomies as treatment for mental disorders. Freeman believed cutting certain nerves in the brain could eliminate excess emotion and stabilize a personality.[209]

The first lobotomies involved drilling holes in the skull and inserting a rotating knife to destroy brain cells in the prefrontal lobes of the brain. Later, Freeman developed a 10-minute trans-orbital lobotomy in which the brain was accessed through the eye sockets with an instrument that resembled an ice pick. Freeman's procedure did not require a surgeon or an operating room, which allowed

[207] http://lvtgw.jadephoenix.org/Info_htm/Herbal_G/ginko_b2.htm
[208] https://www.ncbi.nlm.nih.gov/pmc/articles/PMC2755332/
[209] http://www.npr.org/templates/story/story.php?storyId=5014565&ps=rs

Freeman, who was not a surgeon, to perform the lobotomies. Freeman performed more than 2,500 lobotomies in his lifetime.[210]

Results for patients varied. In "The Lobotomy Files: One Doctor's Legacy," the *Wall Street Journal* says: "Drs. Freeman and Watts considered about one-third of their operations successes in which the patient was able to lead a 'productive life,' Dr. Freeman's son says. Another third were able to return home but not support themselves. The final third were 'failures,' according to Dr. Watts."[211]

During their heyday, both doctors were held in high esteem, but the long-term negative results for a majority of their patients were another regrettable outcome in the history of using surgery to treat mental illness.

Surgery Doesn't Treat Transgenderism

Cotton, Freeman, and Watts were precursors to today's treatment of transgenderism, a mental disorder, with another set of surgeries. They treated patients by pulling teeth, cutting out colons, and scrambling brain tissue, resulting in mortality rates of 30 to 40 percent and a failure rate of 33 percent, respectively. The treatment methods in hindsight seem barbaric.

Today's accepted treatment for gender issues—cutting off body parts and rearranging everything from the Adam's apple, hips, and breasts to the genitalia—seems barbaric as well, and lacking in compassion.

> The compassionate response is to explore other less extreme options first,
> before resorting to surgery.

Our long history with treating transgenderism strongly suggests surgery has not been effective. In my journey to gender change, my psychologist told me surgery was the only answer to my problems, and never asked any questions to discover other possible causes of my gender distress.

Today, people write to me about their gender-change experiences. They consistently share how at the time of their transition they were told gender change was the only treatment for their condition. Parents write to me concerned about their adult children pursuing transition because they know no one is considering that trauma from the person's childhood could be leading to this unusual desire. Parents report that gender therapists don't want to know about childhood events. The therapist says if an adult wants transition, he or she can have it.

As with Cotton, Freeman, and Watts, today's surgical gender-change treatments are not submitted to rigorous scientific study to evaluate their safety, effectiveness over time, and unexpected consequences. Those who regret making the transition, who return to their birth gender, and who are lost to suicide aren't counted in studies because researchers can't find them. The statistics are skewed in favor of positive outcomes because the people experiencing negative outcomes are, in scientific language, "lost to follow-up."

---

[210] http://psychcentral.com/blog/archives/2011/03/21/the-surprising-history-of-the-lobotomy/
[211] http://projects.wsj.com/lobotomyfiles/?ch=two

Suicide Threats Indicate Mental Illness

Gender-distressed teens will often say something along the lines of "If I don't get puberty blockers or hormones and surgery to transition, I'm going to commit suicide." They mean to demonstrate the strength of their cross-gender feelings and the urgency of their need for transition to everyone who might otherwise urge caution, such as parents, psychotherapists, and endocrinologists.

Threatening suicide is a serious matter that points to the presence of serious mental health issues. When a transgender child uses emotional and psychological blackmail to get fast-tracked towards extreme surgery, it should raise concerns about the person's emotional and psychological health. A suicide threat points to the urgent need for intervention and psychotherapy, not hormones and surgery.

Consider early life events that unfold like this, from an email I received recently:

> Help, my daughter is trying to live as a man and desperately wants gender re-assignment surgery.
>
> Her father was a male to male pedophile. He abused our son. Years later my son became homosexual and is married to a man.
>
> My daughter on the other hand was rejected by her dad. She spent her teen years hating men. She began to engorge herself so that guys would be repulsed by her. She developed obsessive disorders and made sure she looked unattractive to men. She accomplished being unattractive and men turned away from her. She decided to be a lesbian. She decided that wasn't for her after a bad break-up. Now she wants to become a transgender.

It's not completely unexpected a young woman like this would seek to become a transgender given the rejection of her father, her appearance calculated to repel men, and a failed lesbian relationship. Her dad's pedophilia, homosexual leanings, and rejection of her would easily keep her from developing a healthy self-image and relationships.

She sees transgenderism as the fix to all this rejection. As a transgender, she can fall in love with herself and avoid rejection. Yes, it is psychologically unhealthy behavior, but it will provide a temporary reprieve from the rejection she has experienced so far in her life.

Young people who consider themselves neglected, abused, or abandoned may turn to self-abusive or attention-getting behaviors. They latch on to anything they can control when all seems out of control. Notice I said "consider." A child can feel rejected when no rejection exists. Perceived rejection can lead a child towards homosexuality or transgenderism because it looks more attractive than the life they have, or allows them to feel in control of their life.

Parents need to take a stand against public schools and government policies that are intended to groom children towards gender change and eliminating male and female sex distinctions. Parents cannot afford to stand silently by while their right to parent their children is eroded.

Chapter 7.
Bruce/Caitlyn Jenner

"Sex Change" Surgery:
What Bruce Jenner, Diane Sawyer, and You Should Know

The dark and troubling history of the contemporary transgender movement, with its enthusiastic approval of gender-reassignment surgery, has left a trail of misery in its wake.

BY WALT HEYER
PUBLIC DISCOURSE, APRIL 27, 2015
WWW.THEPUBLICDISCOURSE.COM/2015/04/14905/

Bruce Jenner and Diane Sawyer could benefit from a history lesson. I know, because I suffered through "sex change" surgery and lived as a woman for eight years. The surgery fixed nothing—it only masked and exacerbated deeper psychological problems.

The beginnings of the transgender movement have gotten lost today in the push for transgender rights, acceptance, and tolerance. If more people were aware of the dark and troubled history of sex-reassignment surgery, perhaps we wouldn't be so quick to push people toward it.

The setting for the first transgender surgeries (mostly male-to-female) was in university-based clinics, starting in the 1950s and progressing through the 1960s and the 1970s. When the researchers tallied the results and found no objective proof that it was successful—and, in fact, evidence that it was harmful—the universities stopped offering sex-reassignment surgery.

Since then, private surgeons have stepped in to take their place. Without any scrutiny or accountability for their results, their practices have grown, leaving shame, regret, and suicide in their wake.

The Founding Fathers of the Transgender Movement

The transgender movement began as the brainchild of three men who shared a common bond: all three were pedophilia activists.

The story starts with the infamous Dr. Alfred Kinsey, a biologist and sexologist whose legacy endures today. Kinsey believed that all sex acts were legitimate—including pedophilia, bestiality, sadomasochism, incest, adultery, prostitution, and group sex. He authorized despicable experiments on infants and toddlers to gather information to justify his view that children of any age enjoyed having sex. Kinsey advocated the normalization of pedophilia and lobbied against laws that would protect innocent children and punish sexual predators.

Transsexualism was added to Kinsey's repertoire when he was presented with the case of an effeminate boy who wanted to become a girl. Kinsey consulted an acquaintance of his, an endocrinologist by the name of Dr. Harry Benjamin. Transvestites, men who dressed as women, were well-known. Kinsey and Benjamin saw this as an opportunity to change a transvestite physically, way beyond dress and make-up. Kinsey and Benjamin became professional collaborators in the first case of what Benjamin would later call "transsexualism."

Benjamin asked several psychiatric doctors to evaluate the boy for possible surgical procedures to feminize his appearance. They couldn't come to a consensus on the appropriateness of feminizing surgery. That didn't stop Benjamin. On his own, he began offering female hormone therapy to the boy. The boy went to Germany for partial surgery, and Benjamin lost all contact with him, making any long-term follow-up impossible.

The Tragic Story of the Reimer Twins

The third co-founder of today's transgender movement was psychologist Dr. John Money, a dedicated disciple of Kinsey and a member of a transsexual research team headed by Benjamin.

Money's first transgender case came in 1967 when he was asked by a Canadian couple, the Reimers, to repair a botched circumcision on their two-year-old son, David. Without any medical justification, Money launched into an experiment to make a name for himself and advance his theories about gender, no matter what the consequences to the child. Money told the distraught parents that the best way to assure David's happiness was to surgically change his genitalia from male to female and raise him as a girl. As many parents do, the Reimers followed their doctor's orders, and David was replaced with Brenda. Money assured the parents that Brenda would adapt to being a girl and that she would never know the difference. He told them that they should keep it a secret, so they did—at least for a while.

Activist doctors like Dr. Money always look brilliant at first, especially if they control the information that the media report. Money played a skilled game of "catch me if you can," reporting the success of the boy's gender change to the medical and scientific community and building his reputation as a leading expert in the emerging field of gender change. It would be decades before the truth was revealed. In reality, David Reimer's "adaptation" to being a girl was completely different from the glowing reports concocted by Money for journal articles. By age twelve, David was severely depressed and refused to return to see Money. In desperation, his parents broke their secrecy, and told him the truth of the gender reassignment. At age fourteen, David chose to undo the gender change and live as a boy.

In 2000, at the age of thirty-five, David and his twin brother finally exposed the sexual abuse Dr. Money had inflicted on them in the privacy of his office. The boys told how Dr. Money took naked photos of them when they were just seven years old. But pictures were not enough for Money. The pedophilic doctor also forced the boys to engage in incestuous sexual activities with each other.

The consequences of Money's abuse were tragic for both boys. In 2003, only three years after going public about their tortured past, David's twin brother, Brian, died from a self-inflicted overdose. A short while later, David also committed suicide. Money had finally been exposed as a fraud, but that didn't help the grieving parents whose twin boys were now dead.

The exposure of Money's fraudulent research results and tendencies came too late for people suffering from gender issues, too. Using surgery had become well-established by then, and no one cared that one of its founders was discredited.

Results from Johns Hopkins: Surgery Gives No Relief

Dr. Money became the co-founder of one of the first university-based gender clinics in the United States at Johns Hopkins University, where gender reassignment surgery was performed. After the clinic had been in operation for several years, Dr. Paul McHugh, the director of psychiatry and behavioral science at Hopkins, wanted more than Money's assurances of success immediately following surgery. McHugh wanted more evidence. Long-term, were patients any better off after surgery?

McHugh assigned the task of evaluating outcomes to Dr. Jon Meyer, the chairman of the Hopkins gender clinic. Meyer selected fifty subjects from those treated at the Hopkins clinic, both those who had undergone gender reassignment surgery and those who had not had surgery. The results of this study completely refuted Money's claims about the positive outcomes of sex-change surgery. The objective report showed no medical necessity for surgery.

On August 10, 1979, Dr. Meyer announced his results: "To say this type of surgery cures psychiatric disturbance is incorrect. We now have objective evidence that there is no real difference in the transsexual's adjustments to life in terms of job, educational attainment, marital adjustment and social stability."[212] He later told *The New York Times*: "My personal feeling is that the surgery is not a proper treatment for a psychiatric disorder, and it's clear to me these patients have severe psychological problems that don't go away following surgery."

Less than six months later, the Johns Hopkins gender clinic closed. Other university-affiliated gender clinics across the country followed suit, completely ceasing to perform gender reassignment surgery. No success was reported anywhere.

Results from Benjamin's Colleague: Too Many Suicides

It was not just the Hopkins clinic reporting lack of outcomes from surgery. Around the same time, serious questions about the effectiveness of gender change came from Dr. Harry Benjamin's partner, endocrinologist Charles Ihlenfeld.

Ihlenfeld worked with Benjamin for six years and administered sex hormones to 500 transsexuals. Ihlenfeld shocked Benjamin by publicly announcing that 80 percent of the people who want to change their gender shouldn't do it. Ihlenfeld said: "There is too much unhappiness among people who have had the surgery…Too many end in suicide." Ihlenfeld stopped administering hormones to patients experiencing gender dysphoria and switched specialties from endocrinology to psychiatry so he could offer such patients the kind of help he thought they really needed.

In the wake of the Hopkins study, the closure of the flagship Hopkins clinic, and the warning sounded by Ihlenfeld, advocates of sex change surgery needed a new strategy. Benjamin and Money looked to their friend, Paul Walker, PhD, a homosexual and transgender activist they knew shared their passion to provide hormones and surgery. A committee was formed to draft standards of care for transgenders that furthered their agenda, with Paul Walker at the helm. The committee included a psychiatrist, a pedophilia activist, two plastic surgeons, and a urologist, all of whom would financially benefit from

[212] http://www.baltimorestyle.com/index.php/style/features_article/ fe_sexchange_jf07

171

keeping gender reassignment surgery available for anyone who wanted it. The "Harry Benjamin International Standards of Care" were published in 1979 and gave fresh life to gender surgery.

My Experience with Dr. Walker

I myself suffered greatly to come to terms with my gender. In 1981, I sought out Dr. Walker to ask him, the man who wrote the standards of care, for help. Walker said I was suffering from gender dysphoria. A mere two years after both the Hopkins study and the public statements of Ihlenfeld drew attention to the increased suicide risk associated with gender change, Walker, even though he was completely aware of both reports, signed my approval letter for hormones and surgery.

Under his guidance, I underwent gender reassignment surgery and lived for eight years as Laura Jensen, female. Eventually, I gathered the courage to admit that the surgery had fixed nothing—it only masked and exacerbated deeper psychological problems. The deception and lack of transparency I experienced in the 1980s still surround gender change surgery today. For the sake of others who struggle with gender dysphoria, I cannot remain silent.

It is intellectually dishonest to ignore the facts that surgery never has been a medically necessary procedure for treating gender dysphoria and that taking cross-gender hormones can be harmful. Modern transgender activists, the descendants of Kinsey, Benjamin, and John Money, keep alive the practice of medically unnecessary gender-change surgery by controlling the flow of published information and by squelching research and personal stories that tell of the regret, unhappiness, and suicide experienced by those who undergo such surgery. Negative outcomes are only acknowledged as a way to blame society for its transphobia.

Transgender clients who regret having taken this path are often full of shame and remorse. Those who regret their decision have few places to turn in a world of pro-transgender activism. For me, it took years to muster the courage to stand up and speak out about the regret.

I only wish Dr. Paul Walker had been required to tell me about both reports when I consulted him: the Hopkins study showing surgery did not alleviate severe psychological problems, and Ihlenfeld's observation of the continuing transgender unhappiness and high incidence of suicide after hormones and surgery. This information might not have stopped me from making that disastrous decision— but at least I would have known the dangers and pain that lay ahead.

Bruce Jenner—In Transition Or Psychological Crisis?

Olympic gold medalist and former Kardashian husband Bruce Jenner is proclaiming his gender change to the world. Will he be able to find himself inside the spectacle he's creating?

BY WALT HEYER
THE FEDERALIST, FEBRUARY 6, 2015
THEFEDERALIST.COM/2015/02/06/BRUCE-
JENNER-IN-TRANSITION-OR-PSYCHOLOGICAL-CRISIS/

Bruce Jenner, Olympic gold medalist, former reality TV show star, former husband to a Kardashian, and father of many children and step-children from his three marriages, at the age of 65 is the new poster "girl" for gender change. The changes in Jenner's appearance make it obvious that he is under the influence of female hormones.

In the next few days, Jenner is expected to appear in a Diane Sawyer interview to discuss his reasoning for undergoing gender change. Jenner's close relatives, his mother and his children, say they didn't see any signs of a gender change coming, but they support his decision because he seems so happy.

The media are swirling around Jenner with their never-ending snapshots, rumors, and innuendo. The piranha are circling, turning a man's most difficult time of life into a salacious spectacle. The media relentlessly study his every move, every action and behavior, and document it for worldwide consumption. They will not stop until they take the last morsel of dignity from this Olympian. I worry that the full national display will end up pushing Jenner from heights of euphoria to depths of depression or worse.

There is no question that Jenner is a willing participant—he and his journey are being filmed as the subject of a reality series. How can anyone go through such a stressful and psychologically emotional time in full view of the media? How can someone experiment with his identity in such a public way? What if he eventually changes his mind?

Take It from Someone Who Understands

I am worried about Jenner because his current journey is the mirror image of mine 30 years ago. I know the journey, the pitfalls, the highs and the lows of changing genders. I look at the pictures of Bruce Jenner plastered on the Internet and it's like I'm witnessing a movie of my own life from 30 years ago, with Bruce playing the leading role.

I had a successful career and had been married for 17 years, with two of the most amazing and wonderful kids any dad could ever have. Like Jenner, I had recently gone through a divorce and my executive position in the automotive industry looked to be in jeopardy. Divorce is stressful enough. Add in the downward spiral of a man's career, and it is toxic to the psyche.

I secretly underwent the full regimen of cross-gender hormones, which caused female changes to my appearance. Then the next step: the gut-wrenching but exciting process of going out as a female with close friends for dancing and drinking in red pumps, bright red lipstick, and long hair.

My gender-change surgery was performed by the most well-known "sex change" surgeon in the world at the time. The California Superior Court accepted my petition to change my birth certificate from male to female. I lived for eight years as a female, Laura Jensen, and worked for the federal government at the Federal Deposit Insurance Corporation and the U.S. Postal service in San Francisco.

I was accepted as Laura, earned a good income, and was even passable as a female. Just like Jenner's, my friends and family, for the most part, supported my new female gender.

Gender Changes Can Conceal Underlying Problems

I'm concerned for Jenner. He's a bright, likable guy who has enjoyed success far beyond what most of us will ever dream. Jenner appeared to function as a normal adult, but stressful life events like his divorce and the loss of the long-running reality show, "Keeping Up with the Kardashians," could be the cause of his crisis of identity. Bruce's desire to be a woman could be the result of the adult onset of a disorder in his psyche triggered by traumatic events.

There are so many unknowns when someone seeks a change of gender. I'm not judging. I've been there and back myself.

After my surgical gender change failed to relieve my distress, I was diagnosed with a dissociative disorder that had been there all along. My desire to be a female was a symptom of something else. Surgery and transition, while it made me happy at first, did not treat the dissociative disorder. In fact, surgery compounded my difficulties and made it harder to recover.

I restored my male identity but it required that I be properly diagnosed. As the underlying disorder was appropriately treated, my desire to change genders faded away like a mist in the bright light of day. One of the hardest things was to admit to myself, my family, and my friends that the whole surgical change had been unnecessary. I had been so adamant beforehand that I needed it.

Jenner has the added complexity of being a celebrity in the glare of the media spotlight. We see so many examples of celebrities who can't cope and end up pushed to their deaths, like Michael Jackson and the misuse of propofol, Elvis Presley, Whitney Houston, and now perhaps even Whitney's only daughter and the excessive use of drugs. Trying to cope with personal problems while living in a public fishbowl certainly intensifies stress.

Enter stage-right Diane Sawyer and the "Mahogany Row" suits of the entertainment industry looking for the titillating story. I wonder if they care about Jenner or only the allure of ratings. Do they see the bridge could be out down the road and it might not end well?

For the past decade, I have received emails from highly successful career people, some with very high incomes, who underwent gender-change surgery only to regret it years later. Several were on the brink of suicide, and they weren't celebrities.

Jenner will be publicly sharing an intimate journey with which I am very familiar. I'm concerned that the media feeding frenzy could push him to the edge.

Bruce Jenner Puts The Brakes On His Transition But Not His SUV

Former Olympian Bruce Jenner has decided he will pause his transition to female in the wake of a devastating car crash.

BY WALT HEYER
THE FEDERALIST, FEBRUARY 17, 2015
THEFEDERALIST.COM/2015/02/17/BRUCE-
JENNER-PUTS-THE-BRAKES-ON-HIS-TRANSITION-BUT-NOT-HIS-SUV/

When I recently wrote about Bruce Jenner[213] I had no idea that only one day later the former Olympian would be in a real-life crisis, in the midst of a multi-vehicle chain-reaction crash on the busy Pacific Coast Highway in Malibu, California. The video footage of the scene showed Jenner visibly shaken and emotionally stressed, standing in the middle of all the wreckage. Jenner had been driving the car which rear-ended another car, pushing it into oncoming traffic where it was then hit head-on. The driver of that vehicle died.

In the blink of an eye there was death, injuries, and lives forever changed. Nothing could be more devastating for Jenner than knowing someone had died in this crash. Jenner isn't alone in his grief; the victim's family is struggling with the loss of a loved one. There is no measure for the depth of the pain this accident has caused. Everyone in each family was injured emotionally even if they were not present at the time. As I look at the pictures of Jenner standing in the street next to the wreckage, I thought how symbolic a picture it is of his life today—the torn wreckage of his marriage and family life, a new female persona painfully and slowly emerging.

Jenner could be facing charges for vehicular manslaughter, and while commencing a gender transition it was too much. Due to the psychological impact of this accident, Jenner came to a crossroad and placed his very public gender transition on hold. Real life has bumped Jenner's transition to the sidelines because the accident took the life of a 69-year-old woman.

Switching Genders Is Complicated Even During Peaceful Times

As a former transgender, I know the difficulty of changing genders even when everything in life is running relatively smoothly. During my transition over 30 years ago, I was emotionally fragile. I swung between anxiety and great anticipation about my future, anxiety over the unknown, and anticipation of finally living free of the intense gender distress that drove me to change genders.

Jenner's unwanted reality show that unfolded on the highway will have a very long running season inside his thought life. No one knows at this point the emotional cost to him of the nightmare he faces each day. The re-runs will be played over and over again with no way to turn them off.

---

[213] https://thefederalist.com/2015/02/06/bruce-jenner-in-transition-or-psychological-crisis/

Most people do not realize how complex the transgender mind is. Many transgenders suffer from depression, anxiety, bipolar, personality, dissociative, schizophrenic, obsessive compulsive, and narcissism disorders, which tag along with the gender dysphoria. More than 40 percent of transgenders report having attempted suicide at some time, and depression is the major cause of suicide. And that's without the added impact of being involved in a fatal car crash.

I'm not saying Jenner has a disorder, but accompanying disorders are often present in transgenders. A transgender during the early stages of gender transition can be depressed and filled with anxiety about transitioning. It is a difficult enough time—then the accident. No one would ever want to deal with what Jenner is facing.

If Bruce Jenner Follows Through, He May Regret It

Jenner has lived his life up to now—65 years—socially identifying with his male biological gender. Now he has paused following through with his desire to identify socially with the female gender. Gender reassignment surgery and hormones will not change his biological DNA from male to female, so the changes will be his appearance, not innate biology.

My concern is, if he follows through with his gender change he, like so many, will end up regretting it. No one can look into the crystal ball and see if his transition would be successful or not. The long-term results of gender reassignment surgery have not been studied. No test can determine who will benefit. No sound research has been published that proves a gender change will be successful.

Every gender change is an experiment.

No one tracks the participants over the long run—not the surgeons doing the surgery and not the psychologists providing the approval.

The media frequently repeats the mantra that regret is rare. Under scrutiny, that claim falls short. Academic researchers admit that up to 90 percent of transgenders cannot be found. That means that any reports of success are based on the 10 percent that could be found, which is hardly a basis for any conclusion about success or failure rates.

Sex-Change Regret Is Quite Common

"Several factors complicate efforts to systematically study the long-term effects of gender reassignment surgery. First, a large proportion of patients (up to 90 percent) are lost to follow up," write Stan Monstrey, Griet De Cuypere, and Randi Ettner in chapter five of "Principles of transgender medicine and surgery" (2007).

If all transgenders are so happy with their choice, why can't they be found afterwards? I suspect they are lost because they committed suicide, are addicted to drugs, or like me, they returned to their birth gender and quietly live out the balance of life in the gender into which they were born.

If regret is so rare, why do I hear from so many regretters?

Regret is more common than many know or will admit.

Gender change regret has been reported for decades. Sure, in the first few weeks after a surgical gender change, almost all transgenders will say life is wonderful. Then with the passing of time—one year, three years, eight years—post-surgical regret sets in when the expectations of the "happy life" they thought would be there for them continue to be unfulfilled. I didn't know how useless changing genders would be in resolving my lifelong gender conflict until the change was complete. I have heard from regretters from three weeks post-op to 35 years after and everything in between. Some of their stories are recounted with their permission on my web site, sexchangeregret.com.

Jenner is experiencing a very difficult time. It could be the wake-up call to stop the madness, or it could drive him deeper into his female self. My prayer is that he will come out the other side of this horrific car accident with a new perspective on life, one that will truly help him. I pray he gets all the support and help he needs and finds the strength to make it through this mess.

Bruce Jenner Wants To Change The World When He Should Change His Mind

Personal and medical experience indicates that switching genders will not give Bruce Jenner peace.

BY WALT HEYER
THE FEDERALIST, APRIL 27, 2015
THEFEDERALIST.COM/2015/04/27/BRUCE-
JENNER-WANTS-TO-CHANGE-THE-WORLD-WHEN-HE-SHOULD-CHANGE-HIS-MIND/

With the airing of his interview with Diane Sawyer last Friday, Bruce Jenner became the most triumphant, celebrated, photographed, and interviewed transgender in the world. Jenner, a longtime transvestite, now at 65 years of age is going to explore his feminine side by transitioning to female. Along the way, he hopes to inspire others.

Jenner's interview opened a window for millions of viewers to see the psychological deliberation of a cross-dresser. Jenner shared that the emotional stress of hiding his secret has become unbearable. His internal struggle led him to the question: Would I be happier living as a full-time transgender female or should I continue living as a transvestite?

But there is reason to be concerned for Jenner's transition. A review of more than 100 international medical studies of post-operative transgenders conducted in the United Kingdom in 2004 found "no robust scientific evidence that gender reassignment surgery is clinically effective." Chris Hyde, the director of the research facility that conducted the review, said: "There is a huge uncertainty over whether changing someone's sex is a good or a bad thing. While no doubt great care is taken to ensure that appropriate patients undergo gender reassignment, there's still a large number of people who have the surgery but remain traumatized—often to the point of committing suicide."[214]

As a former transgender myself, I found it painful to see Jenner looking so fragile, exhibiting an uncertain nervousness throughout the interview. I see Jenner and my heart sinks with sadness; my stomach aches in pain. When Jenner said, "I want to know how this story ends, you know?" a rush of concern filled me. I know one possible outcome of the story—great pain to kids, wife, family and even to himself. I want to yell at him, "Stop! The bridge is out."

Dear Bruce Jenner: I Felt Your Pain

I see my life 32 years ago played out in that interview. I had made comments so eerily similar when I was on the brink of transitioning. Like Jenner, my emotional gender difficulty started at a young age. At age five, I enjoyed dressing up as a girl with my grandmother. When I was about 15 years old, the

---

[214] http://www.theguardian.com/society/2004/jul/30/health.mentalhealth

amazing news of Christine Jorgensen's transition from male to beautiful female was in the headlines and I knew right away that I wanted a sex change.

> I felt deep inside that transition was the only way I would finally be happy
> in my own skin.

Like Jenner, I "came out" to my first wife about my cross-dressing, and we acted as if it were no big deal. But it was a big deal. I started taking hormones and had some feminizing surgeries while I was married. Like Jenner, I was not a homosexual.

My life was an emotional roller coaster. I had the highs of being a successful automotive executive and a dad and the lows of going through divorce. On the one hand, I was ecstatic and excited to finally pursue what I saw as the answer to my lifetime of gender struggles: transition. On the other hand, I was deeply concerned about my relationship with my children.

At age 42, I transitioned from male to female. I was euphoric. I felt the gender change was the best thing I had ever done. Many of my friends supported and affirmed my decision. For example, Bill, my closest friend of many years, told me, "You have never looked happier. You are more at ease as a woman."

The Gender Romance Ends

But after eight years of living as a woman, my once-successful transition turned on me. I mean the exhilaration from the early days wore off, and I found myself reflecting on my transition. I came to realize that all the changes to my appearance, dramatic and effective as they were, were only cosmetic. All the changes to my identity documents—birth certificate, driver's license, Social Security card— were in name only, simply words on the paper. If I only could have remained living in my delusional gender bubble all would have been good, perhaps.

The reality that I was not a woman was just too much for me. Unexpectedly, my emotions plunged downward and overwhelmed me.

> All the gender specialists I consulted assured me I was a true transgender.

They encouraged me to stick with my female gender, but eight years was long enough. It was over.

The shame of being so narcissistic and self-absorbed as a transgender female and knowing I had hurt the ones I loved resulted in deep depression and regret. I started to consider suicide. That's what I mean when I say my once successful transition turned on me. I discovered much too late that gender change surgery was not a medical necessity at all. I can admit that transition was the biggest mistake of my life.

Bruce Jenner's Dramatic Life

In an ironic twist, Jenner's interview aired April 24, 32 years to the day that I underwent gender reassignment surgery.

At the interview's opening, Jenner said, "This will be an emotional roller coaster, but somehow I will get through it." Hasn't his entire life been one mind-boggling ride? Build the most outrageous roller coaster ever, with slow-crawling upward highs followed by swift blink-of-the-eye downward spirals, and you have Jenner's triumph-to-tragedy-filled life. Jenner has ridden this roller coaster more than once in his life.

In 1976, only 90 days after his Olympic triumph, Jenner's younger brother was tragically killed in a horrible accident in Jenner's automobile. Jenner had been given a new Porsche, and his 18-year-old brother, Burt, had wanted to take his sweetheart, Judith, for a ride. On that cold November day in Connecticut, Jenner handed the keys of his Porsche to his little brother, who lost control of the car and hit a utility pole. The crash took the lives of both Burt and Judith.

Life can be unpredictable, especially when you are about to dive into a gender change with no guarantees. In the last year, Jenner has suffered great emotional stress, with his separation and divorce from Kris Kardashian and the end of his participation on the lucrative family reality show, "Keeping Up with the Kardashians." While these difficult losses were still painfully fresh, tragedy struck again on the California Pacific Coast Highway. The car Jenner was driving pushed another car into oncoming traffic and resulted in the second driver's death. Being involved in someone's death creates the kind of emotional pain that never goes away.

No one knows how Jenner's story will end.

> Two deaths, a gender transition, divorce, and a pending trial could psychologically derail the best of us.

The odds are that Jenner's life, like that of many transvestites who transition, will experience the euphoria of extraordinary highs in the beginning followed years later by a downward spiral.

Bruce Jenner Needs Concern, Not Admiration

We should all be concerned for Jenner. A whopping 41 percent of transgenders report attempting suicide. We saw a glimpse of how fragile Jenner is when he shared that he recently considered suicide. The paparazzi had camped outside the clinic where he was undergoing some "feminizing" surgery. Home alone later that day, he said he paced the hallways of his home and considered shooting himself. Thankfully he didn't. It's a measure of his vulnerability that this particular frenzy of tabloid attention shook him up. After all, he has spent his entire adulthood in the public eye. He should know the paparazzi never stop.

As long as the television lights are on and the cameras are rolling, being in the spotlight he enjoys, Jenner will be fine. But when the lights go dim and the cameras are no longer rolling, he will face the most difficult time of his life. His celebrated change of gender could turn on him and become the cause of deep depression, which, left untreated, according to those who study the causes of suicide, is the number one cause for suicide.[215]

---

[215] http://www.suicide.org/suicide-causes.html

I wish I could say I'm the only transgender to regret transitioning, but contrary to what the media would lead us to believe, I know I'm not the first or the last. I get many emails from male-to-female transgenders who eventually regretted their gender change. Some say regret came as early as three months after surgery; others tell me it took 8, 10, 15, even 30 years to admit that gender change was the biggest mistake of their life. I have received comments such as, "How could I have been so stupid?"

What was missing from the interview was a discussion about sex-change regret. Instead, there was no indication that Jenner or Sawyer were aware or understood that the long-term results of changing genders can be dramatically different than one's expectations.

I pray it ends well for Jenner. He says he wants to "change the world" when, in my view, Jenner would do better to change his mind.

Dear Bruce Jenner: You Could Really Be Hurting People

Here's some heartfelt caution for Bruce Jenner from another who had the surgeries, the glamor shots, the excitement, the adulation—and, finally, the regret of going transgender.

BY WALT HEYER
THE FEDERALIST, JUNE 4, 2015
THEFEDERALIST.COM/2015/06/04/DEAR-BRUCE-
JENNER-YOU-COULD-REALLY-BE-HURTING-PEOPLE/

The June issue of *Vanity Fair* has a stunning cover shot of the newly formed transgender Caitlyn Jenner, quite the contrast to the cover shot almost 40 years ago of the newly famous Olympian, Bruce Jenner, on the Wheaties cereal box.

No doubt, this is an exhilarating time in Jenner's life. So exciting it promises to eclipse the notoriety and fame of Jenner's gold-medal accomplishment.

However, too much fame can turn sour and become painfully unwelcome. Some will see the new cover shot as an invitation, an open season to bash and make fun Jenner's transition to Caitlyn. The glare of the media could be difficult, even for someone like Jenner, who made his living from being in the spotlight. Only time will tell if this current media frenzy will turn good people into sharp-teethed piranha who devour him and his new gender.

Jenner is not the first to publicly acknowledge gender-identity struggles, just the latest on the list of transgender celebrities. But unlike those who have gone before, he has the inventiveness and savvy to manage his transition for maximum benefit.

As a former transgender myself, who underwent all the surgeries in mid-life and lived eight years as the female Laura Jensen, I will take care not to be hurtful. But I have concerns.

You Can't Control a Media Circus

Jenner learned valuable self-promotion lessons from his years with the Kardashian women. Like a world-renowned symphony conductor, Jenner has orchestrated an elaborate, well-staged, "coming out" party, and America is caught up in watching his personal life unfold, waiting for the next red high-heeled shoe to drop. The cover of *Vanity Fair* is no accident. Jenner is making big hay out of all this fame.

> The media are completely complicit in his self-promotion, looking like a bunch of drunks surrounding Jenner at Friday-night happy hour tossing back the Caitlyn Kool-Aid.

In April, Jenner's first highly-anticipated media event aired—an interview with Diane Sawyer on "20/20." Jenner's team dictated strict rules of engagement beforehand so the notably sensitive Jenner

183

would not be ruffled. With his tissue in hand, at times he dabbed at his tears like a jilted teenager who had lost his first love.

The interview with Sawyer was the set-up for the *Vanity Fair* cover article this week. Let's face it: Jenner has successfully captured America's attention, "blowing up" social media with his transgender debut on Twitter and Facebook. Everyone is talking about Caitlyn. Each step in the rollout seems deliberately designed to pique interest for the next: the revelation with Sawyer on "20/20," the glamorous photo layout in *Vanity Fair*, and, coming soon, the reality "docu-drama" of the transition process.

While Bruce Jenner Focuses on Himself, Others Suffer

I said I would use caution not to harm Jenner. But sometimes the humor or irony of certain aspects of the media circus are too tempting. When I started thinking about how well-planned this media launch has been, I could not help seeing the humor in using a magazine called "Vanity Fair."

When I looked up the meaning of the word *vanity*, everything fell into place. Vanity is defined as "the quality of having too much pride in one's appearance and/or accomplishments" and also "being excessively proud of oneself or one's qualities or possessions; self-conceit." Perhaps it is no accident Jenner arrange to debut her new appearance on the cover of a magazine called *Vanity Fair*.

What Jenner nor the media has not talked about is that 62.7 percent of those who have the desire to change genders suffer from a variety of other psychological and psychiatric disorders that haven't been diagnosed and therefore haven't been treated. The other disorders range from depression and anxiety to bipolar, dissociative, personality, and obsessive-compulsive disorders and narcissism.[216]

The desire to change genders can be the "acting out" of one of these disorders. When the underlying psychological disorder is treated, the desire for a change of gender subsides.

The Transgender Experts Aren't

That was my experience. I was told by leading gender experts that my lifelong anxiety and gender distress would be alleviated by changing genders. After much soul-searching, I decided to follow their advice. I underwent feminizing procedures and surgeries and lived successfully as a woman for eight years.

But the distress did not go away. The specialists told me to "give it time." I thought eight years was enough of an investment in a strategy that wasn't yielding long-term peace. A fortuitous observation on the part of a psychiatrist with whom I worked led to the definitive diagnosis of a co-existing disorder. After doing the tough work in counseling, I returned to my male gender identity and achieved real serenity.

Those who think gender reassignment is a cure for their depression, anxiety, and gender distress need to be warned. I get hundreds of emails from visitors to my web site, sexchangeregret.com—letters from regretters and their wives, parents, brothers, and sisters who tell me how their lives and the lives of their families are completely broken apart as a result of a family member who wants to, or has

---

[216] http://www.ncbi.nlm.nih.gov/pubmed/25180172?log$=activity

already, changed genders. All because they did not properly diagnose an existing psychological disorder before undergoing the drastic step of gender change.

Jenner did talk about wanting to help reduce the transgender suicide attempt rate[217] (estimated at 41 percent[218]). I have the same goal. However, we come at the problem with different solutions: Jenner by promoting his own gender change and me by suggesting improvements in diagnosis and treatment of disorders prior to changing genders.

My concern is that the extravagant public adulation of Jenner will encourage others to seek out gender-change therapists for the wrong reasons. Many will see the excitement Jenner is enjoying and think they can emulate his life. Unfortunately, gender-change surgery is serious business. The surgery is not reversible. When Snoopy is gone, he's gone. The toll on the rest of the family is also serious, especially if children are involved. Their young lives can be shaken with a catastrophic trauma not of their own making.

---

[217] http://abc.go.com/shows/2020/listing/2015-04/24-bruce-jenner-the-interview
[218] http://www.thetaskforce.org/downloads/reports/reports/ ntds_report_on_health.pdf

Caitlyn Jenner Needs Therapy, Not Awards

Transgender hero Caitlyn Jenner receives an award tonight for courage. But a doctor who regrets his gender change is a better candidate for such an award.

BY WALT HEYER
THE FEDERALIST, JULY 15, 2015
THEFEDERALIST.COM/2015/07/15/CAITLYN-JENNER-NEEDS-THERAPY-NOT-AWARDS/

Caitlyn nee Bruce Jenner is slated to accept the Arthur Ashe Courage Award from ESPN at a Los Angeles gala tonight. The Arthur Ashe award is given to individuals who show strength in the face of adversity, courage in the face of peril, and willingness to stand up for their beliefs, no matter the costs. Jenner does not smack of courage at this point in his life. Insanity perhaps is a better fit: glorifying a transgender life by spending $4 million on a gender change.

Let's see if the award fits the male-to-female transgender Olympian's latest activities.

1) The award recipient must possess strength in the face of adversity. Jenner is being paid $5 million for a TV show on "E." Is $5 million for a TV show really adversity?

2) The recipient must show courage in the face of peril. This suggests Diane Sawyer is the face of peril, given her "coming out" interview with Jenner earlier this year. Sorry, Diane.

3) The recipient must demonstrate willingness to stand up for his or her beliefs. Well, Jenner did stand up for his beliefs no matter the cost. He spent $4 million on plastic surgery and couture to change from Bruce to Caitlyn.

There is the 2015 Arthur Ashe award winner.

Others have preceded Jenner down the path of gender transition and, like Jenner, spared no expense on feminizing procedures and wardrobes. Only time will tell if Jenner will later join the ranks of the regretters who discover too late that changing genders was a terrible mistake.

A Physician Opens Up About His Gender-Change Regret

Although Jenner hasn't displayed courage through his gender transition, I know another man who has. Through my website sexchangeregret.com, people contact me with their stories of regret and hopelessness at living transgender, looking for a way to restore their previous life. One such story, from Dr. Stu, a physician ten years post-op, provides real-life evidence that changing genders can come with a great deal of regret, even when all standards of care and protocols are followed. Dr. Stu and many others share a common bond: regret after changing genders.[219]

Dr. Stu is sharing his personal story publicly for the first time, from the unique perspective of a medical professional. Going public with the reality of regrettable gender-change consequences in

---

[219] http://www.thepublicdiscourse.com/2015/04/14688/

today's environment takes a heaping dose of strength and courage, and demonstrates a willingness to stand up for one's beliefs no matter the cost.

Stu originally contacted me four years ago to share the regrettable consequences of his own gender reassignment surgery. He definitely got my attention in one of his first emails to me in 2011:

> Hurting big time from my sex reassignment surgery six years ago from male to female. I have de-transitioned successfully [gone back to the male gender], but now truly feel at odds with my mutilated body. As a physician, I would like to join forces with you to get the message out that sex reassignment surgery is a terrible mistake for most people.

His is a sobering story that should be taken seriously. In his own words, Dr. Stu tells his story:

> It was a trip to Colorado in March 2005 that ruined my life and erased the very body part that externally separates boys from girls at birth. The sex change surgery that I underwent permanently robbed my wife and me of true sexual intimacy. I still suffer from periods of extreme anxiety and there are bouts of depression that invade my thinking. My urinary tract has suffered from infections and personal hygiene will always take special attention as altered anatomy can easily become problematic. I often feel fatigued, and I worry about the need for ongoing hormone treatment. Testosterone has replaced the estrogen that I used to take, but having to self-administer what my body used to produce is a bimonthly reminder of what I lost by making that trip to Colorado in 2005.
>
> Ten years later I still need help. Seeking a remedy I reached out to the surgeon who performed the gender reassignment surgery. She had ruined me and I needed to resolve ongoing surgical issues that caused me to spray urine everywhere when voiding. All I got from the surgeon was a message that hinted at more fees and a surgeon who was more concerned about her liability than resolving any problems I was having caused by the surgery she had performed.

Gender-Change Surgeon Admits Transition Difficulties

I interrupt Stu's story here for a note that collaborates Stu's experience. After Stu first contacted me, I emailed his surgeon to find out if she was willing to repair the damage she had done. Marci Bowers, known around the world as a gender surgeon and who himself is transgendered from male to female, emailed me back with this response:

> It is tougher to transition later in life. Question is, is life better after or before? I think unequivocally, it is after…but that is what the real life test is all about. I wish it were longer, honestly but I cannot turn someone away on that number alone. Life is full of turns. Individuals need to make wise decisions and this is a big one. I cannot be held responsible when someone makes a bad decision.

Here, a prominent gender surgeon makes the shocking admission that gender transitions are "tougher" late in life and he wishes the real-life test were "longer" that is, that transgenders live as their opposite sex prior to surgery more than the two years specified in the standards of care. Then he makes the blockbuster comments that he "cannot turn someone away" nor can he "be held responsible when someone makes a bad decision." The confessions of a gender reassignment surgeon should be headline news: transitioning is a decision; meaning transgenders are not born that way.

Bowers, the gender surgeon, who was once Mark and is now Marci, earns in excess of a million dollars a year. He cannot "turn someone away" because he benefits financially, not because the surgery is 100 percent or even 98 percent successful.

Dr. Stu Explains How His Transgender Feelings Began

All of this started with my own distorted thoughts that took root when I was only five. As I look back on my life, I realize that the majority of my energies, thoughts, and dreams were centered on trying to do something that was both ludicrous and a societal anathema. I am sad as I realize that my life could have been so much more. The pursuit of changing myself from a man to woman has essentially ruined me, I regard the majority of my life as pretty pathetic, and I am angry about how my obsession with everything female has robbed me since the age of five.

In my case, the feelings that I have had about wanting to be female started at this early age. I must have been a fairly sensitive lad who needed more attention or strokes of affirmation from my parents than I received. As a child, I took note of a pretty girl named Sally, and it seemed that she had so much adoration and praise from those around her. I must have yearned to be like her, and somehow the notion that being a girl would make everything right clung to me. Lifelong feelings and desires do take hold at an early age, and such seeds of thought serve to influence over a lifetime.

Anxiety, for whatever reason—be it a lack of confidence or low self-esteem—has plagued me for the entirely of my life, and I firmly believe that it has driven me to seek the pleasures of cross-dressing as a salve for my inner distress. I believe that the positive emotions that I felt as I wore soft and flowing garments coupled with acts of self-gratification influenced my brain chemistry in such a way that led to the release of neurotransmitters, which in turn acted on the pleasure center of my brain. In doing so, my maladaptive behavior and feelings were reinforced. I became addicted to the idea of transforming into a woman and to the accouterments of femininity. This would make everything right, or so I thought.

I should have placed my endeavors on understanding what it was that made me uncomfortable as a male, not on why I wanted to be female.

Dr. Stu's Advice for People Considering Transgenderism

When contemplating a transition from one gender to another, it is important to seek and obtain wise and unbiased counsel—listen to those who know you best. Variant opinions about the wisdom of changing genders are needed. Balance the media-hyped stories of the high-profile transgendered with the reality of struggling, regretful, and dead transgendered people. Anxiety and depression should be treated or excluded. Addiction, personality disorders, dissociative traits, and mental derangements need to be identified and dealt with.

In all the times that I cried out for help, I never once received honesty or sound mental or medical help.

There are frankly too many "yes practitioners" too willing to take the buck. If this medical machine cared about the gender-confused person, it would not participate in the destruction of normal tissues, and it would not send ill-suited people into the lion's den.

Further, to expect the public at large to accept men in dresses as normal, or allow them into areas of privacy reserved for genetic women and girls, borders on criminal. As a physician, I know of the horror of disease, and let me tell you, this whole notion of gender dysphoria and its treatment have spun out of control into a monster of a problem. Lives are ruined and devastated—it has become a cancer.

As For Studies on Transgenders

I appreciate Dr. Stu's willingness to share his story of regret. The media minions continue to advance the false impression that regret is rare. CNN's Carol Costello did that in her interview with me June 2nd, 2015[220] citing a "Swedish study" conclusion that regret occurs only 2 percent of the time.

The Swedish study does indeed say regret occurred 2 percent of the time. But we have to look at the glaring omission made in how the study authors calculated the percentage of regretters. They calculated the percentage by counting the legal and surgical reversal applications submitted during the time period. The problem is that it left out the number of deaths.

Those who had committed suicide or died by other causes were counted as non-regretters because, of course, they were not able to submit a reversal application.[221]

Suicide and regret are not mutually exclusive but are, in fact, one and the same. A 2004 review of 100 international studies found "no robust scientific evidence that gender reassignment surgery is clinically effective" and "many gender reassignment studies are unsound because researchers lost track of more than half of the participants." After having gender reassignment surgery, a large number of people who had the surgery remained traumatized often to the point of committing suicide. This was the conclusion after reviewing not one study, but 100 international studies.[222]

The results of the 2004 review reflect the real life of Dr. Stu, who himself underwent gender reassignment surgery, found no evidence it was effective, and remains traumatized.

Dr. Stu and I never got an award for strength or courage, but that's okay. We got our lives back, and there's nothing better than that.

---

[220] http://newsbusters.org/blogs/matthew-balan/2015/06/02/shock-cnn-features-former-transgender-jenner-coverage
[221] http://www.ncbi.nlm.nih.gov/pubmed/19816764
[222] http://www.theguardian.com/society/2004/jul/30/health.mentalhealth

Transgender Characters May Win Emmys, But Transgender People Hurt Themselves

---

Asking a surgeon to modify a person's appearance is simply a socially acceptable means of self-mutilation.

BY WALT HEYER
THE FEDERALIST, SEPTEMBER 22, 2015
THEFEDERALIST.COM/2015/09/22/TRANSGENDER-
CHARACTERS-MAY-WIN-EMMYS-BUT-TRANSGENDER-PEOPLE-HURT-THEMSELVES/

Transgender individuals have high levels of mental-health problems such as depression, resulting in increased levels of self-injury and suicidal ideation (thoughts, attempts, and rates), finds a September study from the highly respected Nottingham Centre for Gender Dysphoria in the United Kingdom. The center reviewed 31 papers to arrive at that conclusion.[223]

This is probably not the "trans civil rights problem" recent Emmy winner Jill Soloway meant when accepting her award for directing a comedy show sponsored by Amazon that features a transgender character.[224] But statistics show it deserves to be.

If we examine the medical definition of self-injury, we get a better understanding of why changing genders is a mental health issue. The Mayo Clinic defines self-injury as "an unhealthy way to cope with emotional pain, intense anger and frustration."[225] As someone who has undergone gender change, I know that people who indulge in self-destructive behaviors and suicide ideation have mental issues that beg to be treated and resolved.

Gender Change Is Self-Destructive

To a person undergoing gender transition, in the beginning it feels like the right thing to do, even exciting, for the first few months or years. I felt at peace for the first four or five years after I transitioned. Then I realized the high cost of that tenuous peace. Being transgender required destroying the identity of Walt so my female persona, Laura, would feel unshackled from Walt's past, with all of its hurt, shame, and abuse. It's a marvelous distraction for a while, but it isn't a permanent solution when the underlying issues remain unaddressed.

Gender change is at its heart a self-destructive act. Transgender individuals not only annihilate their birth identity, they destroy everyone and everything in their wake: family, wife, children, brothers or

---

[223] http://www.ncbi.nlm.nih.gov/pubmed/26329283

[224] http://www.9news.com.au/entertainment/2015/09/21/12/17/emmy-winner-jeffrey-tambor-dedicates-award-to-transgender-community

[225] https://www.mayoclinic.org/diseases-conditions/self-injury/symptoms-causes/syc-20350950

sisters, and career. Certainly this demonstrates the behavior of someone hell-bent on total self-destruction and self-harm.

It occurred to me after much self-reflection that asking a surgeon to modify my appearance through a series of cosmetic procedures was simply a socially acceptable means of self-mutilation and self-destruction. Taken to the extreme, self-destruction leads to suicide.

Recovery from Self-Hating Is Possible

My turnaround began when I enrolled at one of California's universities to study psychology, addictions, and recovery. As I studied and applied what I was learning to my own life, it became evident that transgenderism was a psychological disorder and recovery was possible.

For me, the restoration of my sanity would only come by reversing the gender change and going back to living as the male God had made me to be. It took much heart-wrenching anguish to come to that conclusion, but it was the only way to end my self-harm.

Surgery to change my appearance had not been the treatment for my gender dysphoria (the clinical term for persistent gender uneasiness). No amount of surgery can fix a disorder with psychological roots. The biological fact is that no one can change from one gender to another except in appearance.

> Through many years of therapy, I began to see that gender dysphoria had been my survival mechanism to cope with intense emotional pain.

The profound psychological hurts from my early childhood separated me from reality in some ways. Not everyone responds this way to abuse—some cut themselves as teenagers, run away from home, seek solace in substance abuse and addiction, or even bury the pain under seemingly positive pursuits such as achievement. A few of us cope by acting out in a different gender and finding a surgeon to do the cutting for us.

Unhealthy coping behaviors are signs of underlying psychological damage. Who but the psychologically damaged would go to such lengths to eradicate who they are in name, appearance, and gender so they could pretend to be someone they are not?

Powerful Feelings Are Not Reality

The feelings are so powerful and pervasive that we, the gender dysphoric, think our compulsion is real and we start acting out on it. We want to have gender-change surgery because it makes drastic changes in our appearance. The desire for transition becomes an endless obsession, a longing that demands we destroy and erase the histories of our birth and follow whatever "professionals" advise—hormone therapy, cosmetic surgeries, voice modulation lessons—all designed to allow us assume a new identity, one built on hurt, anger, and pain.

This was my story. I was 42 years old, married for 16 years and the father of two outstanding kids. But I had suffered in secret for most of my life from the desire to be female.

> The fantasy of changing genders became a passionate longing at the age of 15 when I first heard someone had done it.

Christine Jorgensen, a retired Marine, had changed from male to female.

Over the next 25 years, I became convinced that gender surgery would be the key, my only option, to resolving the psychodrama going on in my head. Eradicate Walt, become Laura, and life would be lovely. But the reality is the strong feelings and the surgeries put the person in a limbo state, living somewhere between male and female and not fitting into either.

From Regret to Reality

Perhaps life's wisdom is only found by looking back over one's shoulder at the clear view of the carnage that results from the madness of self-destruction.

> Regret, once acknowledged, opened my eyes to see what I had thought was
> reality, "I should be a woman," was only an illusion.

The moment the word "regret" tumbled from my lips, I was open to truth and wisdom. I started to consider the possibility of leaving my surgically-altered life as a transgender woman and resume living as the male gender given me at birth.

With this new wisdom I begin to study, pray, and meditate on a power higher than myself. Rather than focusing on my dissatisfaction with who I was, I became open to putting my broken life behind me. I could choose to remain self-centered and self-obsessed, but if I did, I would stay isolated from reality. The choice was up to me. I chose to try faith.

Although progress came slowly, eventually the manic, self-centered, relentless anxiety no longer drove me. I stopped thinking that what the surgeons had done to my body defined my identity. I came to accept that gender surgery didn't change me into a woman. I was born a man, and I was still a man; my gender never changed. Therefore, even though I couldn't undo all of the feminizing changes to my body, I didn't need what is called "reversal surgery" to be a man.

The Secret World of Detransitioners

Ninety-nine percent of the emails I receive are encouraging. Many come from regretters or their loved ones who validate the findings of this recent Nottingham study about self-destruction and suicide ideation. When I probe regretters gently about experiences in childhood, 100 percent of the time they reveal an abusive or traumatic environment that triggered the onset of gender dysphoria, just like it had for me.

Detransitioners live in secret and hide the shame and disappointment of falling for the fraud of gender change. In the emails I get, I hear how they want to detransition, but do not want to go public or be counted among the ones whose lives were so torn apart. Some will come to Jesus Christ for their redemption and restoration. Others will reject faith but through sheer willpower, driven by strong internal forces, find restoration of the gender once lost. Some lose the fight and give in to suicide.

> The world of regretters that I see and support is vastly different from the
> world of the transition advocates…

...those in a relentless pursuit to convince the world that a transgender identity is the ultimate of all genders.

The advocate world includes intellectuals and medical practitioners, who benefit financially and professionally from providing transition services to this population of hurting people. Some surgeons even perform reversal procedures for regretters who transitioned and want to go back, but the focus is primarily on getting people diagnosed as gender dysphoric and put on the fast-track to transition. Hardly a word is spoken to clients about regret or the high rate of attempted suicide after surgery.

> The regretters who have contacted me report that none of their doctors recommended treatment for underlying psychological distress.

Instead, the psychologists were quick to diagnose them with gender dysphoria, prescribe hormone therapy, and approve them for surgery.

Not All Doctors Approve

Medical community reports of transgender unhappiness even after transition are annotated in my book, "Paper Genders." For example, Charles Ihlenfeld, an endocrinologist who had worked for six years with Dr. Harry Benjamin and administered hormone therapy to some 500 transgenders, concluded that 80 percent of people who expressed the desire to change genders should not do so. Ihlenfeld said there was too much unhappiness and too many suicides among transgenders and, as a result, he quit administering hormone therapy to them.

Back in the late 1970s, Paul McHugh was in charge of the Johns Hopkins Hospital psychiatry department and gender clinic. For ten years, the clinic performed gender surgeries. When a follow-up study was conducted to objectively judge the outcomes...

> ....they found no evidence that changing genders improved the quality of life of transgenders.

McHugh concluded, "Changing genders is collaborating with the madness of mental disorders."

Studies published in the United Kingdom, Italy, Japan, Sweden, and the Netherlands speak of the psychiatric and psychological disorders present in a majority of transgenders, and report on the high rate of suicide in the gender-changing population. Others along the way, like me, have sounded the warning about the lack of medical necessity for gender reassignment surgery.

Fast-forward to this September, to the Nottingham Centre report that transgenders show increased rates of self-harming behaviors and suicidal thoughts and behaviors, and it's the same story of discontent. This study suggests transgenders are hell-bent on self-destruction.

Let's Glamorize Self-Destruction

On the other hand, the media are hell-bent on glamorizing the transgender life. The media find stories of transition newsworthy. Warning signs such as the robust objective research findings apparently are not newsworthy and not reported. Apparently transgender TV shows yield better ratings if the people are shown moving towards their path of self-harm. But when the transgender life loses its luster and today's media darlings experience discontent and question their decisions, where will the coverage be then?

My experience was no different. Everyone was supportive and interested while I lived the transgender life. Now that I have gone back, producers are not interested in my story. Recovery isn't as titillating a subject and doesn't reach the ratings stratosphere.

> My life is living evidence that no matter how broken a person's life seems to be, it can be restored to joy and fullness.

The door to restoration and sanity is open; anyone can live free apart from the madness of being transgender.

I'm the lucky one. I share the my message of hope worldwide, traveling wherever I'm welcomed, writing books and articles, participating on radio and television shows, offering a web site full of info, all in an effort as best as one man can to prevent others from unnecessary gender surgery, regret, and suicide. Through my web site, sexchangeregret.com, alone, the message has reached 180 countries and hundreds of thousands of people.

I share this recent study because it was conducted by a gender dysphoria clinic and points us to a deeper understanding of the transgender mind; that is, transgender individuals have mental health problems that lead to self-injury and suicidal behaviors. If not a civil-rights issue, this is certainly a human compassion issue that ought to call us, not to exploit them for money and attention, but to address their deepest needs.

Chapter 8.
Serving in the Military

I Was Once Transgender. Why I Think Trump Made the Right Decision for the Military.

President Donald Trump announced on Wednesday that transgender individuals would not be permitted to serve in the military.

BY WALT HEYER
THE DAILY SIGNAL, JULY 26, 2017
WWW.DAILYSIGNAL.COM/2017/07/26/WHY-
FORCING-THE-MILITARY-TO-PAY-FOR-SEX-CHANGES-WOULD-BE-DISASTROUS/

On Wednesday, President Donald Trump tweeted that he wouldn't allow transgender individuals to serve in the military:

> After consultation with my Generals and military experts, please be advised that the United States Government will not accept or allow......
>
> — Donald J. Trump (@realDonaldTrump) July 26, 2017[226]

> ....Transgender individuals to serve in any capacity in the U.S. Military. Our military must be focused on decisive and overwhelming.....
>
> — Donald J. Trump (@realDonaldTrump) July 26, 2017[227]

> ....victory and cannot be burdened with the tremendous medical costs and disruption that transgender in the military would entail. Thank you
>
> — Donald J. Trump (@realDonaldTrump) July 26, 2017[228]

I think he made the right decision—and as someone who lived as trans-female for several years, I should know.

When I discovered Congress voted earlier this month to not block funding for transgender-related hormone therapies and sex change surgeries, I wondered if it considered how devastating this will be to the fitness, readiness, and morale of our combat-ready troops.

In July, the House of Representatives voted down Missouri Republican Rep. Vicky Hartzler's amendment to the National Defense Authorization Act, which would have banned the military from funding such treatments.

---

[226] https://twitter.com/realDonaldTrump/status/890193981585444864
[227] https://twitter.com/realDonaldTrump/status/890196164313833472
[228] https://twitter.com/realDonaldTrump/status/890197095151546369

Paying for transition-related surgeries for military service members and their families is beyond comprehensible.

Perhaps they have forgotten that our military was forged to be the world's strongest fighting force, not a government-funded, politically correct, medical sex change clinic for people with gender dysphoria.

Gender dysphoria, the common diagnosis for one who feels at odds with his or her birth gender, develops from prolonged anxiety and depression. People are not born that way.

> The "proof" for a diagnosis of gender dysphoria is having strongly held feelings—but feelings can and often do change over time.

The military is expected to prepare its members in warfare: to kill, destroy, and break our enemies. The most important factors in preparing a strong military are not hormone therapy, surgical sex changes, or politically correct education.

We need psychologically fit, emotionally sound, highly trained troops to protect our nation from its enemies.

While countless homeless vets are currently sleeping under cardboard boxes, or waiting for life-saving care from the Department of Veterans Affairs, we learn that transgender military recruits now qualify for preferential coverage for sex change procedures that are scientifically unproven and extremely costly.

I myself was fully sex-reassigned from male to female, and eventually came to accept my birth gender.

I have over 70 years of firsthand life experience, eight years of living as a woman, 20 years of researching the topic, and 12 years of helping others who, like me, found that transitioning and reassignment surgery failed to be proper treatment and want to restore their lives to their birth gender.

Costly, but Not Effective

Transitioning can be expensive—up to $130,000 per person[229] for numerous body-mutilating and cosmetic procedures over many months (or years) to fashion the body to appear as the opposite sex.

Yet, no matter how skilled the surgeon, or how much money is spent, it is biologically impossible to change a man into a woman or a woman into a man. The change is only cosmetic.

The medical community continues to recommend this radical "treatment" in the absence of scientific evidence that people are better off in the long run. This population attempts suicide at a rate of 40 percent.[230]

Even after the full surgical change, they attempt to end their lives, or tragically succeed.

Over 60 percent of this diverse population suffer from co-existing mental disorders.[231] Consider Bradley Manning (now Chelsea Manning), a former Army soldier who was so psychologically and

---

[229] http://time.com/money/4092680/transgender-surgery-costs/
[230] http://www.transequality.org/sites/default/files/docs/usts/USTS Full Report - FINAL 1.6.17.pdf
[231] https://www.ncbi.nlm.nih.gov/pubmed/25180172

emotionally unbalanced that he stole confidential documents from the military and forwarded them to WikiLeaks.

The Military Is a Fighting Force, Not a Gender Clinic

The military should not provide sex change surgery.

Through my website, sexchangeregret.com, I hear from people who experienced firsthand how damaging and unnecessary reassignment surgeries were. For them, the sex change failed to resolve the emotional and psychological disorders that drove the desire to change gender.

Many write after living the transgender life for years. They write to ask for advice on how to reverse the original surgical change and restore their lives to the original birth gender like I did, a process called detransition.

Some service members will come to regret having undergone the surgery and will want to detransition. Where will the military be then? Will the military pay for the sex change reversal procedure, too?

Failed "sex change surgeries" are not uncommon and will drive up the cost to care for the military transgender population above the projected $3-4 billion 10-year cost.[232]

Beyond the financial cost, there's the question of the service member's military readiness during their transition or detransition, as the process often comes with a great deal of anxiety and emotional instability.

I know of many who have struggled to adapt to the new gender role for years after reassignment surgery.

In my view, as a former trans-female who works every day with regretters, allowing the military to pay for sex change surgeries will make a mockery of the U.S. military.

Advocates are relentless in their pursuit of making others, via the government and insurance companies, cover the cost of sex change procedures.

If the military had been forced to pay, the advocates would have used this as leverage to press every other entity—both government and commercial—to pay for sex change surgeries as well.

As a person who lived the transgender life for eight years, I can attest that assisting, affirming, or paying for hormone therapies and genital mutilation surgeries would not have strengthened our military. They would only have brought adverse long-term consequences, both for individuals and for our armed forces as a whole.

---

[232] https://gohmert.house.gov/news/documentsingle.aspx?DocumentID=398547

Why Trump Keeping Trans People From The Military Is A Good Decision

President Trump is correct to block trans soldiers' attempts to emulate the opposite sex because it will not strengthen our military nor provide transgender people long-term help.

BY WALT HEYER
THE FEDERALIST, JULY 27, 2017
THEFEDERALIST.COM/2017/07/27/TRUMP-
KEEPING-TRANS-PEOPLE-MILITARY-GOOD-DECISION/

In a stunning move, President Trump announced on Twitter that transgender individuals will not serve in the U.S. military. Despite Congress voting in late July to fund gender-reassignment surgery for military service members, Trump tweeted Wednesday: "After consultation with my Generals and military experts, please be advised the United States Government will not accept or allow Transgender individuals to serve in any capacity in the U.S. Military."

It's unclear the mechanisms Trump plans to use to put this policy into effect, however. Activist groups announced plans to sue immediately if Trump codifies this policy in an executive order,[233] and Sen. John McCain, chairman of the Senate Armed Services Committee, issued a statement defending the Department of Defense's decision under President Obama to allow transgender soldiers to remain in the armed forces. He says there's not enough evidence that transgender people will reduce combat effectiveness or that transgender soldiers' elective gender-change surgeries are too steep a price for taxpayers to pay. [234]

McCain is wrong. Iraq combat veteran J.R. Salzman pointed out on Twitter the day of Trump's announcement that in combat all emotional vulnerabilities matter and threaten soldiers' lives and units:

> "War is no place for people who are mentally, emotionally, or physically confused or in turmoil. You have your sh-t together, or you don't. And if you don't, you'll just get people needlessly killed. Political correctness has absolutely no place in the military."[235]

---

[233] https://thefederalist.com/2017/07/26/transgender-people-no-longer-allowed-military-president-trump-tweets/

[234] https://www.mccain.senate.gov/public/index.cfm/2017/7/statement-by-sasc-chairman-john-mccain-on-transgender-americans-in-the-military

[235] https://thefederalist.com/2017/07/26/disabled-combat-veteran-speaks-out-on-trumps-transgender-military-ban/

As a male who had gender reassignment surgery and lived the transgender life, I can also testify that Trump is correct to block taxpayers from assisting, affirming, or paying for hormone therapies and gender reassignment surgeries because it will not in any way strengthen our military nor provide the long-term help individuals diagnosed with gender dysphoria are seeking.

I felt distress at being a boy and longed to be a girl starting at the age of 4. I underwent full gender reassignment at age 43 and lived as a woman for eight years. Now I have more than 70 years of first-hand life experience and 20 years of researching the topic.

For the past 12 years, I've made myself available to others who, like me, found that transitioning and reassignment surgery failed to relieve the gender dysphoria. People from all walks of life—teaching, medicine, law enforcement, aviation—have contacted me for advice for restoring their lives to their birth gender. They are not okay, treatments that pretend they can be the opposite sex are often ineffective, and we have ample evidence to show that.

The Science Isn't Settled

The science is not settled on the effectiveness of gender transitioning, which is a good reason to resist forcing taxpayers to pay for what is quite likely to turn out to harm rather than help gender dysphoric people. Peer-reviewed studies have demonstrated a need for caution. After reassignment surgery, people still have excessive high rates of suicide attempts and unresolved mental disorders,[236] indicating that changing genders is not effective in improving the lives of individuals who suffer with gender dysphoria.

In 2004, an article in *The Guardian* reported that a review of more than 100 international medical studies of post-operative transsexuals found gender reassignment was not effective and in fact, many patients remain traumatized and suicidal afterwards. Chris Hyde, the director of the research facility, said: "There is a huge uncertainty over whether changing someone's sex is a good or a bad thing. While no doubt great care is taken to ensure that appropriate patients undergo gender reassignment, there's still a large number of people who have the surgery but remain traumatized – often to the point of committing suicide."[237]

In 2009, researchers found that 90 percent of the last 10 patients at their gender clinic had at least one other significant form of psychopathology, a key factor in a person's fitness for military service. They said, "This finding seems to be in marked contrast to the public, forensic, and professional rhetoric of many who care for transgendered adults." The researchers also said that "Such clinical certainty would have to be based on carefully established sophisticated follow-up findings. These are lacking."[238]

Transgender People Have High Rates of Mental Illness

An endocrinologist in the early days of the sex change movement, Dr. Charles Ihlenfeld, administered cross-gender hormones to some 500 gender changers over six years. Based on his observations,

---

[236] https://thefederalist.com/2015/08/19/transgender-regret-is-real-even-if-the-media-tell-you-otherwise/
[237] https://www.theguardian.com/society/2004/jul/30/health.mentalhealth
[238] http://www.ncbi.nlm.nih.gov/pubmed/19105079

Ihlenfeld sounded a warning in 1979 about hormone therapy and reassignment surgery: "There is too much unhappiness among people who have had the surgery," he said. "Too many of them end as suicides."[239] Ihlenfeld retrained as a psychiatrist to be better equipped to treat the transgender population.

Ihlenfeld's observations are confirmed in studies:

- A 2011 long-term follow-up of transsexual persons undergoing sex reassignment surgery found that "Persons with transsexualism, after sex reassignment, have considerably higher risks for mortality, suicidal behavior."[240]
- The results of a survey in the Netherlands published in 2003 found that major mood disorders, dissociative disorders, and psychotic disorders are present in 79 percent of transgenders.[241]
- A 2014 study found that more than 60 percent of this population suffer from co-existing mental disorders.[242]

This population attempts suicide at a rate of 40 percent.[243] Even after the full surgical change, they still attempt to end their lives. All of this indicates that the vast majority of gender dysphoric people are not mentally capable of the high-stress conditions of military life. Indeed, it suggests it's cruel to put people like this into the pressure cooker that is war.

The compassionate thing to do for a transgender soldier would be to keep him or her from the military then provide expert care to help resolve the underlying psychological issues that often give rise to gender distress. The cruel thing, both to the soldier and his or her unit, would be to put other people's lives into the hands of such a tender, distressed person.

Gender-Change Surgeries Are Not a Good Solution

The cause of gender dysphoria, the common diagnosis for one who feels at odds with his or her birth gender, is not known. Research has ruled out that people are born that way. To make a diagnosis of gender dysphoria, a medical professional interviews the patient to determine if he or she has strongly held feelings, and whether the feelings have persisted over time.

But the problem is that feelings can, and often do, change over time.

Ihlenfeld called gender transition "a temporary reprieve." Eventually, to put the gender dysphoria to rest, the person will need to confront and treat the anxiety and depression.

Not only is it often ineffective long-term, but transitioning can be expensive, up to $130,000 per person, for numerous cosmetic procedures over many months (or years) to fashion the body to appear

[239] http://lvtgw.jadephoenix.org/Info_htm/Herbal_G/ginko_b2.htm
[240] http://www.ncbi.nlm.nih.gov/pubmed/21364939
[241] https://www.ncbi.nlm.nih.gov/pubmed/12832250
[242] https://www.ncbi.nlm.nih.gov/pubmed/25180172
[243] http://www.transequality.org/sites/default/files/docs/usts/USTS Full Report - FINAL 1.6.17.pdf

as the opposite sex.[244] Yet no matter how skilled the surgeon or how much money is spent, the person's biology hasn't been affected. The gender change is only cosmetic.

The Military Is Not the Place for Confused People

Military recruits with gender doubts should be told to settle their gender identity before enlisting or, if actively serving, should leave the military to undergo gender change at their own expense. To do otherwise has the effect of attracting people who are not so much interested in serving, but in having the hefty expense of transition covered.

Beyond the financial cost, there's the question of military readiness of transgender service members during their transition or detransition because of the anxiety and emotional instability that accompanies the process of changing genders. I know of many who struggle to adapt to the new gender role for years after reassignment surgery.

I hear constantly from people who experienced first-hand how damaging and unnecessary their reassignment surgeries were. For them, the gender change failed to resolve the emotional and psychological disorders that drove the desire to change gender. Many write to me after living the transgender life for many years. They write for advice on how to reverse the original surgical change and restore their lives to the original birth gender like I did, a process called detransition.

The military is not the place to settle gender issues. Civilian life is.

Military readiness demands the absolute highest standards with no compromise, with a full focus on protecting the nation, not personal concerns.

---

[244] http://time.com/money/4092680/transgender-surgery-costs/

President Trump, Do Not Turn The Military Into A Federally Funded Sex Change Clinic

The military is not the place to advance a 'politically correct' experiment with cross-gender hormone therapy on troops and veterans.

BY WALT HEYER

THE FEDERALIST, MARCH 13, 2018

THEFEDERALIST.COM/2018/03/13/TRUMP-
DONT-TURN-THE-MILITARY-INTO-A-FEDERALLY-FUNDED-SEX-CHANGE-CLINIC/

The generally accepted treatment program for gender dysphoria begins with administering cross-sex hormones to feminize or masculinize appearance and to improve mental health. The trouble is, no scientifically strenuous studies have been done to assure the effectiveness and safety of this practice, and people with gender issues are being harmed.

One of these people is Jamie Shupe, retired Sergeant First Class from the U.S. Army. His story of emotional and physical trauma from cross-sex hormone treatment illustrates the sometimes unforeseen consequences of the still-experimental cross-sex hormone therapy prescribed for gender dysphoria.

In his words: "I am a transgender person that has suffered my entire life from gender dysphoria. In early 2013, I regretfully allowed the medical establishment to not only convince me that I am a female, but also to lead me to believe that I could successfully gain female appearance characteristics by taking high doses of female hormones. My four years of treatments and their side effects were paid for by the military health care system."

For over four decades, gender experts have recommended cross-sex hormone therapy to treat those patients who feel they should be the other sex, yet rigorous studies of the effects or efficacy of using powerful hormones in this "off-label" way are lacking. Transgender individuals, adult and children, are being experimented upon, with the full involvement and consent of transgender health care providers.

No link shown between Hormone Therapy and Improved Quality Of Life

In 2016, Boston researchers reviewed all published medical studies available in online medical libraries looking for papers that studied the relationship between hormone therapy and changes in psychological functioning and quality of life in transgender individuals over time. They specifically were searching for studies that used the "gold standard" of research — prospective controlled trials.

The results, published in *Transgender Health*, reveal the paucity of research. The authors shared that…

not one prospective controlled trial could be found,

…and therefore a relationship between hormone therapies and improved mental health and quality of life has not been shown.[245]

Shupe says for him, "The treatments failed to improve my mental health symptoms as promised in the informed consent documents."

Links To Suicide And Depression

However, the relationship between cross-gender hormone use and depression, while not scientifically tested, has been noted.

For men taking female hormones (aka, transgender women, or MTF), depression is a known side-effect. As one study says, "Other associated conditions commonly seen in transgender women include increased risks of depression."[246]

Shupe found this to be true: "I was hospitalized in the psychiatric ward twice at the VA for depression and emotional instability after estrogen injections destabilized my mental health to the point that I was suicidal."

For some women taking testosterone (i.e., transgender men, or FTM), testosterone can cause increased irritability, frustration, and anger. There are reports of testosterone destabilizing FTMs with bipolar disorder, schizoaffective disorder, and schizophrenia. The link to depression and suicide has been noted for decades in transgender individuals who take hormones and go on to undergo gender-change surgery.[247]

In 1979, endocrinologist Dr. Ihlenfeld, who had administered cross-sex hormone therapies at a renowned gender clinic to 500 people diagnosed with gender dysphoria over 6 years, warned, "There is too much unhappiness among people who have had the surgery … Too many of them end as suicides."[248]

In 2004, a *UK Guardian* article headlined, "Sex Changes are Not Effective Say Researchers," quoted researchers who reviewed over 100 studies as saying, "There's still a large number of people who have the surgery but remain traumatized – often to the point of committing suicide."[249]

Cross-Gender Hormone Use Is Not Well Studied

Study after study concludes that more research is needed in every area about hormone use by transgender men and women.

For example, effectiveness. The use of feminizing cross-gender hormones has not been proven to be effective. A 2016 research article, which overall tends to be favorable toward cross-gender hormone use, says that, "No studies have examined the efficacy of the different formulations [of estrogen]

---

[245] https://www.ncbi.nlm.nih.gov/pmc/articles/PMC5010234/

[246] https://www.ncbi.nlm.nih.gov/pubmed/27916515

[247] https://apps.carleton.edu/campus/gsc/assets/hormones_FTM.pdf

[248] http://lvtgw.jadephoenix.org/Info_htm/Herbal_G/ginko_b2.htm

[249] https://www.theguardian.com/society/2004/jul/30/health.mentalhealth

specific to transgender hormone management." The author also admits: "There are no unanimous recommendations for the use of anti-androgens [for transgender women]."[250]

Then there's the question of dosage. Determining the right dose in the right form is a matter of trial and error. As guidebooks, such as one for MTF from The Transgender Health Program in Vancouver, BC, clearly state, there is no typical dose: "Clinical protocols for MTF therapy vary greatly. There is no one right hormone combination, type, or dose."[251]

The transgender-specific guidelines that experts at the World Professional Association for Transgender Health (WPATH) and the Endocrine Society have created are based mostly on clinical experience from experts in the field; not verified by research.[252]

Medical Risks And Complications

More seriously is the issue of medical risk and complications, which vary between testosterone and estrogen.

Testosterone, used to masculinize the appearance of a female to that of a male, can increase the risk of heart disease, stroke, and diabetes. It is not known if testosterone increases the risks of breast cancer, ovarian cancer, or uterine cancer. Most of the studies on hormone therapy track biological men, not women who want to appear as men. Because men's bodies are different than women's and the dosages prescribed are different, the results found[253] for biological men are not transferrable to the transgender male population.

The UCSF Center of Excellence for Transgender Health female-to-male]health booklet[254] shares "a few other risks associated with testosterone therapy that you should know about" —

> Testosterone can make your blood become too thick…which can cause a stroke, heart attack or other conditions. This can be a particular problem if you are taking a dose that is too high for your body's metabolism. Your cholesterol could potentially increase when taking testosterone. Your doctor will perform periodic tests of your blood count, cholesterol, kidney functions, and liver functions, and a diabetes screening test…

Estrogen, used by men wanting to feminize to the appearance of a woman, has medical effects and safety concerns for transgender people which are not fully understood. As the UCSF Transgender Care male-to-female health booklet[255] says, "Since there is not a lot of research on the use of estrogen in transwomen, there may be other risks that we won't know about, especially for those who have used estrogen for many years."

---

[250] https://www.ncbi.nlm.nih.gov/pmc/articles/PMC5182227/
[251] https://apps.carleton.edu/campus/gsc/assets/hormones_MTF.pdf
[252] https://www.ncbi.nlm.nih.gov/pmc/articles/PMC5182227/
[253] https://apps.carleton.edu/campus/gsc/assets/hormones_FTM.pdf
[254] https://transcare.ucsf.edu/article/information-testosterone-hormone-therapy
[255] https://transcare.ucsf.edu/article/information-estrogen-hormone-therapy

Jamie Shupe's Story

Jamie Shupe suffered health complications from his hormone therapy.

He says: "As a result of being prescribed these off-label, high dose hormones, I've suffered numerous serious health complications. I've been treated in the emergency room twice for vasculitis (inflammation of blood vessels) and cellulitis in my legs because of oral cross-sex hormones. Testing at the Department of Veterans Affairs (VA) hospital also revealed that my kidney function was abnormal despite leading a healthy lifestyle. The attending physician emphatically advised that I stop taking the oral cross-sex hormones, which I did."

When Jamie went to an LGBT clinic for follow-up care, to his surprise, the clinic doctor harshly criticized the care he received at the VA, both for putting him on oral hormones the year before (because pill form for someone his age can cause problems in the liver), and for stopping the HRT the month before. The clinic doctor said he had a better plan and wrote Jamie a prescription for weekly intramuscular injections of estrogen, to be self-injected into his thighs.

According to Jamie, in a short time the results proved to be disastrous: "By the fifth week of estrogen injections my mood had spiraled out of control. My energy level had also plummeted. I had rapidly deteriorated from a structured daily routine of exercise and working on my website, to a state of complete and utter despair. I had absolutely no ability to concentrate. Suicidal and in the deepest depression of my life, I angrily threw the syringes and vials of estrogen in the trash, swearing to never take hormones again."

Ashamed and considering suicide, Jamie was admitted into the psychiatric ward at the VA hospital. Despite telling the mental health doctors about the hormone injections and the recent stopping of hormones, they didn't test his hormone levels, and as Jamie says, "They diagnosed me with multiple psychiatric illnesses and, in an effort to cure me, pumped me full of antidepressants, mood stabilizers and antipsychotic drugs."

Nearly five months later and back to writing for the first time, Jamie says he counts himself lucky: "I describe myself as lucky because I never had any transgender surgeries that would have rendered my body unable to restore my natural hormones. Today, my hormones are nearly back to natural male levels. Because of the return of my testosterone, my mood is also beginning to stabilize for the first time in months. Some of my concentration has also returned. I'm by no means out of the woods yet and fully recovered."

President Trump, Do Not Place The Military At Risk

Over the last 40 years, hormone therapies and sex change surgeries have produced high rates of suicides, unhappiness, and for some like Shupe, deep distress that led to medical complications and stopping the therapy. The military is not the place to advance a "politically correct" experiment with cross-gender hormone therapy on troops and veterans. The risks to the individuals and to military readiness are too high.

The military needs to have a psychologically healthy, emotionally sound, physically fit, combat ready fighting force; not individuals who are distracted by the need for hormone injections and gaining access to a sex change clinic at the expense of military fitness, readiness and funds.

Mr. President, stand up for the military and keep your word to stand down on turning the military into a sex change clinic for the gender distressed.

Thanks To The Trump Administration, The U.S. Military Will Not Become A Sex-Change Clinic

Bravo to President Trump and Defense Secretary James Mattis for making a common-sense decision and not being bullied into disastrous military policy by non-military voices.

BY WALT HEYER
THE FEDERALIST, MARCH 27, 2018
THEFEDERALIST.COM/2018/03/27/THANKS-TRUMP-ADMINISTRATION-
U-S-MILITARY-WILL-NOT-BECOME-SEX-CHANGE-CLINIC/

The White House issued a memorandum late on March 23 authorizing Defense Secretary James Mattis to "exercise his authority to implement any appropriate policies concerning military service by transgender individuals."[256] Mattis has already made recommendations for what these policies will be:

Allowed: Transgender persons without a diagnosis of gender dysphoria may serve, "like all other Service members," in their biological sex, providing they meet the usual standards for service.

Disqualified: Transgender persons who require or have undergone gender transition.

Disqualified, with exceptions: Those with gender dysphoria.

One notable exception to the last point is for those already serving. In effect, they are grandfathered in and "may continue to serve in their preferred gender and receive medically necessary treatment for gender dysphoria." This speaks well of the administration advisory panel's integrity to honor previously made commitments, as President Obama had allowed openly transgender soldiers to serve and required taxpayers to pay for their physical alterations.

As a former transgender person, I agree with these policies.

Bravo to President Trump and Mattis for making a common-sense decision based on solid reasoning, and not being bullied into making disastrous military policy to pacify non-military voices.

From Tweet to Studied Policy

President Trump asked Mattis to make policy recommendations last summer, after Trump's infamous tweet announcing a ban on transgender persons from serving in the military and a subsequent court injunction against it.

In response to the president's request, Mattis established a panel of experts "that included senior uniformed and civilian leaders of the Department and U.S. Coast Guard, many with experience

---

[256] http://militarypartners.org/wp-content/uploads/2018/03/March-23-policy-implementation.pdf

leading Service members in peace and war. The Panel made recommendations based on each Panel member's independent military judgment." Mattis charged the panel to "provide its best military advice based on increasing the lethality and readiness of America's armed forces."

The panel received input from transgender service members and their commanders, military medical professionals, and civilian medical professionals with experience in this area. They also had access to the Department of Defense's experience from the past year of open transgender military service.

What the Panel Concluded

From the panel's recommendations came two items:

1) Mattis' three-page memorandum for the president summarizing his recommendations, and
2) A 44-page "Department of Defense Report and Recommendations on Military Service by Transgender Persons (Feb. 2018)" that provided the in-depth reasoning behind the proposals.

The Mattis memorandum starts with definitions that are pivotal to the policy: "transgender" and "gender dysphoria." "Transgender" describes persons whose gender identity differs from their biological sex. Within that group is a *subset* of transgender persons who are diagnosed with "gender dysphoria," a discomfort with their biological sex, which results in significant distress or difficulty functioning.

In general usage, the two groups are often considered one and the same. But by separating those who have "significant distress or difficulty functioning" from those who do not, the military policy can be finely tuned to permit some to serve, while restricting those whose service would come with substantial risks.

The previous administration based its policy on a study prepared by the RAND National Defense Research Institute that calculated the costs and effects of allowing transgender persons to serve and transition during active duty. Further investigation into the RAND report's assumptions found the study contained "significant shortcomings," Mattis's memorandum said. It glossed over the effects of the Obama administration decision on medical costs and unit cohesion. As Mattis said, "In short, this policy issue has proven more complex than the prior administration or RAND assumed."

The panel managed to examine all sides of the many dilemmas the military faced with Solomonic wisdom and opened a way for those serving under the previous policy to continue to serve. The policy promotes and safeguards unit cohesion. The DOD report provides the reasoning behind the decision to deny people with gender dysphoria the privilege of serving.

No Evidence Cross-Sex Procedures Work

While standards of care have evolved over the past four decades for transgender health (WPATH SOC), they are based on LGBT activists' political views and real-life trial and error. What has been lacking for 40 years is any scientific proof of efficacy. It is gratifying to see Mattis's report elaborate on the uncertainty that underlies the recommended transition treatment:

> Underlying these conclusions is the considerable scientific uncertainty and overall lack of high quality scientific evidence demonstrating the extent to which transition-related

treatments, such as cross-sex hormone therapy and sex reassignment surgery—interventions which are unique in psychiatry and medicine—remedy the multifaceted mental health problems associated with gender dysphoria.

It succinctly points to the lack of evidence that cross-sex medical procedures work, how the treatment is unlike any others in all of medicine, and how complex the problems associated with gender dysphoria are. All of these explain why the military should not be the place for such experimentation.

In a previous article, "President Trump, Do Not Turn The Military Into A Federally Funded Sex Change Clinic,"[257] I highlighted the emotional and physical trauma resulting from cross-sex hormone treatment in the case of former transgender person Jamie Shupe, a retired sergeant first class from the U.S. Army. His story illustrates the unforeseen consequences of the still-experimental cross-sex hormone therapy prescribed for gender dysphoria and its real link to suicide and depression.

Over the last 40 years, hormone therapies and sex-alteration surgeries have produced high rates of suicides, unhappiness, and, for some like Shupe, deep distress that led to medical complications and stopping the therapy. The military is not the place to advance a "politically correct" experiment with cross-gender hormone therapy on troops and veterans. The risks to the individuals and to military readiness are too high.

The policies Mattis put forward fulfill the need to have a psychologically healthy, emotionally sound, physically fit, combat-ready fighting force, not individuals who are distracted by the need for hormone injections and gaining access to a sex-alteration clinic at the expense of military fitness, readiness, and public funds.

Trump and the military will take considerable heat from the activists who are relentless in forcing transgender privileges into every cranny and crevice of our society. But the military scored a victory in this case. Mattis and Trump protected military readiness from a political activist agenda, freeing the military to be laser-focused on its mission to prepare and maintain battle-ready forces.

---

[257] https://thefederalist.com/2018/03/13/trump-dont-turn-the-military-into-a-federally-funded-sex-change-clinic/

How The Trump Administration Can Truly Help Gender-Struggling Americans

---

The Trump administration can slow things down for transgender Americans and prevent political advocates from rushing them into sex changes many are likely to regret.

BY WALT HEYER
THE FEDERALIST, JANUARY 12, 2017
THEFEDERALIST.COM/2017/01/12/TRUMP-
ADMINISTRATION-CAN-TRULY-HELP-GENDER-STRUGGLING-AMERICANS/

With a new presidential administration comes an opportunity to make a difference in the lives of gender-distressed people. Instead of being in lock-step with the LGBT activist agenda, which pushes for nonsensical laws and prioritizes gender reassignment to the exclusion of other treatment possibilities, the Trump administration could be a voice for those for whom gender reassignment is not the promised fix-all.

Progressive media activists promote changing genders as a safe, glamorous avenue to a wonderful new life. But I see the letters from those who are dissatisfied or even suicidal after a gender change, and someone needs to speak up for them. The suicide attempt rate of 41 percent in the transgender population[258] is unacceptable.

As a former trans person, I hope that soon-to-be President Trump will encourage the medical community to consider the deeper issues causing the desire for hormone therapy and reassignment surgery. I have some suggestions for getting started.

Suggestions to Improve Care for the Gender-Distressed

End the Obamacare transgender mandate. Cancel the Health and Human Services transgender mandate,[259] which forces doctors to participate in sex changes even if they deem it is not in the best interests of the patient.

Issue better medical guidelines. Establish a blue-ribbon team of doctors—internal medicine, psychiatrists, and endocrinologists—who have a history of questioning the current LGBT emphasis on gender change as the only treatment. Task the team with setting federal treatment guidelines focused on the emotional, psychiatric, and psychological needs of gender-distressed individuals and on treating underlying psychological disorders, suicide risk, depression, and anxiety. Investigate ways to reduce the number of unnecessary reassignment surgeries.

---

[258] http://www.msnbc.msn.com/id/40279043/ns/health-health_care/
[259] https://www.gpo.gov/fdsys/pkg/FR-2016-05-18/pdf/2016-11458.pdf

Stop pushing sex changes. Direct the Department of Health and Human Services to stop pushing gender-reassignment surgeries.

Use the power of the purse. Stop federal funding to any organization, such as medical facilities, public schools, and Planned Parenthood offices, if they do not comply with the guidelines. Redirect federal financial resources towards organizations that take a holistic approach.

Don't Push People Into Things Many Will Regret

Let me explain why the Trump administration should reduce the current emphasis on immediate transition for those who are gender-distressed. More than 30 years ago I transitioned from male to female and lived as a female for eight years. In the first few days and months after the "change" I was 100 percent sure the gender transformation was a dream come true.

Like me, most people who make a gender change are happy at first. But as the years pass, for various reasons the idealized dream fails to become reality and the glamorous magazine version of life is gone. Depression takes hold and suicide looks good.

"Regret is rare," say the activists. If they talk about dissatisfaction, suicides, and regret in the transgender population at all, they routinely blame the "transphobic" Right. Carol Costello of CNN interviewed me[260] in 2015 at the height of the Caitlyn Jenner media frenzy. She listened respectfully to my story but then inserted a trans activist talking point: A Swedish study says only 2 percent of people regret their transition.

I have subsequently seen and heard this statistic bandied about, as if it were an indisputable truth. By digging into the source and looking at what other researchers say, a far higher number emerges.

The Swedish study Costello quoted measured regret by counting the number of transgendered people who later applied for reversal to the original sex (called a "regret application").[261] But as other researchers have pointed out, the 2.2 percent number doesn't include the additional patients who died by suicide or made suicide attempts.[262] Obviously, people who are happy with their life don't try to end it. With those included, the number rises to 7.9 percent. That figure also doesn't address those who regret their change but didn't in the study interval apply to reverse it.

Other studies indicate a higher percentage of dissatisfaction. A 2004 United Kingdom review of more than 100 studies said: "Research from the US and Holland suggests that up to a fifth of patients regret changing sex."[263] That's 20 percent, not 2 or 3. A recent systematic review of 28 studies examined outcomes of sex reassignment in 1,833 participants and found that from 16 to 29 percent of patients do *not* experience significant improvement in their gender dysphoria.[264]

---

[260] https://www.youtube.com/watch?v=ZWb9vtl5n1c

[261] https://www.researchgate.net/publication/262734734_An_Analysis_of_All_Applications_for_Sex_Reassignment_Surgery_in_Sweden_1960-2010_Prevalence_Incidence_and_Regrets

[262] http://www.klinefelter.se/wp-content/uploads/ Gender_Dysphoria_In_Adults.pdf

[263] https://www.theguardian.com/society/2004/jul/30/health.mentalhealth

[264] https://www.ncbi.nlm.nih.gov/pubmed/19473181

Regret Is Not Rare, It's Common

As I have studied gender reassignment dissatisfaction over the last 10 years I've become convinced that the current treatment protocol of hormones and gender reassignment surgery ignores underlying problems. The issues go much deeper than a change of gender persona can reach or resolve.

Poor evaluations allow too many who lack psychological or emotional fitness to undergo gender reassignment surgery. Other factors like alcohol, drugs, and high-risk behaviors play a role in poor long-term outcome for the transgender population. As Richard B. Corradi, M.D., a professor of psychiatry at Case Western Reserve University School of Medicine, wrote recently: "People with a chronically unstable self-image, poor self-esteem, and an ill-defined sense of self are poorly equipped to deal with the stresses of ordinary life. This group constitutes the vast majority of the self-identified transgendered who undertake the full sex-change regimen of hormone treatment and 'sex-reassignment' surgery."[265]

Now to trans-advocates, Corradi's words are "hate speech." That means they hate the accurate assessment of a psychiatric doctor. Regardless, he's not by any means an isolated case. Dr. Charles Ihlenfeld, after spending six years administering hormone therapy to 500 transgender patients in the 1970s, said the same thing: "There is too much unhappiness among people who have had the surgery. Too many of them end as suicides."

"It's not just a question of surgery or of screening out those who are psychotic or emotionally unstable; it's the question of what the patient is going to do with the rest of his life that has to be resolved. Therapy can give him insight into himself and into his feelings that he needs to change his anatomical sex," Ihlenfeld said. [266] As a former transgender who underwent the complete gender reassignment protocol, I can tell you Dr. Ihlenfeld spoke the truth in 1979, but no one was listening. I attempted suicide after cross-gender hormones and a radical surgery.

Today I see similar regrettable outcomes of these protocols in the letters I receive, each one telling his or her own pain-filled, chilling story of dissatisfaction with being transgender, a label they no longer take pride in. Now they want a way back to sanity.

> Corradi found chronically unstable self-image, poor self-esteem, and an ill-defined sense of self among transgender patients.

How can a change of gender persona and appearance be a singular, permanent solution for people who suffer this way? The issues go much deeper for many such people.

Chris Hyde, the director of the University of Birmingham's research facility (Arif) in the UK, said: "There is a huge uncertainty over whether changing someone's sex is a good or a bad thing. While no doubt great care is taken to ensure that appropriate patients undergo gender reassignment, there's

---

[265] https://thefederalist.com/2016/11/17/psychiatry-professor-transgenderism-mass-hysteria-similar-1980s-era-junk-science/

[266] http://lvtgw.jadephoenix.org/Info_htm/Herbal_G/ginko_b2.htm

still a large number of people who have the surgery but remain traumatized—often to the point of committing suicide."[267]

A large population-based study released in 2011 from Sweden (Dhejne et al. 2011) found that patients who underwent gender reassignment surgery had a much higher incidence of co-occurring (or comorbid) psychopathology, death by suicide, and suicide attempts.[268]

Recent studies offer a possible explanation for the feeling that one needs to change anatomical sex. They show that two-thirds of transgender people have other co-existing psychological disorders. A 2014 study found 62.7 percent of patients diagnosed with gender dysphoria had at least one co-occurring disorder, and 33 percent were found to have major depressive disorders, which are linked to suicide ideation.[269] Another 2014 study of transgender individuals in four European countries found that almost 70 percent of participants showed one or more Axis I disorders, mainly affective (mood) disorders and anxiety.[270]

In 2007, the Department of Psychiatry at Case Western Reserve University in Cleveland, Ohio, in a clinical review of the comorbid disorders of patients interviewed at their Gender Identity Clinic, found that "90% of these diverse patients had at least one other significant form of psychopathology … [including] problems of mood and anxiety regulation and adapting in the world. Two of the 10 have had persistent significant regrets about their previous transitions."[271]

Stop Experimenting With Sad People's Lives

The combination of 41 percent attempting suicide and 20 percent or more reporting dissatisfaction does not square with a community of happy and healthy people where "regret is rare."

I would love to set the record straight to benefit people who are being led astray by false talking points. Surgical and hormonal gender reassignment is not without risk. Unhappiness with the outcome is not rare. To those who think transgender people are happy with their gender changes: Why, then, do they spend their days contemplating suicide?

I know from the letters I receive that too many people encounter dissatisfaction in post-surgical life and have nowhere to turn for help. For some, unhappiness is due to social difficulties, such as broken family relationships, divorce, loss of long-term relationships, or strain maintaining a career. For others, it's attributable to the physical results: disappointment with the outcome of surgery or problems "passing" in one's new gender.

Too many U.S. medical practitioners direct all gender-distressed people toward the extreme measures of conforming the body to the mind, rather than exploring the psychological issues that lie beneath the feelings.

[267] https://www.theguardian.com/society/2004/jul/30/health.mentalhealth
[268] https://www.ncbi.nlm.nih.gov/pubmed/21364939
[269] http://www.ncbi.nlm.nih.gov/pubmed/25180172
[270] http://bjp.rcpsych.org/content/204/2/151.full
[271] http://www.ncbi.nlm.nih.gov/pubmed/19105079

Underestimating the level of dissatisfaction with gender change lulls lawmakers, medical personnel, and the patients themselves into experimenting with people's lives and making public policy based on a lie.

It encourages an attitude of "There's no harm in trying," which is false. Giving powerful hormones and recommending radical surgeries without screening for psychological issues first causes great harm to the patients and their families.

It is not homophobic, transphobic, or bigoted to look at the causes of dissatisfaction and suicide among the transgender population. Rather, it is a caring, heartfelt way to prevent dissatisfaction and suicides. Improvement in treatment begins with acknowledging and using solid facts and statistics. Many people who are regretful and suicidal followed to the letter the generally accepted treatment protocol of doctor-prescribed hormone therapy and genital surgery.

President-elect Trump has an opportunity to change the transgender talking points and stop federal agencies from pushing the radical transgender agenda, opting instead to put the emphasis on giving gender-troubled folks access to well-rounded care that includes more than a quick path to cross-gender hormones and surgery.

Trump's Proposed Rollback of Transgender Policy Is Good News for Many Who Are Suffering

The Trump administration is considering restoring the long-established definition of "sex" in Title IX civil rights law prior to the Obama administration.

BY WALT HEYER
THE DAILY SIGNAL, OCTOBER 23, 2018
WWW.DAILYSIGNAL.COM/2018/10/23/TRUMPS-PROPOSED-ROLLBACK-OF-
TRANSGENDER-POLICY-IS-GOOD-NEWS-FOR-MANY-WHO-ARE-SUFFERING/

Thank you, Mr. President, for moving to make male and female great again.

In the last few years, biological girls have seen their rights violated in school bathrooms and in sports. National confusion has ensued ever since the previous administration decided to reinterpret Title IX's sex anti-discrimination clause to include self-proclaimed "gender identity."

That may soon come to an end under the Trump administration.

The Department of Health and Human Services has drafted a memo that would reverse the Obama administration's action and return the legal definition of "sex" under Title IX civil rights law to what its authors meant: sex rooted in unchanging biological reality. According to The New York Times, the memo was drafted last spring and has been circulating ever since.[272]

Title IX bans sex discrimination in education programs that receive government financial assistance, meaning schools have to abide by the government's interpretation of Title IX or risk losing federal funds.

When the Obama administration announced it was including "gender identity" under the word "sex," many schools felt they had to treat gender identity as the standard for determining access to bathrooms, sports teams, etc. The result was headlines like "Transgender Athletes Dominate High School Women's Sports."

The memo spells out the proposed definition of "sex" as applied to federal statutes as "a person's status as male or female based on immutable biological traits identifiable by or before birth." The proposed definition won't include a "select a gender" option, as was offered under the Obama administration.

This is simply a return to reality. Sex is an immutable biological reality, while gender identity is a social construct that can change over time. The two terms are not interchangeable. The authors of Title IX meant biological sex, not gender identity.

---

[272] https://www.nytimes.com/2018/10/21/us/politics/transgender-trump-administration-sex-definition.html

The Obama administration's conflation of the two was not just legally problematic—it also pushed transgender ideology further into the mainstream. That's regrettable, because transgender ideology has real and harmful effects on people who are suffering and need help.

> When individuals try to live out life in an ideology that has no basis in
> biological fact, the consequences are stark.

I know, because I lived the trans life for eight years.

I have received hundreds of regret letters from trans people who now realize—too late—that gender-pretending is damaging. Regretters have called gender change "the biggest mistake of my life." The late transgender movie actress Alexis Arquette called her gender transition "bulls***" because no one can really change their gender.

So many have written me personally about the unhappy consequences of imitating the opposite gender for so many years, telling of lives needlessly torn apart and thoughts of suicide. I put those emails into a book, "Trans Life Survivors," which shows the human toll caused by encouraging distressed people to undergo permanent surgeries and take powerful hormones without considering other causes and treatments.

This past weekend, I opened my email as I do each morning and found another message from a person who had ignored biology and went head-first into trans ideology. Now, this person wants out:

> I am now 40 years old, post op male to female transgender person. And to put it simply, very miserable in life now. I have followed you on YouTube … and totally agree with your theories! I am at my wits' end with life and what I have done to myself. It's an inspiration to see and read about what I would call "survivors!"

Many trans folks, after years of "living the life," now want to detransition. Many report to me that they were sexually abused, raped, or molested at a young age—in one case, as a toddler.

Teenage girls are flocking to gender change as an escape. One 15-year-old girl, who the gender experts diagnosed with gender dysphoria, explained to her mother that she wanted to "erase my past" because she was sexually abused by her dad.

In another case, a young 14-year-old girl confessed that "I used being trans to try and escape being scared about being small and weak. I thought that if I presented myself as a man I'd be safer."

Another girl's mother wrote that her daughter was raped at age 19 and desperately "is trying to remove any connection to her being female visually or sexually."

This is the kind of suffering that has driven many to change genders. As a society, we need to honestly consider:

> Is changing genders an effective long-term treatment for past sexual abuse
> and feelings of insecurity?

> Obviously not.

Billy, another trans life survivor, had been sexually abused at age 11 during a summer swimming camp by his diving coach. Billy explained to me that after the abuse, he hated his genitalia and wanted to become a female. Abuse can do that.

Billy, like so many abused as children, was diagnosed by the "gender specialist" with gender dysphoria and given cross-sex hormones and reassignment surgery. He lived fully as a transgender female until regret set in.

Now he has detransitioned back to male and is married—a true trans life survivor who prefers to live a biologically authentic life.

Trans ideology ruined the life of another friend, born male and now living as a trans female. After being diagnosed with gender dysphoria, his excellent employment allowed him financially to transition from male to female. But sex change regret has set in, and now he wants to detransition.

This nice-looking, tall, slender, intelligent transgender person is another who had been sexually abused as a child.

Too many people tell me that even when they establish a history of sexual abuse and communicate that to the gender therapist, the therapist disregards it. If a client wants to change their gender, the therapist will affirm them without reservation and help them down that path.

As a former trans person, and as someone who daily receives stories of physical and emotional devastation wrought by trans ideology, I look forward to a federal definition of sex as being rooted in immutable biology, without the option of being self-selected.

The science is absolutely clear. Sex doesn't change over time, even with hormones and surgery—and that's a good thing.

Chapter 9.
Ideology and Politics

The Transgender Matrix: It's Time to Choose the Red Pill

The transgender community isn't sympathetic to members of the trans-matrix who want to leave. Even so, the red pill population is growing every day.

BY WALT HEYER
PUBLIC DISCOURSE, OCTOBER 10, 2017
WWW.THEPUBLICDISCOURSE.COM/2017/10/20169/

In the 1999 sci-fi movie *The Matrix*, the hero, Neo, is given a choice of two colored pills: red or blue. It's a monumental decision, because his choice will determine how he understands everything around him.

If Neo chooses the blue pill, he will remain blissfully unaware that what he perceives as reality is an illusion: a simulation called "The Matrix." People who take the blue pill can believe in whatever reality they want, but they never know that they are being manipulated and used by nefarious entities.

On the other hand, if Neo takes the red pill, he will awake from the dream and see that everything he has believed since birth is a lie. He will see things as they truly are, and that will make him an enemy of the status quo.

I Took the Blue Pill, and Then the Red Pill

People with gender dysphoria are encouraged to change genders so they can live happily ever after. In the trans-world, all inhabitants fashion their own "reality" based on their feelings and desires.

That's exactly what I did. Even though I was born male, I chose the blue pill and pursued my lifelong dream of being a woman. I believed the "reality" that I wanted to believe. I took on an elaborate alternate identity, made possible by hormones and surgery, and lived as a transgender woman.

But a funny thing happened. After about eight years, I gradually awoke. I realized the simple biological truth: I was still a man, had always been a man, and always would be a man. In terms of *The Matrix*, I took the red pill.

> With newfound clarity of vision, I could see that everything I had believed about the trans-life was a lie.

God's original design of two innate biological sexes, male and female, cannot be overthrown by taking hormones, having surgery, and living a masquerade.

I wanted "true reality," and I found it in Jesus Christ. No longer was I willing to live an artificial life. When I realized the peace and joy of living in the true reality of my God-given sex, I decided that I needed to share my life story. My goal is to empower and help others who no longer want to live the trans-life to see a way out, too.

The War on God Wants Your Redemption Silenced

But the proponents and inhabitants of the trans-matrix consider me an enemy. When I step out and talk publicly about my experience, the blue pill people attack, saying my viewpoint is "hate speech."

In their version of reality, there are two things you must never do: 1) talk about being restored from a former trans-life and 2) testify that it was due to an encounter with Jesus Christ. I'm guilty of both.

Pure Passion Ministries (purepassion.us) also violates both rules of political correctness. They recently released a gripping documentary of fifteen former transgender men and women (including myself) who, through Christ, abandoned their transgender life. All of them speak candidly of the gut-wrenching events that led to living a transgender life and how God intervened in love to personally redeem and restore them back to living fully in their birth gender. For me and the other fourteen people in the documentary, Jesus opened our eyes to "true reality" and transported each of us into a new life, one where we are free, no longer enslaved. It is a powerful movie worth watching—find out more at tranzformed.org.

When the producer and director, David Kyle Foster, himself a former homosexual, released the movie, the consequences from the political correctness police were swift. His ads were rejected from Facebook and YouTube numerous times, and he was denied the use of an e-blast mailing list he had used previously to promote other projects to Christians. He found out that his organization has been designated as "hateful" or "offensive" and blacklisted from using the mailing list by a secular entity.

In a column on *TownHall*, Dr. Michael L. Brown tells how Foster also had been targeted by the popular video hosting service, Vimeo, which demanded that Foster remove videos that the company found offensive.[273] He defended his organization and received a few months' reprieve, but unfortunately, on March 24th of this year, Vimeo removed all 850 of his videos and shut down Pure Passion's account. In one of the emails Foster received, the representative for Vimeo said:

> Your statement equating homosexuality to "sexual brokenness" betrays the underlying stance of your organization. To put it plainly, we don't believe that homosexuality requires a cure and we don't allow videos on our platform that espouse this point of view.

Vimeo said it was offensive to suggest that the blood of Jesus Christ could bring healing to the homosexual. For that reason, they also removed the Pure Passion videos that helped sex abuse victims, sex-trafficked people, people addicted to porn, and people seeking God for help with other issues, including gender dysphoria.

Michael Brown concludes, "Vimeo is engaging in blatant, unapologetic, aggressive anti-Christian censorship."

The Vimeo viewpoint about homosexuality mirrors the viewpoints I heard expressed by transgender and homosexual advocates at a public hearing in March in Massachusetts. Versions of legislation being proposed[274] have already been passed in nine states and the District of Columbia. The law

---

[273] https://townhall.com/columnists/michaelbrown/2017/03/27/vimeo-declares-war-on-gospel-transformation-n2304830
[274] https://www.thepublicdiscourse.com/2017/06/19515/

makes it illegal to provide any therapy for minors that fails to affirm them in their homosexuality or transgender identity. Any therapist who seeks to discover and treat the underlying psychological causes of such issues can be charged with child abuse and lose his or her license.[275]

Rejecting Reality Means Ignoring Science

The trans-matrix requires its members to believe some outlandish claims. The claims deserve to be scientifically scrutinized, but scrutiny is considered blasphemy. Here are just a few of the most egregious of these claims:

"Transition is the answer."

> The trans-matrix claims that gender transition is the answer that will solve all of the problems of those who suffer from gender dysphoria. Yet, studies show that two-thirds of people with gender dysphoria also have other co-existing psychological disorders, which if treated, could ease or eliminate the gender distress without the need for surgery or cross-sex hormones.[276]

"Transgender people are born that way."

> The trans-matrix claims that people with gender dysphoria are born that way—that the transgender brain is wired that way from birth. But no definitive evidence has been found to support that belief.

> An article in *Scientific American* that begins by saying that "Imaging studies and other research suggest that there is a biological basis for transgender identity" concludes with the following contradictory statement:

> "But given the variety of transgender people and the variation in the brains of men and women generally, it will be a long time, if ever, before a doctor can do a brain scan on a child and say, 'Yes, this child is trans.'"[277]

"A person's sex can be changed."

> People who live in the unreality of the trans-world believe that men can become women and women can become men. I've written elsewhere[278] about the physical impossibility of that belief:

> - Underneath all the cosmetic procedures, vocal training, and hair growth or hair removal lies a physical reality. Biologically, the person has not changed from a man into a woman or vice versa.

> - In a recent study, genetic researchers at Israel's Weizmann Institute of Science found evidence that at least 6,500 genes contain sex-specific instructions for males and females.[279] Changing from one sex to the other is not physically possible.

---

[275] http://www.lgbtmap.org/equality-maps/conversion_therapy

[276] https://www.ncbi.nlm.nih.gov/pubmed/25180172

[277] https://www.scientificamerican.com/article/is-there-something-unique-about-the-transgender-brain/

[278] http://dailysignal.com/2017/08/23/sex-change-myth-trying-change-ones-sex-will-always-fail/

[279] http://mobile.wnd.com/2017/05/study-more-proof-a-man-can-never-become-a-woman/

Leaving the Delusions of the Trans-Matrix Behind

Psychiatrist Richard Corradi calls transgenderism a "contagion of mass delusion."[280] As the authors of a report on the ethics of sex reassignment surgery explain:

> Candidates for SRS may believe that they are trapped in the bodies of the wrong sex and therefore desire or, more accurately, demand SRS; however, this belief is generated by a disordered perception of self. Such a fixed, irrational belief is appropriately described as a delusion.[281]

Having lived the trans-life as a woman for eight years, I wholeheartedly agree. For people who identify as transgender, true reality is found in what is called "de-transitioning," which involves coming to terms with and accepting one's birth gender.

People who no longer find satisfaction in the trans-matrix and desire to leave the illusionary world often contact me for support. Resources and information are scarce, to say the least. The process of de-transitioning is emotionally, socially, and legally difficult for most people. The transgender community isn't sympathetic to members of the trans-matrix who want to leave.

To help expand these resources, a gathering of former members of the trans-matrix world like myself, all of whom now see reality as it is, will take place at a secret location in the next few weeks. Each person involved has found the joy of "true gender reality" and wants to help others who have awakened to the same mindset and desire to vacate the artificial transgender life.

The red pill population is growing each day. I will continue to share my story, knowing it can be hope-giving and life-saving, as it affirms the truth of God's original design of innate biological facts.

---

[280] https://thefederalist.com/2016/11/17/psychiatry-professor-transgenderism-mass-hysteria-similar-1980s-era-junk-science/
[281] https://couragerc.org/wp-content/uploads/SRS_217-1.pdf

Bravo to the Truth: What's Wrong with Transgender Ideology

The problem with basing a diagnosis and irreversible treatment on people's feelings, no matter how deeply felt, is that feelings can change.

BY WALT HEYER
PUBLIC DISCOURSE, APRIL 27, 2017
WWW.THEPUBLICDISCOURSE.COM/2017/04/19080/

A recent *New York Post* article tells the story of a Detroit mom named Erica who changed into a transgender dad named Eric. If that is not enough, his son had already changed genders: born a boy, he transitioned to living as a girl. Thus, mom became dad and son became daughter.[282] Similarly, back in 2015, a fifty-two-year-old Canadian man made the news when he traded in his wife and seven kids to fulfill his "true identity" as a six-year-old transgender girl.[283]

Stories like these remind us that transgender identity is a product of LGBTQ social ideology, not of each human person's innate identity as male or female. Transgender identity is not authentic gender but man's attempt to socially engineer the family, sex, and gender identity.

What Makes a Person Trans?

The accepted LGBTQ standard for being a "real" trans woman or trans man is simply that a person desires to self-identify as the opposite of his or her biological sex and to be socially accepted as such. If a person feels distressed about his or her birth gender, then the politically correct action is for everyone to affirm the new and "authentic" gender identity—the one that exists only in the trans person's feelings.

In a recent interview on Fox News, transgender lawyer Jillian Weiss, executive director of the Transgender Legal Defense and Education Fund, was asked repeatedly by host Tucker Carlson, "What are the legal standards to be transgender?" Finally, the legal specialist admitted, "There are no legal standards."[284]

That's right—

No legal standards or legal definitions of transgender exist.

---

[282] http://nypost.com/2017/03/14/transgender-dad-and-daughter-transition-together/

[283] http://www.dailymail.co.uk/femail/article-3356084/I-ve-gone-child-Husband-father-seven-52-leaves-wife-kids-live-transgender-SIX-YEAR-OLD-girl-named-Stef

[284]

http://www.realclearpolitics.com/video/2017/02/27/tucker_carlson_vs_transgender_activist_its_fair_to_ask_what_it_means_to_be_a_woman_or_a_man.html

Yet, as Carlson pointed out, $11 billion of federal money is spent on sex-specific programs, such as the Small Business Administration investing in businesses owned by women. Without a legal definition, these funds become easy prey for, as Carlson puts it, "charlatans" who will claim to be women simply to get the money.

When people feel that their biological sex doesn't match their internal sense of gender, they are typically diagnosed with gender dysphoria. This is defined as "discomfort or distress that is caused by a discrepancy between a person's gender identity and that person's sex assigned at birth." [285] In other words, the medical diagnostician simply listens to and affirms the patient's own verbal self-identification and self-diagnosis.

No objective tests can prove that the transgender condition exists.

No physical examination, blood test, bone marrow test, chromosome test, or brain test will show that a person has gender dysphoria. It is a condition revealed solely by the patient's feelings. Yet the recommended treatment is extreme—cross-gender hormones and sex-reassigning surgery.

Don't be duped when trans activists conflate the unrelated condition of intersexuality[286] with transgenderism to gain sympathy for a trans agenda. People with intersex conditions are not the same as self-identified transgender people. Being intersex is verifiable in the physical body; being transgender is not. People who identify as transgender usually have typical male or female anatomies.

How to Become Transgender

The wikiHow article entitled "How to Transition from Male to Female (Transgender)"[287] outlines a simple five-part system for men who want to become women. Here is a small sample:

> Seek a qualified therapist. . . . Ask your friends in the trans community to recommend a therapist. Browse the internet in search of a therapist experienced working with members of the trans community. . . .

> Receive a diagnosis. Over the course of a series of sessions, your therapist will evaluate your individual situation issuing a diagnosis. After determining that you have consistently experienced symptoms such as disgust with your genitals, a desire to remove signs of your biological sex, and or a certainty that your biological sex does not align with your true gender, your therapist will likely diagnose you with Gender Dysphoria.

These instructions are typical of the advice offered to those who believe they may be transgender. I myself followed a similar series of steps. Yet, in hindsight, after transitioning from male to female and back again, I see that many important topics are ignored by such advice, placing vulnerable people at risk. Four crucial omissions are most obvious and problematic.

285

http://www.wpath.org/site_page.cfm?pk_association_webpage_menu=1351&pk_association_webpage=3926
[286] http://www.isna.org/faq/what_is_intersex
[287] http://www.wikihow.com/Transition-from-Male-to-Female-(Transgender)

First, these instructions fail to caution the reader about therapist bias. Asking friends in the trans community to recommend a therapist guarantees that the therapist will be biased toward recommending the radical step of transitioning.

Second, no mention is made or warning given about sexual fetishes. If a person has been sexually, emotionally, or physically abused or is addicted to masturbation, cross-dressing, or pornography, he could be suffering from a sexual fetish disorder. As such, he is probably not going to be helped by gender dysphoria treatment protocols.

Third, the high incidence of comorbid mental conditions is not mentioned. Those who have been diagnosed with bipolar disorder, obsessive-compulsive disorder, oppositional defiance behaviors, narcissism, autism, or other such disorders need to proceed cautiously when considering transitioning, because these disorders can cause symptoms of gender dysphoria.[288] When the comorbid disorder is effectively treated, the gender discomfort may relent as well.

Fourth, regret after transition is real, and the attempted suicide rate is high. Unhappiness, depression, and inability to socially adapt have been linked to high rates of attempted suicide both before and after gender transition and sexual reassignment surgery. My website[289] gathers academic research on this topic and reports the personal experiences of people who regret transitioning.

Standards of Care?

In theory, the medical community follows certain standards of care for transgender health, now in the seventh revision, which were developed by The World Professional Association for Transgender Health (WPATH).[290] The standards provide guidelines for treating people who report having discomfort with their gender identity.

People think that because standards exist, people will be properly screened before undergoing the radical gender transition. Unfortunately, the overwhelming theme of these standards is affirmation. Again, clinical practitioners do not diagnose gender dysphoria. Their job is to approve and affirm the client's self-diagnosis of gender dysphoria and help the patient fulfill the desire for transition. The standards also advise that each patient's case is different, so the medical practitioners may (and should) adapt the protocols to the individual.

> The patient controls the diagnosis of gender dysphoria.

If a gender specialist or the patient wants to skip the screening protocols and move forward with hormone treatment and surgical procedures, they are free to do so. The standards of care do not come with any requirement that they be followed.

For example, the standards do, in fact, recommend that patients be pre-screened for other mental health conditions. But I routinely hear from family members who say that obvious comorbid

---

[288] https://www.ncbi.nlm.nih.gov/pubmed/25180172
[289] https://www.SexChangeRegret.com
290

http://www.wpath.org/site_page.cfm?pk_association_webpage_menu=1351&pk_association_webpage=3926

conditions, such as autism or a history of abuse, are ignored. The physician or the counselor simply concludes that the psychological history is unimportant and allows the patient to proceed with hormone treatment.

When Real Looks Fake

As simple as it is to become a "real" transgender person, it's even easier to turn into a fake one. "Fake" transgender people like me start out as real, but when they eventually see through the delusion of gender change and stop living the transgender life, transgender activists give them the disparaging label of "fake."

If someone comes to the difficult and honest conclusion that transitioning didn't result in a change of sex, then he or she is perceived as a threat to the transgender movement and must be discredited.

Name-calling and bullying ensues.

To be considered real, the transgender person must continue in the delusion that his or her gender changed. The problem with basing a diagnosis and irreversible treatment on people's feelings, no matter how sincerely held, is that feelings can change.

My message attempts to help others avoid regret, yet the warning is not welcome to the advocates whose voice for transgender rights rings strong and loud. Some will find my words offensive, but then the truth can be offensive. Personally, I cannot think of anything more offensive than men diminishing the wonder and uniqueness of biological women by suggesting women are nothing more than men who have been pumped with hormones and may or may not have undergone cosmetic surgery.

Cheers and bravo to the offensive truth. Let's reclaim the beautiful reality of male and female sexual difference and reject transgender ideology.

Why A Compromise On Transgender Politics Would Be Capitulation

At National Review Online, gay columnist J.J. McCullough makes some sweeping generalizations about what conservatives think about transgenderism that are worth questioning.

BY WALT HEYER
THE FEDERALIST, MAY 16, 2018
THEFEDERALIST.COM/2018/05/16/
COMPROMISE-TRANSGENDER-POLITICS-CAPITULATION/

J.J. McCullough, a gay man and columnist for National Review Online, recently argued it is time for conservatives and progressives to compromise on transgenderism, just as they did decades ago on homosexuality, to preserve a free and peaceful social order.[291] He makes some sweeping generalizations about what conservatives think about homosexuality and *should* think about transgenderism that I think are worth questioning.

First: McCullough says transgenderism is not bizarre. "Through education, and especially exposure, homosexuality is no longer regarded as bizarre, threatening, or mysterious," he notes. Then he says the same should be true about transgenderism.

Yet transgenderism *is* bizarre, threatening and mysterious. Any transgender person who wants to detransition back to his or her birth gender—and there are many—knows transgenderism is a bizarre way to live and destructive. Its modern origins were motivated by evil, and that legacy has not faded.

In the United States, transgenderism began more than 60 years ago in the sick, twisted minds of three men, as I detail in my book "Paper Genders": Alfred Kinsey, a pedophile activist who was addicted to masturbation; Dr. Harry Benjamin, a pedophile activist, who coined the term "transsexual" and was obsessed with cross-gender hormone therapy and sex change surgery; and John Money, a pedophile activist who fabricated his transgender research results.

The pedophile activity of the early days of transgenderism lives on today.[292] I recently received an email from a Canadian drag queen entertainer named Onyx. Drag queens are men, mostly gay, who dress flamboyantly and behave with over-the-top exaggerated feminine mannerisms. Some, like Onyx, become entertainers, and others are featured in news coverage of gay pride parades. Some, but not all, will go on to change their gender.

Onyx describes his disillusionment with the pedophilia creeping into gay bars with transgenderism and with the drag queen lifestyle he now sees as an illusion. I share his email with permission.

---

[291] https://www.nationalreview.com/2018/05/transgenderism-compromise-necessary-to-preserve-social-order/
[292] https://gendertrender.wordpress.com/2012/11/21/what-many-transgender-activists-dont-want-you-to-know-and-why-you-should-know-it-anyway/

> I wanted to follow my own egoistic path and…my thirst for glitter and shows led me into a superficial world. I have been a Drag Queen entertainer named Onyx for about 4 years around Quebec and Montreal. I discovered…corrupted ideas of gender and sexual freedom that are becoming harmful to our society.
>
> Many things woke me up. I couldn't accept seeing last year's Montreal Pride's leading light Drag Queen 'Lactatia' who was only 8 years old. As I have been working in gay bars, I became aware of the pedophilia that was creeping in there. I've decided to quit the Drag scene because I couldn't live this illusion anymore. Everything was getting fake to my eyes and I didn't like to be called 'she'.

A social movement that celebrates elementary school children cross-dressing and dressing and dancing seductively in adult venues for titillation, and pushes for severing natural and healthy human organs even from children,[293] is not one decent people should *ever* "compromise" with.

Homosexuality Doesn't Require Cutting Off Body Parts

McCullough makes another comparison between homosexuality and transgenderism regarding those who consider gender dysphoria as something that can be fixed. He says "only the tiniest fringe still consider the [gay] orientation something worth trying to 'fix.'" He cites California legislation that outlaws the sale of any book, counseling service, or conference that suggests homosexuality or gender confusion can be changed as proof that this perception is correct.

But in fact, *all trans activists* consider the transgender identity something worth trying to fix. The proof is the existence of an entire industry dedicated to medical procedures and cross-gender services to "fix" the transgender person. The problem is, the fix trans-activists push is to change the body to supposedly "match the mind" through cross-gender hormones and surgery, rather than helping the person to find peace with his or her natural body.

The tiniest fringe, as McCullough detractingly calls them, are dissenters from political correctness who demand evidence, such as long-term studies, to show the effectiveness of such "fixes" and demand alternative treatments, such as what has helped me and countless others: sound psychotherapy to address the coexisting disorders that make a person want to be someone they can never become. If this is a fringe, it is growing, and with good reason.

All Attempts to Treat Unnatural Anguish Are Not Quackish

McCullough makes another sweeping assumption about the critics of transgenderism with this statement: "As with homosexuality in the 1980s and '90s, the loud revulsion of critics conceals a fading interest in actually attempting to 'solve' transgenderism, as even those most offended by it seem to quietly regard purported cures as quackish and authoritarian."

---

[293] https://4thwavenow.com/2018/03/26/update-san-francisco-phalloplasty-surgeon-now-with-8-malpractice-suits/

I was a transgender female, and I'm living proof that cures for what drives transgender behaviors and desires are neither quackish nor authoritarian.

> The restoration of my life as a man demonstrates that cures for gender dysphoria are possible, valid, and can lead to desirable outcomes in patients' lives.

The "authoritarian" behavior on display comes not from conservatives, but from trans activists who push for legislation to outlaw unfettered access to psychotherapy, books, and other materials, as California is threatening to do. No government should prohibit people from freely seeking help to change unwanted personal behavior.

The "quackish purported cures" perpetrated on vulnerable people come not from conservatives, but from progressives who maintain that cross-hormones and surgery are the only path to good outcomes, despite decades of contrary evidence.

In 1979, the leading endocrinologist at the gender clinic of trailblazing transgender endocrinologist Harry Benjamin, Dr. Charles Ihlenfeld, relayed his conclusions after treating some 500 people with cross-gender hormones over six years. He urged caution in prescribing cross-gender hormones because 80 percent of people who want to change their gender shouldn't. "There is too much unhappiness among people who have had the surgery," Ihlenfeld said. "Too many of them end as suicides."[294]

The high suicide rate of transsexuals, even after surgery, continues to this day. Treatment that leads many patients to commit suicide is not good medicine. To borrow McCullough's terminology, it's quack medicine. The true quacks are people who demand we further damage hurting people with opposite-sex hormones and plastic surgery rather than help them compassionately and rationally with therapy and relationship supports.

Our Common Ground Is Protecting Children

One area of McCullough's article is applause-worthy. He acknowledges the need to protect children from embracing transgender identities and for protecting the right of parents:

> In particular, the risk of psychologically and physically damaging children by encouraging or enabling them to embrace transgender identities before pubescence must be acknowledged as a valid concern backed by credible evidence. Protecting children from the confusing, anxious, dangerous world of adult sexuality and sexual identity before their developing minds can fully conceptualize its complexities is not bigotry, it is good sense, and the sovereign right of every parent.

With 73 years of experience behind me, starting as a four-year-old boy who was affirmed in crossdressing as a girl and eventually lived eight years as a "trans-female," I can say that McCullough is right on target: affirming young children toward cross-gender behavior plants the seed of gender dysphoria that will cause long-term emotional, psychological, and gender identity incongruency.

---

[294] http://lvtgw.jadephoenix.org/Info_htm/Herbal_G/ginko_b2.htm

McCullough calls for a compromise in which conservatives acknowledge "that arbitrary discrimination against transgender people is a cruel bigotry like any other" and progressives stop using state authority "to impose accommodation of transgenderism in a fashion far more totalitarian than is rationally justified." That sounds great; both sides could agree.

But this "compromise" ignores that *no* conservative leaders are calling for "arbitrary discrimination against transgender people." For example, Ryan Anderson, perhaps the most prominent conservative to speak on transgenderism, constantly advocates compassionate treatment of transgender people. McCullough also misses the core disagreement between progressives and conservatives. Our real disagreement is whether "compassion" means enabling destructive behavior or constructive assistance to come to peace with reality.

The progressive idea of compassion and treatment is to lock people into cross-gender hormones and body part removal and refashioning surgeries, ignore contributing factors, and silence the voice of anyone who disagrees.

The conservative view of compassion and treatment is to encourage open, robust scientific discussion and research to discover treatments that work long-term, and to treat coexisting emotional conditions such as depression and anxiety. One relies on intimidation, censorship, and legislation; the other on scientific methods and free exchange of ideas. Compromise isn't possible.

Have We Finally Reached Peak Transgender?

Men competing as women at the Olympics, LGBT themes on 30 to 45 percent of prime-time television, and influence at the White House—please tell me we've reached the transgender high-water mark.

BY WALT HEYER
THE FEDERALIST, FEBRUARY 16, 2016
THEFEDERALIST.COM/2016/02/16/HAVE-WE-FINALLY-REACHED-PEAK-TRANSGENDER/

State and local lawmakers across the country are dealing with a barrage of proposals about whether men and boys claiming to be transgender will get legal cover to force their way into both public and privately owned bathrooms and showers with women and girls.

For the 2016 spring Olympics in Rio de Janeiro, officials have indicated they will allow a man who is still packing his "tools" to compete as a female if he has low testosterone and claims to be a female. Under the new Olympic standard, a man with low T can now compete equally with biologically correct females even with all his male parts intact.

Future Olympic competitions could look more like a "Saturday Night Live" skit than a world-class athletic event. I hope the biologically correct females open a can of "whoop-up" on the low-T guys.

On Television, Too Much LGBT

On almost every television network, the preponderance of lesbian, gay, bisexual and transgender (LGBT) characters and storylines is inescapable, almost to the point of saturation, even though it's completely out of proportion to the real-world LGBT population of an estimated 3.4 percent.

Six transgender-community-related shows are on the air right now.[295] Terri Ryan, a TV producer and advocate for the cross-dressing community, in Huffington Post asked questions that suggest even an advocate working in the entertainment industry may be uncomfortable with the current over-exposure of transgenders on TV: [296]

> Are there too many TV shows depicting transgender people? Is it just too much at one time for an audience to absorb? Are we in the TG community attempting to force acceptance through highly scripted and well-staged reality shows that may or may not be representing the majority of the TG community? Will having so many transgender topic shows educate or turn off the very people they are attempting to appeal to, because it is too much, too soon?

Arguing that gays and transgenders are ignored or oppressed falls flat on its face these days. Gay, lesbian, and transgender characters are often shown in a pathetic or sympathetic light—abused,

---

[295] http://www.huffingtonpost.com/terri-lee-ryan/are-there-too-many-transg_b_7845150.html
[296] http://www.huffingtonpost.com/terri-lee-ryan/are-there-too-many-transg_b_7845150.html

oppressed, or mistreated—in an effort to make the viewer more open to them and feel sorry for them. But they are not abused. They are our Olympic athletes and TV stars.

The Transgender Push Is Purposeful and Planned

Is it deliberate? Yes. The push to normalize LGBT characters has become all too predictable. We're in the midst of a major, deliberate, well-executed social indoctrination coming from the entertainment industry, the White House, and pro-trans LGBT activists.

Since 2006, the Gay Lesbian Alliance Against Defamation (GLAAD) has evaluated the quantity and quality of LGBT characters during primetime television. Their annual report, the Network Responsibility Index, ranks the networks in a type of scorecard. Their objective is to push for positive representation and to increase the amount of representation. "TV hasn't merely reflected the changes in social attitudes; it has also had an important role in bringing them about," said the 2013 Network Responsibility Index.[297]

The 2015 rankings and score, based on percentage of LGBT-inclusive original programming hours during primetime, show this programming is at an all-time high on broadcast and cable networks.[298]

Broadcast Networks

FOX	45%	Excellent
The CW	45%	Good
ABC	32%	Good
NBC	28%	Adequate
CBS	27%	Adequate

Cable Networks

ABC Family	74%	Excellent
FX	54%	Good
Showtime	41%	Good
HBO	31%	Good
MTV	30%	Good
USA	23%	Adequate

[297] http://www.glaad.org/files/2013NRI.pdf
[298] http://www.glaad.org/files/GLAAD-2015-NRI.pdf

TNT	19%	Adequate
TLC	18%	Adequate
A&E	8%	Failing
History	0%	Failing

LGBT people comprise only 3.4 percent of the population, yet the advocate organization GLAAD considers 28 percent of programming as merely "adequate" and 8 percent as "failing." GLAAD has met with top network executives at networks to discuss how TV can "improve." [299]

Television Networks' Political Connections

When these folks get together for LGBT advocates to set TV programming, they're not so much negotiating as they are strategizing in unison. This is evident from the deep personal affiliations between the LGBT-driven Obama White House and many top TV executives.

Pillow talk and sibling connections can be powerful influences to inspire the networks to support the White House agenda. An article at Breitbart.com explored the many personal connections between White House staffers and network honchos in 2013: [300]

- White House national security advisor Ben Rhoades is the brother of David Rhoades, president of CBS News.
- Press Secretary Jay Carney is married to Claire Shipman, a senior national correspondent at ABC News.
- Special advisor to the president Elizabeth Sherwood-Randall is the sister of Ben Sherwood, president of ABC News.
- Former House Deputy Secretary of State Tom Nides is married to Virginia Moseley, CNN's vice president and Washington bureau chief.

These network execs spend time with family and professional connections who might as well themselves be LGBT advocates. It's no secret that the White House celebrates gay and transgender causes. President Obama uses the power and influence of the "bully pulpit" to get behind the LGBT agenda. In fact, the White House now considers itself to be a medical expert, weighing in on whether certain psychotherapies for lesbian, gay, and transgender people are effective. [301]

When the Supreme Court ruled in favor of gay marriage, the White House "spiked the ball" by blazing an LGBT rainbow across the face of the building. On its website, the White House has a special section dedicated to "President Obama and the LGBT Community." [302]

---

[299] http://sdgln.com/causes/2013/06/28/glaad-meets-cbs-executives-discuss-transgender-images
[300] http://www.breitbart.com/big-journalism/2013/09/07/mainstream-media-honchos-related-towhite-house-officials/
[301] https://www.whitehouse.gov/share/watch-and-share-why-we-must-ban-conversion-therapy
[302] https://www.whitehouse.gov/lgbt

The current administration has appointed more than 250 openly LGBT people to full-time and advisory positions in the executive branch,[303] several of them openly transgender.[304] The Obama administration hired the first transgender to White House staff: LGBT activist Raffi Freeman-Gurspan.[305] In November 2015, only four short months after Freeman-Gurspan started working in the West Wing, the White House announced it was prepared to amend the Civil Rights Act of 1964 to sexual orientation and gender identity, effectively turning sexual preference and gender identity confusion into a civil rights issue.

Why You'll Never See a Formerly Gay Hero

LGBT staffers in the executive branch greatly influence the positions that the White House takes on issues and the positions the White House professes profoundly influence American social values, policy, and legislation.

> This overbearing media and activist push is not favorable to freedom of speech, nor is it an organic social development.

The LGBT lobby is small in numbers but has enormous financial and political power.

No network will ever get approval from GLAAD to feature a script about a homosexual, lesbian, or transgender who changed his or her life after undergoing sound psychotherapy and found freedom from the lifestyle he or she once loved.

When I speak at conferences around the country, I hear speakers who had been gay, lesbian, or transgender. They share their personal stories of coming out of the homosexual life and transgender delusions. Airing realistic underdog stories such as these, of people who are conflicted about being gay or transgender and want to leave the lifestyle, won't win a GLAAD "excellent" rating or any Screen Actors Guild awards. It won't ever get aired.

To pre-empt the wackos who might line up to bash me for my remarks, I'll share some of my history to demonstrate that I'm not homophobic or transphobic. During the years I was living my transgender life, for a time I lived in West Los Angeles in a large house owned by my Alcoholics Anonymous sponsor, a homosexual. He shared his home with men like me who were in early recovery from drugs and alcohol. All of them were homosexual except for me.

We lived together, often sharing dinner and social times, and attending AA meetings together. I lived in the community. Like TV producer Terri Ryan, I say the level of attention on transgender and gay characters and storylines on television is too much.

---

[303] https://www.victoryfund.org/our-work/presidential-appointments

[304] https://www.washingtonpost.com/news/the-fix/wp/2015/08/18/the-white-house-has-appointed-its-first-transgender-staffer/

[305] http://abcnews.go.com/US/meet-1st-openly-transgender-official-working-white-house/story?id=33156360

Protections for Some but Not Others

Think about it. We live in an era when people are encouraged to "select a gender" with not two choices, but a spectrum of "fluidity." Laws are being stretched to accommodate new extremes and trample the rights of anyone who doesn't comply.

These advocates want any boy or man, whether gender-confused or a sexual pervert, to have free access to a female-specific bathroom or locker room by simply saying he identifies as a woman. Obama pushes to accommodate the demands of these men at the expense of girls and women.

New York City has gone even further in its anti-discrimination law, to regulate what must be *spoken*. According to the December 2015 clarification of the New York City Human Rights Law, employers, landlords, and public accommodations are required to use a person's preferred name and pronoun, "regardless of the individual's sex assigned at birth, anatomy, gender, medical history, appearance, or the sex indicated on the individual's identification" or be subject to civil penalties. "The Commission can impose civil penalties up to $125,000 for violations, and up to $250,000 for violations that are the result of willful, wanton, or malicious conduct." [306]

Ignorant Cheerleading Means More Suffering People

I lived the delusional transgender life for eight years, and I can tell you: the LGBT lobby is serving us a boatload of pure malarkey. I hear from transgenders who needed psychological help but instead were put on the surgical slice-and-dice assembly line and now live with the awful consequences. Transgenders attempt suicide at a rate higher than 40 percent and, as I've reported elsewhere, studies show that more than 60 percent of transgenders have co-existing mental disorders. [307]

I'm concerned about the people who are not getting appropriate psychological care and end up committing suicide.

Meanwhile, the entertainment industry refuses to include in their scripts an accurate portrayal of the mental illness and the suicides prevalent in the LGBT population. [308]

The White House focuses on so-called civil rights rather than mental health. These special-interest groups refuse to acknowledge that mental disorders have become the largest single risk factor in the high suicidal behavior within the lesbian, gay, and bisexual community.

The scariest and most feared persons to the LGBT sympathizers are the ones who once lived "the life" but now realize they were not born to that lifestyle and wholeheartedly reject it. I do not hate the LGBT. I just hate the mess that buying into their lifestyle made of my life.

[306] http://www.nyc.gov/html/cchr/downloads/pdf/publications/GenderID_InterpretiveGuide_2015.pdf
[307] https://thefederalist.com/2016/01/06/politicians-response-to-transgenders-is-likely-to-increase-suicides/
[308] http://www.ncbi.nlm.nih.gov/pmc/articles/PMC3662085/

My 'Sex Change' Was a Myth. Why Trying to Change One's Sex Will Always Fail.

According to the most widely accepted definition of "sex" and America's most famous sex-change doctor, a true change of sex is biologically impossible.

BY WALT HEYER
THE DAILY SIGNAL, AUGUST 27, 2017
WWW.DAILYSIGNAL.COM/2017/08/23/
SEX-CHANGE-MYTH-TRYING-CHANGE-ONES-SEX-WILL-ALWAYS-FAIL/

Recently, during a radio show on which I appeared as a guest, a caller posed a question I frequently get asked: "Do the administration of cross-gender hormones and genital surgery change a boy into a girl or a girl into a boy?"

The answer is simple: biologically, not at all.

Underneath all the cosmetic procedures, vocal training, and hair growth or hair removal lies a physical reality. Biologically, the person has not changed from a man into a woman or vice versa.

Sex is an indelible fact of a person's biology. Specifically, it describes one's biological makeup with respect to its organization for reproduction. As Lawrence S. Mayer and Paul R. McHugh explain in The New Atlantis:

> In biology, an organism is male or female if it is structured to perform one of the respective roles in reproduction. This definition does not require any arbitrary measurable or quantifiable physical characteristics or behaviors; it requires understanding the reproductive system and the reproduction process.[309]

The authors go on to note that "[t]here is no other widely accepted biological classification for the sexes." Sex pertains to the two different ways males and females are structured for reproduction, and these structures are permanently engrained in one's biology. They cannot be chosen at will.

A man can mutilate his body, but he can never transform it to be organized as a female—and vice versa for the woman.

This makes sense of the head-snapping (and false) headline many of us saw about a man having a baby.[310] The "man" featured in the story is simply a biological woman who kept her childbearing anatomy intact.

---

[309] http://www.thenewatlantis.com/publications/part-three-gender-identity-sexuality-and-gender
[310] http://abcnews.go.com/Health/story?id=5302756&page=1

My Sex Change Fiction

My "sex change" surgery from male to female was performed by Dr. Stanley Biber in Trinidad, Colorado.

His unusual field of expertise drew clients from around the world and earned the small mountain town the nickname "Sex Change Capital of the World." The surgeon estimated that he performed over 5,000 such surgeries during his career.[311]

I lived legally and socially as a female for eight years, but I came to the realization that I wanted to go back to living as a man. To legally change my gender back to male, I needed to file a petition with the California Superior Court that verified I met certain criteria. (The process has since changed.)

My surgeon wrote a letter to the court stating that I met the medical criteria for the courts to legally change my birth certificate back to male. The very surgeon who earlier said that hormones and surgery had changed me to female, now admitted that it did not.

In the letter, he testified that the surgery and cross-gender hormones had the effect of neutering my external appearance and genitalia, but my internal biological structure and my genetics were still male.

> That's the key to understand: Hormones and surgical changes can affect
> one's external appearance, but no innate biological change of sex occurs.

This truth should seem obvious, but discontented trans women contact me who say they didn't know that they could never become a "real" woman. They are unhappy and opting to go back to the gender of their birth.

False Hope Could Lead to More Suicide

A 2004 U.K. Guardian article, "Sex Changes Not Effective," points out: "While no doubt great care is taken to ensure that appropriate patients undergo gender reassignment, there's still a large number of people who have the surgery but remain traumatized—often to the point of committing suicide."[312]

Too many post-surgical patients contact me to report they deeply regret the gender change surgery and that the false hope of surgical outcomes was a factor. For children, the focus on encouraging, assisting, and affirming them toward changing genders at earlier and earlier ages, with no research showing the outcomes, may lead to more suicides.

Others Advocate Less Surgery

A growing number of people like me, 50 years after the first surgery at Johns Hopkins University Gender Clinic in 1966, are advocating the scaling back of the radical, irreversible, often unnecessary genital mutilation surgeries.

---

[311] http://articles.latimes.com/1995-01-23/news/ls-23267_1_stanley-biber
[312] https://www.theguardian.com/society/2004/jul/30/health.mentalhealth

Rene Jax, in his 2016 book, "DON'T Get on The Plane!" says, "Sex change surgery will ruin your life."

Jax and I have had similar experiences. Both of us were approved for hormones and surgery to resolve our gender dysphoria, and after following the medically prescribed full regimen of hormones and genitalia surgery, and living as women, both of us came away with the same conclusions:

- Gender change surgery was a destructive body mutilation and a waste of time and money.

- After the medically-certified gender change, life didn't improve.

- Gender dysphoria, that feeling of unease with one's gender, persisted, and was not relieved as promised.

Surgery as a Last Resort

Based on the emails I receive, I would urge the person who thinks that gender change is the answer in their situation to delay any surgical changes, or at the very least to restrict any physical changes to ones that are reversible.

This is especially important for younger people who may want to have children one day.

Today in 10 states, only a verbal declaration and a doctor's letter supporting the change are needed to legally change the gender on a birth certificate. Cross-gender hormones or surgery are not required. Only 10 states affirm that surgery and hormones do not change biology.

Studies show that two-thirds of people with gender dysphoria have co-existing disorders, such as depression and anxiety.[313]

I've become an outspoken critic of gender reassignment surgeries because many people are not being treated for other co-existing problems first. Instead, they are quickly prescribed cross-gender hormones and shuttled on a path toward surgery.

But as noted earlier, this surgery cannot succeed in delivering what it promises. It will only mutilate the body, a far cry from the promised "sex change."

---

[313] http://www.thepublicdiscourse.com/2016/02/16376/

Fifty-Six Shades Of Gender Insanity

The LGBT lobby is pushing Facebook and universities to redefine gender norms. This means suffering for everyone, and especially people who struggle with their gender identity.

BY WALT HEYER
THE FEDERALIST, MARCH 10, 2015
THEFEDERALIST.COM/2015/03/10/FIFTY-SIX-SHADES-OF-GENDER-INSANITY/

As a former transgender, I am concerned with the attempts underway to change the words we use for gender:

- Facebook expanded its possible designation of gender to 56 choices last year, with the explicit help of LGBT organizations.

- Public and private universities are teaching a similar LGBT version of gender in human sexuality and public health courses. Professors and administrators are telling students that gender is more than male and female—in fact, those designations are simple and passé.

- The new term for those who live life in their birth gender is "cisgender," or "cis" for short, to distinguish them from "transgender."

The list reads like something out of a comedy routine, except it isn't funny when people who need psychological treatment don't seek it because they see their condition in a list of "normal" genders. They will miss out on hope—the hope that they aren't stuck in confusion. My concern is that they won't get treatment, which can help prevent anti-social behaviors and regrettable suicides.

Fostering Confusion Exacerbates Suffering

It used to be that the men with behaviors such as cross-dressing, sexual fetish, transvestite or drag queen dress-up, female impersonation, and taking cross-gender hormones were considered to have psychological disorders. Some were homosexual; some not.

> Now, the pressure is on to insist that our society accepts and tolerates all oddities as mainstream.

It used to be that those who suffered from gender confusion and distress were considered to have a mental disorder. That's all changed now with the politicizing of the Diagnostic and Statistical Manual of Mental Disorders (DSM), published by the American Psychiatric Association. Gender confusion is not a disorder anymore, it's a dysphoria, and as such, it shouldn't be treated as something to overcome.

Gender distress is now something to embrace and enhance. "You're born that way," they say. Take a new gender name from the list of 56 possibilities, take hormones, and perhaps even have surgery to change your body to match your mental image. Get a new birth certificate and be granted equal status with those born in your adopted gender.

Gender Confusion Is Not Biological, It's Psychological

But what does the research say? Has any biological basis been found that indicates who will develop into a transgender? Is there a genetic marker in transgenders? The answer is no. Researchers have looked for evidence to prove that transgenders are different biologically but they haven't found any.

- One study published in 2014 looked at certain suspected areas of the brain for an association with male-to-female (MtF) transsexualism and found none.[314]

- Another study, published in 2009, looked for "evidence that genetic variants of sex hormone-related genes confer individual susceptibility to MtF or FtM transsexualism" and didn't find any.[315]

- Yet another study, published in 2013, found that "gender disorder does not seem to be associated with any molecular mutations of some of the main genes involved in sexual differentiation." [316]

Not a smidgeon of abnormality can be found in the genetic makeup of transgenders so, no, transgenders are not born that way. They are normal males and females.

What researchers *have* found is that transgenders attempt suicide at an alarming rate.[317]

What researchers *have* found is that a majority of transgenders have at least one psychiatric co-existing (co-morbid) disorder, the most prevalent being major depressive disorder, specific phobia and adjustment disorder.[318]

What researchers *have* found is that 30 percent of gender dysphoria patients have a lifetime diagnosis of dissociative disorder[319] (formerly called multiple personality disorder). Dissociative disorder and gender dysphoria appear very similar, and clinicians often cannot distinguish between the two in the transgender patient.

I think psychologists quickly default to the diagnosis of gender dysphoria and don't consider the possibility of other disorders. I know: this is what happened with me. The most highly regarded gender specialist in the nation diagnosed me with gender dysphoria. He told me that I was a transgender and recommended that I undergo surgery to transition from male to female. All my discomfort would go away after surgery, he said. He was wrong.

---

[314] http://www.ncbi.nlm.nih.gov/pubmed/25124466

[315] http://www.ncbi.nlm.nih.gov/pubmed/19604497

[316] http://www.ncbi.nlm.nih.gov/pubmed/23324476

[317] http://www.thetaskforce.org/static_html/downloads/reports/reports/ntds_full.pdf

[318] http://www.ncbi.nlm.nih.gov/pubmed/25180172

[319] http://www.ncbi.nlm.nih.gov/pubmed/25656174

Surgery Can't Define Who I Am

I lived eight years successfully as a transgender female, but after the initial euphoria wore off, I was still confused and even more depressed. Having surgery and living fully as a woman didn't alleviate the distress. Later, when I received the proper diagnosis and treatment of my dissociative disorder, I no longer needed to play the role of a woman and I regretted that I had been duped by the redefinition madness. The surgery can't define who I am.

> The idea of 56 different genders is repugnant to this former transgender.
> I am a man, not some nonsense name contrived by the LGBT.

I report stories of regret at the website sexchangeregret.com because today's social-political correctness would have us believe that no one regrets sex change. But for some transgenders, regret is real. People contact me with their painful stories and tell me they feel all alone. Some are contemplating suicide because they are so despondent over having had needless surgery. Most had difficult childhood experiences that haven't yet been resolved. Many want to return to their birth gender. All of them tell me that, for them, being a transgender is crazy-making.

My concern is that providing 56 different gender identities deters people who are in gender confusion or distress from seeking proper treatment, which needlessly places them at risk for unhealthy behaviors and possibly suicide. The organizations that propose this apparently are willing to spend time devising new designations and recommending irreversible surgery, but hostile to uncovering the psychological or psychiatric disorders that often accompany gender distress and lead to the high rate of suicide and suicide attempts.

Drop The T From LGBT

Transgender people have high rates of psychological problems that contribute to their identity expression and victimization. The rest of the LGBT crowd should consider how that reflects on them.

BY WALT HEYER
THE FEDERALIST, APRIL 21, 2016
THEFEDERALIST.COM/2016/04/21/DROP-THE-T-FROM-LGBT/

The post-marriage culture war is asymmetrical in the group known as LGBT. Gay, lesbian, and bisexual activists have carried the rainbow banner for transgenders for issues that truly matter, such as employment and housing. Now the time has come for a genuine sanity check for them to stop enabling kookier parts of the trans agenda.

The current bathroom policy debate illuminates the growing gap between the concerns of the transgender community and of the LGB community. Perhaps those who favor gay marriage do not want any part of enabling pedophiles in wigs having easier access to kids in bathrooms.

Trans activists paint the entire LGBT group in an unsympathetic light when they lobby for laws to criminalize such trivialities as misusing pronouns, as passed recently in New York City. Practical LGB members might want to take this opportunity to disentangle themselves from the lunacy of today's trans-rights movement. This will disassociate their movement in the public eye from people whom research shows have high incidents of psychological disorders linked with their transgender expression, and offers an opportunity to protect transgender people from being exploited by high-priced medical quacks.

The differences between the groups now seem glaring. Let's list a few.

Difference 1: Same-Sex Attraction vs. Gender Perception

Many transgenders are not homosexual, lesbian, or bisexual.[320] Unlike people who identify as LGB, transgenders suffer from self-deception disorders (gender dysphoria). They are convinced that they are in the wrong body, and with the help of enablers and affirmers of their delusion, undergo drastic body-mutilating surgeries to enhance the deception and deny the plain and simple truth of their gender. While some LGB people may be transgender, too, the majority are not.

Difference 2: Bathroom Access

The transgender public restroom issue, a hot topic in the news today, is exclusively a transgender cause not shared by those who are lesbian, gay, or bisexual. Transgender bills being debated at the

---

[320] http://www.glaad.org/transgender/transfaq

state and local levels exclusively address gender identity and have nothing to do with sexual preference. This includes bills to legally change one's gender marker on one's birth certificate without surgically altering the appearance of one's genitals. It also includes bills to allow any man to use women's public restrooms and locker rooms if he says he feels like a woman—no surgery or birth-record change required.

> Gay men might care that deviants invoke such laws to indulge their sexual perversions, bringing a backlash on the LGBT community.

Many gay men don't care whether transgenders get access to the public restroom of the opposite sex. But gay men might care that pedophiles and deviants invoke such laws to indulge their sexual perversions in public restrooms and in doing so, bring a backlash on the LGBT community. Most women, lesbian or not, prefer to keep a man who has his toolbox intact out of the women's restrooms and locker rooms, no matter how much he insists he is a woman. This applies particularly to women who have been sexually assaulted in the past.

The freedom to change genders without surgery and to enter gender-segregated spaces is an open invitation to perverts to use public restrooms to indulge their sexual corruptions at the expense of women and girls.

Difference 3: Mental Disorders

Studies show the transgender population has a wide range of co-existing mental disorders. Besides the obvious gender dysphoria, they suffer at high rates from a wide range of undiagnosed and untreated mental issues: body dysmorphic disorders, sexual fetishes like autogynephilia (arousal at the thought of being a woman), and masturbation addictions, to name just a few.

"We found 90% of these diverse patients had at least one other significant form of psychopathology," says a 2009 study by the Department of Psychiatry at Case Western Reserve University. The psychopathologies found were "mood and anxiety regulation and adaption in the world." [321]

A 2011 long-term follow-up of transsexual persons undergoing sex-reassignment surgery concluded: "Persons with transsexualism, after sex reassignment, have considerably higher risks for mortality, suicidal behaviour, and psychiatric morbidity than the general population." [322]

People who are transgender have a higher risk of suicidal behavior, and suicide is known to be caused by depression and anxiety.

> The recommended treatment for depression, anxiety, or other mental disorders is *not* gender surgery.

The staggering number of co-existing disorders in the gender dysphoric population sets the transgender group apart from the lesbian, gay, and bisexual population. The deep psychological and psychiatric depression that results from the self-deception of gender identity and the untreated mental

---

[321] http://www.ncbi.nlm.nih.gov/pubmed/19105079
[322] http://www.ncbi.nlm.nih.gov/pubmed/21364939

disorders has been the major contributor to transgenders' position at the top of the most-likely-to commit-suicide list.

An Opportunity for LGB to Actually Help the T

Now that we've discussed some major points on which the trans agenda does not align with gay and bisexual priorities, let's further discuss how gay, lesbian, and bisexual activists can benefit trans people by shifting their advocacy.

First, this will help reduce the political pressure that is currently resulting in gender dysphoric people being pushed into treatments that hurt rather than help them.

The high rate of mental disorders among transgenders has been well-documented for 50 years. But instead of diagnosing and treating those issues first, rushing the gender dysphoric person into hormones and surgery ignores any childhood trauma or other mental disorders that might be masquerading as gender dysphoria and leaps directly to the extreme measures of injecting cross-gender hormones and scheduling surgery to remove the original "equipment."

In my own case, I was approved for surgery after one session with a gender specialist. That was in the 1980s. Today, according to the letters I receive, approval still happens that quickly, and the other psychological problems are deemed not important.

Perhaps when transgenders are considered apart from LGB there can be a fresh new insurgence of improved psychiatric screening, effective diagnoses of the underlining comorbid disorders, and effective treatment that does not include hormones and gender reassignment. That should reduce the number of suicides in this population.

Here is some more information about the history of medical treatments for trans people to help LGB folks understand why they need to step up now, and have done so in the past.

Trans Has Long Been Recognized as a Psychological Issue

In the United States, the practice of treating the gender-confused with hormones and surgery was started by Dr. Harry Benjamin, an endocrinologist and sexologist who is credited with coining the term transsexualism. Benjamin's New York gender clinic was in full swing during the 1970s. From that clinic emerged some of the first signs that unhappiness with one's gender and the desire to change gender largely evolved from untreated mental disorders, which hormones and surgery did nothing to relieve.

The leading endocrinologist at Benjamin's clinic in the 1970s, a homosexual named Dr. Charles Ihlenfeld, administered cross-gender hormone therapy to some 500 transgenders over a six-year period. He came to the conclusion that the desire to change genders most likely stemmed from powerful psychological factors, and he left endocrinology (and Benjamin's clinic) to begin a residency in psychiatry, a field in which he felt he could be a help to people with gender identity issues. Ihlenfeld said in "Transgender Subjectivities: A Clinician's Guide,"

"Whatever surgery did, it did not fulfill a basic yearning for something that is difficult to define. This goes along with the idea that we are trying to treat superficially something that is much deeper."

Almost simultaneously, similar findings were coming from Johns Hopkins Hospital's gender clinic, an early provider of gender reassignment surgery. Dr. Paul McHugh joined the clinic as the director of psychiatry and behavioral science in the mid-1970s and asked Dr. Jon Meyer, director of the clinic at the time, to conduct a thorough study of the outcomes of the clinic's patients who underwent gender reassignment at the clinic.

McHugh says, "[Those who underwent surgery] were little changed in their psychological condition. They had much the same problems with relationships, work, and emotions as before. The hope that they would emerge now from their emotional difficulties to flourish psychologically had not been fulfilled." [323] These two different reports came to the same conclusion in the late 1970s.

Research Has Continued to Make This Case

Fast-forward to July 30, 2004, when a review of 100 medical studies delivered another powerful rebuke of surgical genders.[324] David Batty wrote in *The Guardian* in the UK:

> There is no conclusive evidence that sex change operations improve the lives of transsexuals, with many people remaining severely distressed and even suicidal after the operation, according to a medical review conducted exclusively for Guardian Weekend tomorrow.
>
> The review of more than 100 international medical studies of post-operative transsexuals by the University of Birmingham's aggressive research intelligence facility (Arif) found no robust scientific evidence that gender reassignment surgery is clinically effective.

Some have argued that transgenderism could be due to genetic factors, in a parallel argument to those suggesting a "gay gene." So far, research has found no such thing for transsexuals. Studies from 2013[325] and 2009[326] showed no alterations in the DNA of the main sex-determining genes in transsexuals, proving born-male transgenders are normal males; not a smidgeon of abnormality in their genetic make-up causes them to be transgender. Gender issues are not inherent to the genetic makeup.

Transgender People's Lives Are On the Line

Four studies published in 2016 alone show that nothing has changed since Ihlenfeld left Benjamin's gender clinic in the 1970s: Mental disorders are prevalent among the transgender population. The most commonly occurring disorders were major depressive episode, suicidality, generalized anxiety disorder, posttraumatic stress disorder, and alcohol dependence.

[323] http://www.firstthings.com/article/2004/11/surgical-sex
[324] http://www.theguardian.com/society/2004/jul/30/health.mentalhealth
[325] http://www.ncbi.nlm.nih.gov/pubmed/23324476
[326] http://www.sciencedirect.com/science/article/pii/S027858460900222X

A study published in *JAMA Pediatrics* in March 2016 shows a high prevalence of psychiatric diagnoses in a sample of 298 young transgender women aged 16 through 29 years. More than 40 percent had coexisting mental health or substance dependence diagnoses. One in five had two or more psychiatric diagnoses. The most commonly occurring disorders were major depressive episode, suicidality, generalized anxiety disorder, posttraumatic stress disorder, alcohol dependence, and non-alcohol psychoactive substance use dependence.[327]

The study concluded that improved access to medical and psychological care "are urgently needed to address mental health and substance dependence disorders in this population."

Another study comparing 20 Lebanese transgender participants to 20 control subjects (the mean age of both groups was 23.55 years) reported that transgender individuals suffer from more psychiatric pathologies compared to the general population. More than half had active suicidal thoughts; 45 percent had a major depressive episode.[328]

The introduction of the third study says there is no consensus among medical professionals on the early medical treatment (giving puberty-suppressing drugs) for children and adolescents with gender dysphoria.[329] The current adolescent treatment guidelines published by The Endocrine Society and the World Professional Association for Transgender Health recommend suppressing puberty with drugs until age 16, after which cross-sex hormones may be given, and deferring surgery until the individual is at least 18 years old.[330] Some medical teams say these guidelines are too liberal and others say they are too limiting, which shows the wide range of opinions.

This study aimed to gather input from pediatric endocrinologists, psychologists, psychiatrists, and ethicists—both those in favor and those opposed to early treatment—to further the ethical debate. The results showed no consensus on many basic topics of childhood gender dysphoria and insufficient research to support any recommendations for childhood treatments, including the currently published guidelines. Nevertheless, many treatment teams using the guidelines are exploring the possibility of lowering the current age limits.

In the meantime, children are being given experimental treatment that has life-long consequences. Of the 38 referrals for gender dysphoria to the Pediatric Endocrinology Clinic at the University School of Medicine in Indianapolis, more than half had psychiatric and/or developmental comorbidities, says the fourth 2016 study.[331]

T and LGB Are Distinct Populations

Reading these studies brings me to the conclusion that "T" is very different from LGB. The scientific community doesn't comingle LGB with T in research studies because they know the obvious truth: people who are transgender are different from those who are homosexual.

---

[327] http://www.ncbi.nlm.nih.gov/pubmed/26999485
[328] http://www.ncbi.nlm.nih.gov/pubmed/27017319
[329] http://www.ncbi.nlm.nih.gov/pubmed/26119518
[330] http://press.endocrine.org/doi/full/10.1210/jc.2009-0345
[331] http://www.ncbi.nlm.nih.gov/pubmed/26903434

Time to pull the "T" from LGBT. No good reason remains to co-mingle people with mental disorders with people who are homosexual. Nor is it necessary to continue to give social credibility to this tiny group of delusional people who need psychiatric or psychotherapy first and foremost, not pronoun protection or gender reassignment.

Speaking for the non-transgendered or recovered transgendered among us, I am through with the political correctness traps of preferred pronouns and allowing men access to women's facilities and activities. It's time to express our compassion for this group and stop participating in their denial. True compassion is acknowledging that serious mental disorders are found in this population and insisting that the medical community stop treating all gender-dysphoric people with hormones and gender reassignment before caring for their mental health.

A good first step is to remove the T from LGBT.

Index

More information

More information about this topic can be found at Walt's websites:

- SexChangeRegret.com: Latest news, research and stories
- WaltHeyer.com: Videos

Contact the author

Contact the author at waltsbook@yahoo.com.

More Books by Walt Heyer

Trans Life Survivors
Why Living the Trans Life Didn't Work

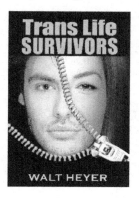

Experience for yourself the raw emotions and "aha" moments from 30 people who were convinced sex change was the answer but came to see it was not.

This book is packed with:

– emails from 30 trans survivors

– the latest research and resources

– a special section on teens and children

Paper Genders
Pulling the Mask off the Transgender Phenomenon

A fresh perspective on the medical treatment for gender identity issues, combining well-researched facts with personal accounts. Exposes and debunks the promises of sex change surgery and shines a light on the suicides and dissatisfaction that the advocates would prefer to keep hidden.

"The research, reason, passion (even outrage) and compassion makes for compelling reading."

Gender, Lies and Suicide
A Whistleblower Speaks Out

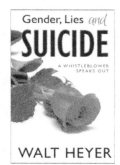

Transgender people undergo hormone injections and irreversible surgeries in a desperate effort to feel better, yet they attempt and commit suicide at an alarming rate, even after treatment.

Walt Heyer digs into the issues behind transgender suicide and shares heart-wrenching letters from those who regret the decision to change genders.

A Transgender's Faith

A true story of betrayals, bad choices, love and the journey home

"Walt's story...a true miracle story

...about a very personal and powerful struggle..."

Perfected with Love
A powerful and inspiring true story

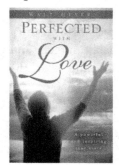

One church says "No" to a scary person. Another church says "Yes" and the astonishing results demonstrate why Scripture says of faith, hope and love that "the greatest of these is love."

This inspiring true story will encourage and equip you and your church with ways to show God's love to a transgender person.

Available at SexChangeRegret.com, Amazon.com, and Ingram Spark.

For bulk sales, contact Walt Heyer at waltsbook@yahoo.com.

Made in the USA
Coppell, TX
11 February 2020